# AN INTRODUCTION TO FUEL CELLS

# AN INTRODUCTION TO FUEL CELLS

EDITED BY

## KEITH R. WILLIAMS

*Head of Surface Reactions Division, 'Shell' Research Limited,
Thornton Research Centre, Chester, England*

CONTRIBUTORS

M. R. ANDREW    R. W. GLAZEBROOK    F. JONES
J. W. PEARSON    J. G. SMITH

ELSEVIER PUBLISHING COMPANY

AMSTERDAM–LONDON–NEW YORK

1966

ELSEVIER PUBLISHING COMPANY
335 JAN VAN GALENSTRAAT, P.O. BOX 211, AMSTERDAM


AMERICAN ELSEVIER PUBLISHING COMPANY, INC.
52 VANDERBILT AVENUE, NEW YORK, N.Y. 10017


ELSEVIER PUBLISHING COMPANY LIMITED
RIPPLESIDE COMMERCIAL ESTATE, BARKING, ESSEX

LIBRARY OF CONGRESS CATALOG CARD NUMBER 65-13902
WITH 112 ILLUSTRATIONS AND 15 TABLES

ALL RIGHTS RESERVED
THIS BOOK OR ANY PART THEREOF MAY NOT BE REPRODUCED IN ANY FORM,
INCLUDING PHOTOSTATIC OR MICROFILM FORM,
WITHOUT WRITTEN PERMISSION FROM THE PUBLISHERS

PRINTED IN THE NETHERLANDS

621.3 12429
W72 i 429

# PREFACE

During the past few years my colleagues and I have frequently been asked to recommend a book on fuel cells which gives a co-ordinated account of the scientific principles on which they are based, together with some indication of their current state of development. These requests have come both from industry and from those concerned with technical education. Unfortunately, the only books so far published have been collections of individual papers by workers in particular fields. While these books are often of great interest to those actively engaged in fuel cell research, they lack the continuity of a volume produced by one author or by a team who work together. Also, in these books, some aspects of fuel cell technology receive undue emphasis while others are neglected. We therefore welcomed the invitation from Elsevier Publishing Company to compile a book which provided a general introduction to fuel cells.

The present volume is concerned more with underlying principles than with specific details of fuel cell construction. As the engineering aspects of fuel cells are those which are changing most rapidly, we have thought it unwise to provide extensive details of the construction of existing fuel cells. Nevertheless, the relevant chapters in this book should give an adequate background to anyone wishing to develop fuel cells and batteries.

We have not assumed that the reader is very familiar with electrochemistry, and electrochemists will therefore find little that is new to them in the earlier chapters of the book. The emphasis, particularly on mass transport, is, however, different from that normally encountered in text books of electrochemistry. We have not attempted a rigorous approach to electrode potentials and kinetics but have tried to give a simple account of the principles involved. Similarly, rather than discussing electrochemical techniques in detail, we hope to have provided a guide for those wishing to read the literature concerned with the fundamentals of the reactions occurring in a fuel cell.

63322

Fuel cells have not yet reached the stage of development where they are suitable for widespread commercial exploitation. While the hopes of the optimists of a few years ago have not yet been realized, my colleagues and I hope that this book will show that considerable progress has been made and that there is good reason to believe that ultimately fuel cells will be used extensively.

We should like to express our gratitude to Lord Rothschild, Chairman of 'Shell' Research Limited, for his encouragement in our research, to Dr. A. Hickling of Liverpool University for the many helpful discussions we have had during the writing of this book, and to Mrs. Jean Minnis for her patient typing of our manuscript.

Thornton Research Centre,                              KEITH R. WILLIAMS
Chester, England

# ACKNOWLEDGEMENTS

Thanks are due to various industrial organizations and to the authors, editors and publishers of a number of books and journals for permission to reproduce the figures specified.

*Figure*

30     Pratt & Whitney Aircraft Division of United Aircraft Corporation. (Power-cell Performance demonstrated at East Hartford, Conn., U.S.A.)

31     P. RUETSCHI, J. C. DUDDEY AND D. T. FERRELL, *Proc. 3rd Intern. Symp. on Batteries, Bournemouth, 1962*, (ed. by D. H. COLLINS,), Pergamon, Oxford, 1963.

32     E. JUSTI AND A. WINSEL, *Kalte Verbrennung—Fuel Cells*, Franz Steiner Verlag, Wiesbaden, 1962.

35     H. G. OSWIN AND S. M. CHODOSH, *Fuel Cell Systems*, (Advan. Chem. Ser. No. 47), Am. Chem. Soc., Washington, D.C., 1965.

36     L. W. NIEDRACH AND W. T. GRUBB, *Fuel Cells*, (ed. by W. MITCHELL), Academic Press, New York, 1963.

37     General Electric Research Laboratories.

38     J. N. MURRAY AND P. G. GRIMES, *Fuel Cells*, (Chem. Eng. Progr. Tech. Manual), Am. Inst. Chem. Engrs., 1963, p. 57. (Table 62)

39     T. O. PAVELA, *Ann. Acad. Sci. Fennicae, AII*, **59** (1954) 7.

40     J. GINER, *Electrochim. Acta*, **9** (1964) 63.

41, 42     M. J. SCHLATTER, *Fuel Cells*, (ed. by G. J. YOUNG), Vol. 2, Reinhold, New York, 1963, p. 190.

43     M. W. BREITER AND S. GILMAN, *J. Electrochem. Soc.*, **109** (1962) 622.

44, 45     S. GILMAN AND M. W. BREITER, *J. Electrochem. Soc.*, **109** (1962) 1099.

46     S. B. BRUMMER AND A. C. MAKRIDES, *J. Phys. Chem.*, **68** (1964) 1448.

47, 48     M. I. GILLIBRAND AND G. R. LOMAX, *Proc. 3rd Intern. Symp. on Batteries, Bournemouth, 1962*, (ed. by D. H. COLLINS), Pergamon, Oxford, 1963.

49     R. A. WYNVEEN, *Fuel Cells*, (ed. by G. J. YOUNG), Vol. 2, Reinhold, New York, 1963, p. 190.

50     W. EITEL AND W. SKALIKS, *Z. Anorg. Chem.*, **183** (1929) 270.

51–54     G. H. J. BROERS AND J. A. A. KETELAAR, *Fuel Cells*, (ed. by G. J. YOUNG), Vol. 1, Reinhold, New York, 1960, p. 78.

55, 56     I. TRACHTENBERG, *Fuel Cell Systems*, (Advan. Chem Ser. No. 47), Am. Chem. Soc., Washington, D.C., 1965.

57     G. H. J. BROERS AND M. SCHENKE, *Fuel Cells*, (ed. by G. J. YOUNG), Vol. 2, Reinhold, New York, 1963, p. 6.

viii ACKNOWLEDGEMENTS

*Figure*

58     G. H. J. BROERS, *Fuel Cells*, (Chem. Eng. Progr. Tech. Manual), Am. Inst. Chem. Engrs., 1963, p. 57.

59, 60     B. S. BAKER *et al.*, *Fuel Cell Systems*, (Advan. Chem. Ser. No. 47), Am. Chem. Soc., Washington, D.C., 1965. (From work done at the Institute of Gas Technology and American Gas Association support.)

64     W. D. KINGERY *et al.*, *J. Am. Ceram. Soc.*, **42** (1959) 397.

68–72     J. M. DIXON *et al.*, *J. Electrochem. Soc.*, **110** (1963) 276.

73–76     J. WEISSBART AND R. RUKA, *J. Electrochem. Soc.*, **109** (1962) 723.

77     General Electric Research Laboratories.

78–80     Westinghouse Electric Corporation Research and Development Centre.

81, 82     General Electric Research Laboratories.

83–86     E. J. CAIRNS *et al.*, *J. Electrochem. Soc.*, **110** (1963) 1025.

87–89     H. BINDER *et al.*, *Electrochim. Acta*, **8** (1963) 781.

90–92     C. E. HEATH AND C. H. WORSHAM, *Fuel Cells*, (ed. by G. J. YOUNG), Vol. 2, Reinhold, New York, 1963.

93–95     General Electric Research Laboratories.

96     W. T. GRUBB AND L. W. NIEDRACH, *J. Electrochem. Soc.*, **110** (1963) 1086.

97     W. T. GRUBB, *Nature*, **301** (1964) 699.

98     W. T. GRUBB, *Proc. Ann. Power Sources Conf.*, **16** (1962) 34. (Fig. 7)

99     W. T. GRUBB AND C. J. MICHALSKE, *Nature*, **201** (1964) 287.

100, 101     L. W. NIEDRACH, *J. Electrochem. Soc.*, **109** (1962) 1092.

104     E. YEAGER, *Fuel Cells*, (ed. by W. MITCHELL), Academic Press, New York, 1963.

105     Dr. E. JUSTI *et al.*, High drain hydrogen-diffusion electrodes operating at ambient temperature and low pressure, Franz Steiner Verlag, Wiesbaden, 1959.

106     S. GILMAN, *J. Phys Chem.*, **66** (1962) 2657.

108     Pratt & Whitney Aircraft Division of United Aircraft Corporation. (Power-cell Performance demonstrated at East Hartford, Conn., U.S.A.)

109     General Electric Research Laboratories.

110, 111     'Shell' Research Ltd.

# CONTENTS

Preface . . . . . . . . . . . . . . . . . . . . . . . . . . . . .   v
Acknowledgements . . . . . . . . . . . . . . . . . . . . . .   vii
List of the principal symbols . . . . . . . . . . . . . . . . .   xiii

Chapter 1. INTRODUCTION
by K. R. WILLIAMS . . . . . . . . . . . . . . . . . . . . . .   1
1. Historical background . . . . . . . . . . . . . . . . . .   1
2. Classification . . . . . . . . . . . . . . . . . . . . . . .   7
3. The fuel cell in power systems . . . . . . . . . . . . . .   11
References . . . . . . . . . . . . . . . . . . . . . . . . . .   13

Chapter 2. ELECTRODE POTENTIALS AND EFFICIENCY
by M. R. ANDREW AND F. JONES . . . . . . . . . . . . . .   14
1. Reversible electrode potentials . . . . . . . . . . . . . .   14
2. Efficiency . . . . . . . . . . . . . . . . . . . . . . . . .   20
3. Measurement of current efficiency . . . . . . . . . . . .   23
4. Reference electrodes . . . . . . . . . . . . . . . . . . .   24
References . . . . . . . . . . . . . . . . . . . . . . . . . .   26

Chapter 3. KINETIC EFFECTS—PART 1
by M. R. ANDREW AND F. JONES . . . . . . . . . . . . . .   27
1. Activation polarization . . . . . . . . . . . . . . . . . .   27
2. Concentration polarization . . . . . . . . . . . . . . . .   36
3. Ohmic polarization . . . . . . . . . . . . . . . . . . . .   42
4. Polarization in porous electrodes . . . . . . . . . . . . .   43
5. Current/voltage curves . . . . . . . . . . . . . . . . . .   46
6. Apparatus and measurements . . . . . . . . . . . . . . .   50
References . . . . . . . . . . . . . . . . . . . . . . . . . .   63

Chapter 4. KINETIC EFFECTS—PART 2
by M. R. ANDREW . . . . . . . . . . . . . . . . . . . .   65
1. Principles of chronopotentiometry . . . . . . . . . . . . .   65
2. Principles of chronoamperometry. . . . . . . . . . . . . .   74
3. Other electrochemical techniques used in fuel cell research . . . .   77
References . . . . . . . . . . . . . . . . . . . . . . . . .   83

Chapter 5. HYDROGEN–OXYGEN (AIR) FUEL CELLS
by K. R. WILLIAMS . . . . . . . . . . . . . . . . . . . .   86
1. Type of electrode. . . . . . . . . . . . . . . . . . . . .   86
2. Electrode structure . . . . . . . . . . . . . . . . . . . .   92
3. Relative merits of different hydrogen–oxygen cells . . . . . . .  105
References . . . . . . . . . . . . . . . . . . . . . . . . .  107

Chapter 6. ELECTROLYTE-SOLUBLE FUELS
by M. R. ANDREW AND R. W. GLAZEBROOK . . . . . . . . . .  109
1. The methanol fuel cell . . . . . . . . . . . . . . . . . .  111
2. The hydrazine fuel cell . . . . . . . . . . . . . . . . . .  147
3. The ammonia fuel cell . . . . . . . . . . . . . . . . . .  151
4. Conclusions . . . . . . . . . . . . . . . . . . . . . . .  152
References . . . . . . . . . . . . . . . . . . . . . . . . .  153

Chapter 7. FUEL CELLS WITH MOLTEN CARBONATE
ELECTROLYTES
by F. JONES . . . . . . . . . . . . . . . . . . . . . . . .  156
1. Introduction . . . . . . . . . . . . . . . . . . . . . . .  156
2. Molten carbonate electrolytes . . . . . . . . . . . . . . .  157
3. Electrodes used in molten carbonate cells . . . . . . . . . .  160
4. Thermodynamics. . . . . . . . . . . . . . . . . . . . .  161
5. Kinetics of molten carbonate cells . . . . . . . . . . . . .  162
6. Practical cells . . . . . . . . . . . . . . . . . . . . . .  166
7. Prospects for molten carbonate fuel cells . . . . . . . . . .  180
References . . . . . . . . . . . . . . . . . . . . . . . . .  181

Chapter 8. SOLID OXIDE ELECTROLYTES
by J. G. SMITH . . . . . . . . . . . . . . . . . . . . . .  183
1. Historical background . . . . . . . . . . . . . . . . . .  183

2. Properties of oxide electrolytes . . . . . . . . . . . . . . . . .   186
3. Thermodynamics of a solid oxide cell . . . . . . . . . . . . .   200
4. Practical fuel cells with solid oxide electrolytes . . . . . . . .   203
References . . . . . . . . . . . . . . . . . . . . . . . . . . . . .   212

Chapter 9. HYDROCARBON FUELS
by J. G. SMITH . . . . . . . . . . . . . . . . . . . . . . . . .   214
1. Historical background . . . . . . . . . . . . . . . . . . .   214
2. Electrochemical oxidation of hydrocarbons at high temperatures .   215
3. Electrochemical oxidation of hydrocarbons in cells with aqueous
    electrolytes . . . . . . . . . . . . . . . . . . . . . . . . . .   230
References . . . . . . . . . . . . . . . . . . . . . . . . . . . . .   246

Chapter 10. MISCELLANEOUS FUEL CELLS
by R. W. GLAZEBROOK AND F. JONES . . . . . . . . . . . . . . .   248
1. The biochemical fuel cell . . . . . . . . . . . . . . . . . . .   248
2. Regenerative fuel cells . . . . . . . . . . . . . . . . . . . .   257
3. Amalgam cells . . . . . . . . . . . . . . . . . . . . . . . . .   272
4. Low temperature carbon monoxide fuel cells . . . . . . . . . .   275
References . . . . . . . . . . . . . . . . . . . . . . . . . . . . .   281

Chapter 11. COMPLETE POWER SOURCES
by J. W. PEARSON . . . . . . . . . . . . . . . . . . . . . . . .   284
1. Batteries . . . . . . . . . . . . . . . . . . . . . . . . . . .   284
2. Production of hydrogen . . . . . . . . . . . . . . . . . . . .   300
References . . . . . . . . . . . . . . . . . . . . . . . . . . . . .   308

Chapter 12. THE STATUS, PROBABLE DEVELOPMENT AND
APPLICATIONS OF FUEL CELLS
by K. R. WILLIAMS . . . . . . . . . . . . . . . . . . . . . . .   310
1. The current status of fuel cells . . . . . . . . . . . . . . . .   310
2. Probable development and applications of fuel cells . . . . . . .   313
Reference . . . . . . . . . . . . . . . . . . . . . . . . . . . . .   318

Author Index . . . . . . . . . . . . . . . . . . . . . . . . . .   319
Subject Index . . . . . . . . . . . . . . . . . . . . . . . . . .   321

# LIST OF THE PRINCIPAL SYMBOLS

| | |
|---|---|
| $a$ | activity |
| $A$ | area of an electrode |
| $C_d$ | differential double layer capacitance per unit area |
| $C_e$ | concentration in the vicinity of the electrode |
| $C_0$ | concentration in the bulk of solution |
| $d$ | electrode thickness |
| $C_p^\circ$ | heat capacity at constant pressure |
| $D$ | diffusion coefficient |
| $D_e$ | effective diffusion coefficient |
| $e$ | an electron |
| $E$ | equilibrium potential of a reversible electrode process |
| $E^\circ$ | standard potential of a reversible electrode process |
| $E_A$ | anode potential |
| $E_C$ | cathode potential |
| $f$ | frequency |
| $F$ | the faraday (96,500 coulombs) |
| $\Delta G$ | change in free energy accompanying a reaction occurring at constant temperature and pressure |
| $\Delta G^\circ$ | standard free energy change |
| $\Delta H$ | change in heat content accompanying a reaction occurring at constant temperature and pressure |
| $\Delta H^\circ$ | standard heat content change |
| $i$ | current density |
| $i_a$ | anodic current density |
| $i_c$ | cathodic current density |
| $i_L$ | limiting current density |
| $i_0$ | exchange current density |
| $I$ | current |
| $I_L$ | limiting current |
| $k$ | rate constant |
| $k_f$ | rate constant of the forward reaction |

| | |
|---|---|
| $k_b$ | rate constant of the backward reaction |
| $K$ | equilibrium constant |
| $l$ | distance between the two electrodes of a cell |
| $n$ | number of electrons involved in an electrochemical reaction |
| $n_a$ | number of electrons involved in the rate determining step of an electrochemical reaction |
| $p$ | pressure |
| $p_e$ | pressure of a gas in the vicinity of the electro-active sites |
| $p_0$ | pressure with which a gas is supplied to an electrode |
| $r$ | resistance of the electrolyte |
| $R$ | the gas constant |
| $R_A$ | ohmic resistance of the anode |
| $R_C$ | ohmic resistance of the cathode |
| $R_I$ | total internal resistance of a cell |
| $\Delta S$ | change in entropy associated with a reaction |
| $S_Z$ | ionic mobility of species $Z$ |
| $t$ | time |
| $t_Z$ | transport number of species $Z$ |
| $T$ | temperature |
| $V$ | cell e.m.f. |
| $V^\circ$ | cell e.m.f. under standard conditions |
| $V_T$ | terminal voltage |
| $x$ | mole fraction |
| $\alpha$ | transfer coefficient |
| $\delta$ | thickness of the diffusion layer |
| $\varepsilon_C$ | current efficiency |
| $\varepsilon_G$ | free energy efficiency |
| $\varepsilon_T$ | comparative thermal efficiency |
| $\varepsilon_V$ | voltage efficiency |
| $\eta$ | overpotential |
| $\eta_a$ | activation overpotential |
| $\eta_c$ | concentration overpotential |
| $\eta_r$ | ohmic overpotential |
| $\theta$ | fractional surface coverage |
| $\kappa$ | specific conductance |
| $\rho$ | specific resistance |
| $\tau$ | transition time |

*Chapter 1*

# INTRODUCTION

## 1. HISTORICAL BACKGROUND

In 1839 Grove[1] described experiments in which electricity was generated by supplying hydrogen and oxygen to two separate electrodes immersed in sulphuric acid. We now know that in this cell hydrogen was ionized at one electrode releasing electrons to the external circuit. The positively charged hydrogen ions were effectively transported through the sulphuric acid electrolyte to the oxygen electrode. There they reacted with negative hydroxyl ions formed by a reaction between oxygen, water and electrons. Electrons in traversing the external circuit gave rise to an electric current. Thus, this early device incorporated the essential features of what are now called fuel cells. Despite the time which has elapsed since the principle was established, no commercially exploited fuel cell has yet emerged. From this observation it may be inferred, rightly, that the problems to be solved are difficult ones.

The immediate attraction of the fuel cell is its potentially high efficiency. With perfect electrodes and an electrolyte having negligible electrical resistance the whole of the free energy change $\Delta G$ of the overall chemical reactions occurring in the fuel cell is available to do useful work. This was appreciated by Ostwald[2] in 1894. On the other hand the thermal efficiency $\varepsilon$ of a reversible heat engine working between absolute temperatures $T_1 - T_2$ is given by the relation

$$\varepsilon = \frac{T_1 - T_2}{T_1} \quad \text{(Carnot's Theorem).} \tag{1}$$

Since practical heat engines are irreversible and normally operate with a lower temperature of at least 300°K while the upper temperature is limited by the materials of which they are made, thermal efficiencies in excess of 40% are seldom achieved. In considering the efficiency of a heat engine we are concerned with the enthalpy change $\Delta H$ resulting from oxidation of the fuel. The free energy change $\Delta G$ of a chemical reaction is related to the enthalpy change by the equation

$$\Delta G = \Delta H - T\Delta S \qquad (2)$$

where $T$ is the absolute temperature and $\Delta S$ the entropy change. As it is the free energy change which determines the output of a fuel cell, whether the thermal efficiency of a fuel cell is greater than or less than the free energy depends upon the magnitude and sign of $T\Delta S$.

We shall define a fuel cell as a primary cell in which a conventional fuel is supplied to one electrode and an oxidant, usually oxygen or air, to the other. Both electrodes should be unaffected by the reaction as should the electrolyte which separates them. At the "fuel" electrode (anode) of a fuel cell, the fuel is oxidized and electrons are released to the external circuit. Correspondingly at the oxygen electrode (cathode) oxygen is reduced and electrons accepted from the external circuit. The term "conventional fuel" is interpreted fairly liberally and is normally taken to include hydrogen.

It is only fair to point out that there is not universal agreement that a fuel cell should be defined as in the last paragraph. Originally the term was restricted to primary cells intended to oxidize coal, while recently so-called "regenerative fuel cells" have been developed which are more akin to secondary cells.

As fuel cells are essentially low voltage devices giving outputs of about one volt or less, they are usually connected in series to produce a useful output. Such a collection of fuel cells is usually referred to as a fuel cell battery or, more simply, a fuel battery.

Following Grove's original experiments, fuel cell developments followed two different lines which persist to this day. One was to convert the available fuel, then coal, to hydrogen by the water gas process. The hydrogen was then to be used in a hydrogen–oxygen (air) cell. The other was to oxidize the fuel (carbon) directly in a fuel cell.

As long ago as 1855 Becquerel attempted to make a fuel cell which consumed carbon directly. He melted "nitre" in a platinum vessel, placed a carbon rod in the fused salt and obtained a current between the carbon and the platinum. Jablockoff[3] made a similar cell using cast iron instead of platinum for the vessel which retained the electrolyte. These cells were quite unsound in principle as the carbon was attacked by the fused nitrate mainly in a manner which produced no current. It is doubtful if air entered into the reactions of these fuel cells at all although in a true carbon-consuming fuel cell carbon and oxygen derived from the air would be the only reactants consumed.

The concept of a fused electrolyte was also adopted by Jacques[4] who in 1896–97 designed and built a 1.5 kW battery of fuel cells. Each cell consisted of an iron pot containing fused sodium hydroxide into which was placed a carbon rod. Air was bubbled through the fused electrolyte, and current drawn between the iron pot and the carbon rod. Haber and Brunner[5] showed that this was not a true carbon–oxygen cell, hydrogen being produced at the carbon electrode by reaction between carbon and sodium hydroxide. The hydrogen was then oxidized electrolytically at the carbon electrode which presumably contained impurities that catalysed the electrode reaction. It was also found that the presence of a trace of manganese as an impurity was essential to the operation of the cell. Manganese was oxidized to manganate by the air bubbled through the bath of fused alkali. Since the electrolyte in the Jacques cell was not invariant, hydroxide being converted to carbonate, the cell was in no sense a practicable fuel cell.

Taitelbaum (1910)[6] modified the Jacques cell by introducing a porous ceramic diaphragm between the two electrodes. He used fused sodium hydroxide as the electrolyte but added manganate directly to electrolyte adjacent to the oxygen electrode. Reed[7] in 1918 substituted fused borax containing manganese dioxide for the fused sodium hydroxide of Taitelbaum's cell and gold for the iron pots. Air was not bubbled through the electrolyte and it is doubtful if this was a true fuel cell. In all probability the manganese dioxide was the reactant at the cathode. Baur and Ehrenburgh[8] used molten silver containing dissolved oxygen as the cathode in association with a fused borax electrolyte and a carbon fuel electrode. Baur and Preis[9] in 1937 described carbon-consuming fuel cells using solid electrolytes of zirconia stabilized with magnesia or yttria. The penalty paid for having such a stable electrolyte was the necessity of using an operating temperature of 1050°C.

Because of the difficulties associated with carbon-consuming fuel cells, many workers tried the alternative of using hydrogen or carbon monoxide as the fuel. It was intended to derive these gases from coal if a practicable fuel cell resulted from the research.

In 1889 Mond and Langer[10] built a hydrogen–oxygen fuel battery using electrodes made of platinum sheets pierced with many small holes and covered with platinum black. The electrolyte, dilute sulphuric acid, was retained in a porous plaster of Paris diaphragm sandwiched between each pair of electrodes. The output was poor and the cell expensive; it was, however, probably the first fuel cell to give measurable power under reasonably invariant conditions. Siegl[11] reduced the cost of the Mond and Langer cell by supporting the platinum on carbon particles.

Other workers used fused salts as electrolytes for hydrogen–oxygen cells. Beutner[12] used a mixture of molten potassium fluoride and sodium chloride into which he inserted, as electrodes, platinum tubes closed at the end by pieces of thin palladium foil. Although its performance was very poor, this cell probably functioned as a hydrogen concentration cell, hydrogen diffusing in through palladium at the hydrogen electrode and being removed at the oxygen electrode. The mechanism of ionic conduction in the cell is obscure. Baur and Ehrenburgh[8] used their fused borax electrolyte cell with various metals for the hydrogen electrode and an oxygen electrode made of molten silver. Using a nickel fuel electrode they were able to make carbon monoxide and oxygen react in their fuel cell.

It was not until 1939 that Greger[13] proposed the first fuel cell reaction scheme for a fused salt (carbonate) electrolyte that could be considered an invariant system. Oxygen and carbon dioxide were fed to and reacted at the "air" electrode to form carbonate ions:

$$O_2 + 2 CO_2 + 4 e \rightarrow 2 CO_3^{2-} . \tag{3}$$

These ions would transport the charge through the electrolyte and be discharged at the fuel electrode where they would react with hydrogen or carbon monoxide:

$$H_2 + CO_3^{2-} \rightarrow H_2O + CO_2 + 2 e \tag{4}$$

$$CO + CO_3^{2-} \rightarrow 2 CO_2 + 2 e . \tag{5}$$

Apparently this remained only a proposal until after World War II.

Haber and Moser[14] used a hot glass tube as the electrolyte of a carbon monoxide fuel cell. The electrodes were of porous platinum coated inside and outside the tube. Although a good open-circuit potential was obtained when carbon monoxide and oxygen were fed to the electrodes, useful currents could not be drawn from the cell, the internal resistance of which was undoubtedly very high and its mechanism of conduction obscure; it may have been an oxygen concentration cell, oxide ions being formed at the cathode and discharged at the fuel electrode. As for the vast majority of fuel cell work until the 1940's, the investigators' approach was empirical and their reports usually failed to give a clear account of the supposed mechanism of electrode reactions.

This empirical approach also led to attempts to avoid the problems of making fuels and oxygen react directly at electrodes by using "redox" electrodes. The essence of this type of fuel cell electrode is that the chemical and the electrode reactions are physically separated. At the anode an ion present in the electrolyte in a reduced state is oxidized. The oxidized ion is then chemically reduced by fuel in a separate compartment. Correspondingly at a redox cathode an oxidized ion is reduced and then reoxidized by the air. In a fuel cell either one or both electrodes could be of the redox type. The principles of this type of cell are illustrated in Fig. 1, where it will be noted that anode and cathode compartments of the cell are separated by a diaphragm. In this example stannous ions $Sn^{2+}$ are oxidized to stannic ions $Sn^{4+}$ at the "fuel" electrode (anode). Electrons are released to the external circuit by this process. In the fuel regenerator the stannic ions are reduced to stannous ions by the fuel (hydrogen) with the release of hydrogen ions. Hydrogen ions transport the current across the diaphragm (shown dotted) which separates the anode and cathode compartments of the cell. Correspondingly, at the cathode, bromine is reduced to bromide ions which are reoxidized to bromine by oxygen in the oxygen regenerator.

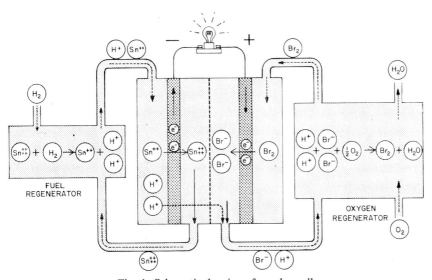

Fig. 1. Schematic drawing of a redox cell.

Jungner[15] was probably the first to employ a redox cell. He used a cell consisting of two carbon electrodes immersed in warm concentrated sulphuric acid, a porous partition separating the anode and cathode. Usually the cathode was of graphite, and air was bubbled into the electrolyte which contained an "oxygen carrier" such as nitric oxide. The fuel and anode consisted of lumps of carbonized matter (*e.g.* charcoal) which may have reduced the sulphuric acid to sulphurous acid. In any event the cells were not very successful. Taitelbaum[6] also made redox cells using hot concentrated sulphuric acid as electrolyte. He introduced various metallic ions capable of existing in two states of oxidation, *e.g.* iron, mercury, cerium and vanadium. He preferred vanadium in both compartments and used cells operating at 200°C. However, as considerations of the potentials and mass transport required will show, it is unsound to use the same redox couple in both sides of a fuel cell. Nernst[16] made similar fuel cells operating at 40–60°C and favoured titanium, thallium and cerium ions. He also suggested the use of chlorine gas produced and regenerated by the Deacon process in order to solve the problems of the oxygen electrode.

Rideal and Evans[17] made redox fuel cells with fused electrolytes which were of a glass-like nature and which used ferric and manganese ions in the electrolyte in both anode and cathode compartments. These cells were not successful. Rideal and Evans had more success with a "regenerable metal electrode". The idea was to use a metal electrode (zinc or preferably tin) which formed an insoluble hydroxide when oxidized anodically in dilute hydrochloric acid. It was intended to reduce the tin externally and return it to the cell. The associated air electrode employed a ferric ferrous redox couple. Although this fuel cell gave some output, it was very inefficient.

As many workers were fascinated by the potentialities of the fuel cell this historical account is not complete, but further descriptions of early work are given in the review by Baur and Tobler[18]. Nevertheless it is clear that by 1930 most of the potential fuel cell systems had been outlined in principle. There had, however, been no real attempt to engineer a useful power unit. Then, in 1932 Bacon working at Cambridge (England) started to investigate the possibility of building a powerful fuel battery.

Bacon's engineering approach contrasted with that of earlier workers as well as of his contemporaries. Whereas others had concentrated on laboratory studies of the electrochemical aspects of fuel cells, usually with the object of burning conventional fuels, Bacon courageously set out to make a useful power source based on a simple hydrogen–oxygen cell. This pioneer work which culminated in the demonstration of a five kilowatt hydrogen–oxygen fuel battery in 1959[19] undoubtedly did much to stimulate the current wave of interest in fuel cells.

One of the concepts introduced by Bacon was that of the use of fuel batteries as replacements for secondary batteries, instead of as primary energy convertors. He saw that when substantial power outputs were required over prolonged periods, the hydrogen–oxygen fuel battery associated with high pressure gas storage cylinders would be much more compact than secondary batteries, and it is for this purpose that fuel batteries are finding their first use. In particular, the paramount need for lightness has stimulated the development of hydrogen–oxygen fuel batteries for the United States space programme. As will be apparent from the rest of this book, the many problems in making practical fuel cells for more widespread use are being tackled with resolution and this will undoubtedly result in the production of commercially useful fuel batteries.

## 2. CLASSIFICATION

To illustrate the problems to be solved in fuel cells it is convenient to consider the main processes occurring in a simple hydrogen–oxygen fuel cell (Fig. 2). The hydrogen (fuel) electrode is the anode and has negative polarity. Correspondingly, the oxygen electrode or cathode is positive. It will be noted that this is the reverse of the electrolysis cell or voltameter. Hydrogen gas must be transported to the surface of the hydrogen electrode where it is in

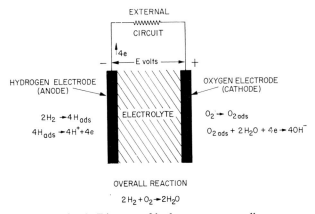

Fig. 2. Diagram of hydrogen–oxygen cell.

contact with the electrolyte. The adsorbed hydrogen must then ionize into positive hydrogen ions and electrons which are released to the external circuit. At the oxygen electrode oxygen gas must be transported to the electrode surface at which electrons from the external circuit react with adsorbed oxygen and water to form negative hydroxyl ions. An ionic transport mechanism has to exist between the two electrodes such that hydrogen and hydroxyl ions react to form water. In a practical fuel cell provision must be made for removal of this water. The e.m.f., $E$, between the electrodes of an ideal or reversible fuel cell is determined by the thermodynamics of the overall cell reaction. This subject is considered in detail in the next chapter. When current is drawn from a fuel cell its e.m.f. is always less than that of an ideal fuel cell. This is because various losses or forms of polarization are introduced when the electrode reactions occur at a finite rate. Chapters 3 and 4 are devoted to consideration of these kinetic effects and the means by which they may be measured, calculated or otherwise investigated.

Before considering fuel cells and their electrode processes in detail it is perhaps useful to outline the main types of fuel cell and this will now be done.

### *(a) Fuel cells with aqueous electrolytes (hydrated ion transport)*

*Liquid electrolytes*

Historically the oldest and still, in many ways, the most important fuel cells are those employing aqueous electrolytes. In all of these cells hydrogen or hydroxyl ions play an important part in both the electrode processes and the current transport through the electrolyte. The first fuel cells used *acid electrolytes*, as do many modern ones. In such fuel cells hydrogen ions are formed at the fuel electrode by electrochemical oxidation of the fuel. If the fuel is hydrogen, then the hydrogen ions are formed by direct ionization:

$$H_2 \rightarrow 2\,H^+ + 2\,e\,. \tag{6}$$

Although it is usual to refer to the "hydrogen ion" $H^+$ in electrochemistry, in aqueous solution the hydrogen ion is invariably hydrated to form the hydronium ion $H_3O^+$. To simplify equations, this water of hydration is usually ignored.

Fuel cells in which the hydrogen ions are derived directly from hydrogen are described in Chapter 5. Alternatively, more complex fuels such as carbon monoxide, methyl alcohol and hydrocarbons may be used in which case the fuel electrode processes are more involved. However, the net electrochemical result must still be the oxidation of the fuel to hydrogen ions, the oxidation of the carbon in the molecule to carbon dioxide being part of the overall process. The hydrogen ions formed at the fuel electrode in an acid electrolyte are ultimately discharged at the oxygen (air) electrode to form water:

$$O_2 + 4\,H^+ + 4\,e \rightarrow 2\,H_2O\,. \tag{7}$$

Sulphuric acid is usually used as electrolyte for acid fuel cells intended to operate below 80°C, and phosphoric acid at higher temperatures.

Alkaline electrolytes are frequently used, usually a strong solution of potassium hydroxide. In this type of fuel cell hydroxyl ions play a dominant role in transport processes within the electrolyte. They are formed at the oxygen electrode by electrochemical reduction of oxygen and reaction with water:

$$O_2 + 2\,H_2O + 4\,e \rightarrow 4\,OH^-\,. \tag{8}$$

Strongly alkaline electrolytes are usually limited to hydrogen, hydrazine $(N_2H_4)$ and ammonia $(NH_3)$ as fuels, *i.e.* fuels which do not contain carbon. This is because alkaline electrolytes react with carbon dioxide formed from the oxidation of carbon-containing fuels:

$$CO_2 + 2\,OH^- \rightarrow CO_3^{2-} + H_2O\,. \tag{9}$$

Instead of using a strongly alkaline electrolyte it is possible to use strong buffer solutions. The most common example of this type of electrolyte is potassium carbonate. In such electrolytes hydroxyl ions are in equilibrium with carbonate and bicarbonate ions:

$$CO_3^{2-} + H_2O \rightleftharpoons OH^- + HCO_3^- \tag{10}$$

$$HCO_3^- + H_2O \rightleftharpoons OH^- + H_2CO_3\,. \tag{11}$$

As hydroxyl ions are removed at the fuel electrode they are replaced immediately by hydrolysis. Although these hydroxyl ions take part in the electrode reactions, the carbonate and bicarbonate ions are the negative ions primarily responsible for current transport.

While acid buffer solutions could presumably be used in a similar manner to carbonate and bicarbonate electrolytes, they have received little attention apart from their use in some "biochemical" fuel cells which use live bacteria or enzymes to catalyse electrode reactions. Certainly the low electrical conductivity and poor performance of oxygen electrodes in such electrolytes is no encouragement to their use.

*References p. 13*

## Immobilized aqueous electrolytes

An aqueous electrolyte need not necessarily be mobile, and various methods have been proposed for retaining both acid and alkaline electrolytes in matrices or gel form. Mond and Langer[10] used a porous sheet (plaster of Paris) to retain the sulphuric acid electrolyte of their hydrogen–oxygen cell. Garner and Williams[20] proposed the use of a gelled electrolyte using, for example, finely divided silica as the gelling agent with an acid electrolyte. Wynveen[21] has emphasized the advantages of absorbing an alkaline electrolyte with asbestos fibres.

## Ion exchange electrolytes

Instead of an electrolyte solution it is possible, as Grubb[22] showed, to use ion exchange membranes to separate the electrodes of a fuel cell. Both organic and inorganic ion exchange materials have been used. It is usual to employ cationic (hydrogen) exchange membranes as they are more stable and have higher conductivities than anionic exchange membranes. If air is used as the oxidant, the carbon dioxide which it contains forms carbonate ions which would gradually replace the hydroxyl groups on an anionic exchange membrane and reduce its performance as an electrolyte.

## Electrode systems for fuel cells with aqueous electrolytes

The cathode of low temperature fuel cells with aqueous electrolytes is almost invariably supplied with oxygen or air. This necessitates some form of three-phase electrode which stabilizes a gas liquid interface in contact with the electrode catalyst which must be an electronic conductor. Occasionally hydrogen peroxide has been used directly as the source of oxygen for a fuel cell cathode. In such cases the oxidant is dissolved in the electrolyte and a two-phase system is achieved, an electrically conducting plate coated with catalyst immersed in the electrolyte sufficing as the cathode.

The corresponding fuel electrodes are usually of the three-phase type when gaseous fuels such as hydrogen are used. Occasionally hydrogen-permeable membranes are employed. Where a fuel, such as methanol or hydrazine, which is soluble in the electrolyte is used in a low temperature fuel cell a two-phase system again results. As the electrode may be wholly immersed in the electrolyte, its physical form is less important than it is for three-phase electrodes. Such electrodes are considered in Chapter 6.

It is essential that electrodes and their catalysts should not be chemically attacked by the electrolyte at any potential likely to be attained in the fuel cell. This is a stringent requirement for all fuel cells.

*(b)  Fuel cells with non-aqueous electrolytes*

In high temperature fuel cells operating at 500°C or higher there are two major types of electrolyte, fused alkali metal carbonates described in Chapter 7 and solid ionically conducting oxides (Chapter 8).

The fused carbonates have higher electrical conductivity and permit much lower operating temperatures than the oxide electrolytes but, as already noted in eqn. (3), carbonate electrolytes require the addition of carbon dioxide to the gas supplied to the cathode. For the oxide electrolyte the cathode reaction is very simple:

$$O_2 + 4\,e \to 2\,O^{2-} . \tag{12}$$

The anode reactions for this type of fuel cell are correspondingly simple, *e.g.*

$$H_2 + O^{2-} \to H_2O + 2\,e \tag{13}$$

$$CO + O^{2-} \to CO_2 + 2\,e . \tag{14}$$

Corresponding anode reactions for fuel cells with fused carbonate electrolytes were given in eqns. (4) and (5).

The electrodes for carbonate cells are usually of the three-phase type, although hydrogen-permeable silver–palladium membranes are sometimes used as fuel electrodes. Oxide cells usually employ porous metal electrodes for both anode and cathode, although sometimes molten silver containing dissolved oxygen is used as the cathode.

### 3. THE FUEL CELL IN POWER SYSTEMS

It is usual to specify the performance of a fuel cell in terms of the current density given by the electrodes at a stated output voltage. Current densities are always quoted in terms of the area determined by the linear dimensions of the electrode although the true surface area of the electrode is usually very much greater than this.

Unlike most heat engines, the efficiency of a simple fuel cell is greatest at low loads and falls as the load is increased. If still more current is drawn from the fuel cell, both power and efficiency are further reduced. These points are illustrated by Fig. 3.

Although the current/voltage characteristic is an important index of electrode performance with fuel cells it is by no means the whole story. Weight, volume, efficiency, life and cost are all interrelated. There are prob-

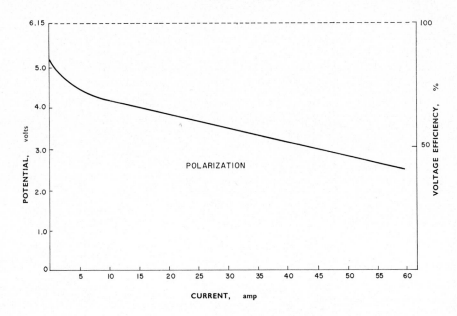

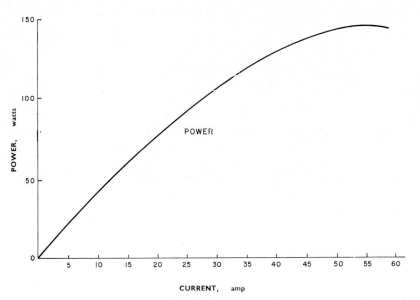

Fig. 3. Polarization and power curves for a hydrogen–air fuel cell battery; 5-cell unit (electrolyte 6$N$ KOH at 45°C).

lems too, both of power output and carbon formation associated with the uses of hydrocarbon fuels and these are discussed in Chapter 9.

For completeness, a variety of fuel cells other than those already discussed are described in Chapter 10. This chapter may perhaps be considered to illustrate the fertility of the minds which have endeavoured to bypass the problems of the fuel cells described in the previous chapters.

When a suitable fuel cell electrode system has been developed, there are many engineering problems to be solved before a useful power source can be built and these are considered in Chapter 11. In the concluding chapter, the state of development of fuel cells at the time of writing is considered. From this final chapter it will be clear that while fuel cells have been developed very considerably during the past few years, much remains to be done before they become power sources suitable for widespread commercial use.

## REFERENCES

1 W. R. GROVE, *Phil. Mag.*, **14** (1839) 127.
2 W. OSTWALD, *Z. Elektrochem.*, **1** (1894) 122.
3 P. JABLOCKOFF, *Compt. Rend.*, **85** (1877) 1052.
4 W. W. JACQUES, *Z. Elektrochem.*, **4** (1897) 129.
5 F. HABER AND R. BRUNNER, *Z. Elektrochem.*, **10** (1904) 697; *ibid.*, **12** (1906) 78.
6 J. TAITELBAUM, *Z. Elektrochem.*, **16** (1910) 286.
7 A. REED, *Trans. Electrochem. Soc.*, **33** (1918) 89.
8 E. BAUR AND H. EHRENBURGH, *Z. Elektrochem.*, **18** (1912) 1002.
9 E. BAUR AND H. PREIS, *Z. Elektrochem.*, **43** (1937) 727.
10 L. MOND AND C. LANGER, *Proc. Roy. Soc.*, **46** (1889) 296.
11 K. SIEGL, *Elektrotech. Z.*, **34** (1913) 1317.
12 R. BEUTNER, *Z. Elektrochem.*, **17** (1911) 91.
13 H. H. GREGER, *U.S.Patent 2,175,523* (1939).
14 F. HABER AND A. MOSER, *Z. Elektrochem.*, **11** (1904) 593.
15 E. W. JUNGNER, *U.S.Patent 884,664* (1908).
16 W. NERNST, *German Patents 259,241* (1912), *264,026* (1912), *and 265,414* (1912).
17 E. N. RIDEAL AND U. R. EVANS, *Trans. Faraday Soc.*, **17** (1921–2) 466.
18 E. BAUR AND J. TOBLER, *Z. Elektrochem.*, **39** (1933) 169.
19 F. T. BACON, Chap. 5 in *Fuel Cells*, (ed. by G. J. YOUNG), Vol. 1, Reinhold, New York, 1960.
20 P. J. GARNER AND K. R. WILLIAMS, *Brit. Patent 884,584* (1960).
21 R. A. WYNVEEN, Chap. 10 in *Fuel Cells*, (ed. by W. MITCHELL), Academic Press, New York, 1963.
22 W. T. GRUBB, *U.S.Patent 2,913,511* (1959).

# Chapter 2

# ELECTRODE POTENTIALS AND EFFICIENCY

It has been noted in Chapter 1 that, as the fuel cell is not a heat engine, its efficiency is not restricted by the Carnot cycle. Thus fuel cells may be capable of higher efficiencies than heat engines. It is the purpose of this chapter to discuss the significance of electrode potentials and efficiency and to do this it is necessary to remind the reader of standard aspects of electrochemistry. Since the derivations of the thermodynamic equations used can be found in many textbooks[1] only the equations themselves are stated here as required.

### 1. REVERSIBLE ELECTRODE POTENTIALS

Processes occurring at electrodes involve an interchange of electrons and are therefore oxidation–reduction reactions which may reach a position of equilibrium that can be expressed as

$$x\,O + n\,e \rightleftharpoons y\,R \qquad (1)$$

where $O$ is an oxidized species and $R$ a reduced species.

A simple example of this type of reaction is the equilibrium between ferric and ferrous ions

$$Fe^{3+} + e \rightleftharpoons Fe^{2+}$$

In the special case where reaction (1) is in a state of reversible equilibrium (*i.e.* a state in which every stage in the reaction is in dynamic equilibrium and there is no *net* reaction), there will be a difference in potential between the electrode and electrolyte. This is called the electrode potential of the system. Nernst[2] derived an equation correlating the equilibrium potential $E$, of the electrode and the activities of the species involved for a metal in equilibrium with its cation. More generally, his equation is written as

$$E = E^\circ + \frac{RT}{nF} \ln \frac{a_O^x}{a_R^y} \qquad (2)$$

where $R$ is the gas constant (joules/°C/mole), $T$ is the absolute temperature (°K), $F$ is the faraday (96,500 coulombs/equivalent), $a$ is the activity of the species involved, $n$ is the number of electrons involved (equivalents/mole).

When $a_O = a_R = 1$, $E = E°$, $E°$ being defined as the potential of the system when all the species involved in the equilibrium are at unit activity. This potential is called the standard (or normal) potential of the reaction at equilibrium. $E°$ is directly related to the standard free energies of the species involved in the equilibrium by the relationship $\Delta G° = -nFE°$ ($\Delta G°$, the standard free energy change for the reaction, must be expressed in joules/mole for $E°$ to be in volts).

So far only a single electrode reaction has been considered but it is not possible to measure the potential corresponding to a single equilibrium since only potential differences can be measured. Thus there must be some second process to give a point of reference and some arbitrary zero of potential must be chosen. By convention the potential corresponding to the reversible equilibrium between hydrogen gas at one atmosphere pressure and hydrogen ions at unit activity is taken as zero at all temperatures. This defines the *standard hydrogen potential* to which all other potentials may be related.

As an example, the potential of the equilibrium

$$O_2 + 2\,H_2O + 4\,e \rightleftharpoons 4\,OH^- \tag{3}$$

may be calculated on the hydrogen scale. For this reaction

$$E = E° + \frac{RT}{4F} \ln \frac{a_{O_2}}{a_{OH^-}^4} \tag{4}$$

$a_{H_2O}$ being taken as unity.

From free energy data $E°$ is calculated to be 0.401 volt at 25°C and if the oxygen is at one atmosphere pressure then

$$E = 0.401 - \frac{RT}{F} \ln a_{OH^-} \text{ at } 25°C$$

$$= 0.401 - 0.059 \log_{10} a_{OH^-}.$$

Hence,

$$E = 1.229 \text{ volt for } a_{OH^-} = 10^{-14}$$

or

$$E = 0.401 \text{ volt for } a_{OH^-} = 1.$$

That is, on the hydrogen scale the potential of the equilibrium (3) is 1.229 volt at pH=0 or 0.401 volt at pH=14.

In a solution containing hydroxyl ions at unit activity the potential of the equilibrium between hydrogen, hydroxyl ions and water can be calculated to be −0.828 volt. It follows that any cell comprising an oxygen electrode and a hydrogen electrode, *both operating reversibly*, with the gases at one atmosphere pressure will have a voltage of 1.229 volt. This voltage will be independent of the hydrogen ion concentration of the medium *provided the activity of water remains at unity* (Fig. 4).

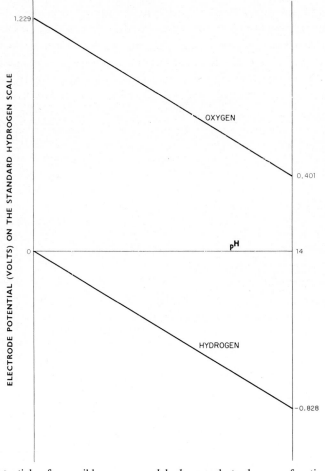

Fig. 4. Potentials of reversible oxygen and hydrogen electrodes as a function of pH.

The potential of 1.229 volt calculated above is the theoretical difference in potential between the two equilibria

and
$$O_2 + 2 H_2O + 4 e \rightleftharpoons 4 OH^-$$
$$2 H^+ + 2 e \rightleftharpoons H_2$$

at a temperature of 25°C with the gases at one atmosphere pressure when *no* current is flowing in any external circuit. The hydrogen equilibrium is readily established but special precautions must be taken to ensure that oxygen is in equilibrium with hydroxyl ions according to the equation written above. Consequently, an accurate check of the theoretical potential has rarely been made. Bockris and Huq[3], using highly purified solutions, measured a potential of $1.24 \pm 0.02$ volt which was stable for about an hour but Hoare[4] considered that this value was probably that of a mixed potential, *i.e.* not an equilibrium potential but a steady state one. It was considered that reaction (3) and the reaction

$$PtO + 2 H^+ + 2 e \rightleftharpoons Pt + H_2O$$

might both be involved. In more recent work Hoare[5], using platinum electrodes covered with an oxide film formed by prolonged contact with nitric acid, measured a potential of $1.225 \pm 0.010$ volt which was stable for about 24 hours. With rhodium electrodes similarly passivated, a potential of $1.225 \pm 0.003$ volt, stable for about 2 hours, was measured. Hoare suggests that only when the electrode surface is completely covered with oxide, is equilibrium (3) established; the electrode surface is thereby inert towards oxygen and a true equilibrium potential is established.

Recently, Schuldiner and Roe[6] have claimed that the equilibria involved on a platinum surface are

$$O_2 + H^+ + e \rightleftharpoons HO_2 \qquad \text{at pH 0–0.75}$$

$$O_2 + 2 H^+ + 2 e \rightleftharpoons H_2O_2 \qquad \text{at higher pH}$$

and these processes agree well with the mechanism proposed by Berl[7], who showed that oxygen is reduced on carbon electrodes by a process involving hydrogen peroxide

$$O_2 + H_2O + 2 e \rightleftharpoons HO_2^- + OH^- \tag{5}$$

from which the equation

$$E = -0.076 + \frac{RT}{2F} \ln \frac{a_{O_2}}{a_{HO_2^-} a_{OH^-}}$$

may be written. Because of the high rate of decomposition of $HO_2^-$ its steady state concentration is very low and $E$ is about one volt on effective peroxide-decomposing catalysts. The oxygen formed by the decomposition

$$HO_2^- \rightarrow OH^- + \tfrac{1}{2} O_2 \qquad (6)$$

is used again in the electrochemical reaction. Since the overall reaction as expressed by eqns. (5) and (6) is identical with reaction (3) it follows that, as the ability of a series of catalysts to decompose peroxide increases, the closer to 1.229 volt will be the measured potential.

*(a) Effect of pressure on electrode potentials and cell e.m.f.'s*

For reaction (3), by applying the Nernst equation at two different oxygen pressures it is easily shown that

$$\Delta E = E_2 - E_1 = \frac{RT}{4F} \ln \frac{p_2}{p_1}$$

where $E_1$ and $E_2$ are the electrode potentials at pressures $p_1$ and $p_2$ respectively. It is clear that $\Delta E$ remains small even if $p_1$ and $p_2$ differ quite appreciably. Thus an electrode supplied with air instead of pure oxygen has a theoretical potential only a few millivolts lower than a true oxygen electrode. Similar considerations apply to fuel electrodes and an electrode supplied with diluted hydrogen will have a potential only a few millivolts higher than one provided with hydrogen at a pressure of one atmosphere. These facts are important as they indicate that fuel cells may be able to use dilute reactants without the cell e.m.f. being seriously affected.

The pressure variation of the e.m.f. of a reversible cell reaction occurring at constant temperature is expressed by

$$-nF \frac{\delta V}{\delta p} = \frac{\delta \Delta G}{\delta p} = \Delta v \qquad (7)$$

where $\Delta v$ is the volume change for the reaction. It is clear from eqn. (7) that if all the reactants and products are liquids (or solids) then, since $\Delta v$ will be very small, pressure will have little influence on $\Delta G$ and the variation of e.m.f. with pressure will be small. With a hydrogen–oxygen fuel cell in which large volume changes may occur, a reasonably large pressure coefficient will be observed.

### (b) Effect of electrolyte concentration on cell e.m.f.'s

Lee[8] has evaluated the effect of potassium hydroxide concentration on the theoretical e.m.f. of a hydrogen–oxygen cell. If ideal gas behaviour is assumed, $\Delta v$ for the hydrogen–oxygen reaction is expressed as

$$\Delta v = RT \left\{ \frac{2}{p_{H_2O}} - \left( \frac{2}{p_{H_2}} + \frac{1}{p_{O_2}} \right) \right\} \tag{8}$$

where $p_{H_2O}$ is in the partial pressure of water vapour in equilibrium with the electrolyte. As the electrolyte concentration increases, $p_{H_2O}$ decreases and from eqns. (7) and (8) $V$ increases (Table 1).

TABLE 1

CALCULATED VARIATION OF THE CELL e.m.f. FOR THE REACTION $H_2 + \frac{1}{2} O_2 \rightleftharpoons H_2O$ WITH POTASSIUM HYDROXIDE ELECTROLYTE CONCENTRATION AT $25°C$

| KOH concentration (%wt.) | Standard e.m.f. (volts) |
| --- | --- |
| 1 | 1.229 |
| 10 | 1.230 |
| 20 | 1.232 |
| 30 | 1.235 |
| 40 | 1.243 |
| 50 | 1.251 |

### (c) Effect of temperature on cell e.m.f.'s

The standard e.m.f. of a cell at any temperature is calculated from the standard free energy change for the cell reaction at that temperature. This can be computed from the temperature coefficients of the heat capacities ($C_p^{\circ}$) of the species involved as a function of temperature and a value of both $\Delta S^{\circ}$ and $\Delta H^{\circ}$ at one particular temperature (usually $298°K$).

Empirically it is found that

$$C_p^{\circ} = a + bT + cT^2$$

whence

$$\Delta C_p^{\circ} = \Delta a + \Delta bT + \Delta cT^2$$

where $\Delta$ (function) represents the difference between the values of (function) for the products and reactants involved in the stoichiometric equation.

Since

$$\Delta H_T^\circ = \Delta H_{298}^\circ + \int \Delta C_p^\circ dT$$

and

$$\Delta S_T^\circ = \Delta S_{298}^\circ + \int \frac{\Delta C_p^\circ}{T} dT$$

it follows that

$$\Delta H_T^\circ = \Delta H_{298}^\circ + \Delta a T + \tfrac{1}{2}\Delta b T^2 + \tfrac{1}{3}\Delta c T^3 \qquad (9)$$

and

$$\Delta S_T^\circ = \Delta S_{298}^\circ + \Delta a \ln T + \Delta b T + \tfrac{1}{2}\Delta c T^2 . \qquad (10)$$

Values of $a$, $b$, $c$, $\Delta H_{298}^\circ$, $\Delta S_{298}^\circ$ are available from tables[9] and may be used to calculate $\Delta H_T^\circ$ and $\Delta S_T^\circ$. From the results $\Delta G_T^\circ$ (and hence $V_T^\circ$) can be calculated from the Gibbs–Helmholtz equation

$$\Delta G = \Delta H - T \Delta S \qquad (11)$$

A simpler, though less accurate, method of finding values of $\Delta G_T^\circ$ for elevated temperature hydrogen–oxygen cells and for carbon monoxide–oxygen cells is to use the data of Richardson and Jeffes[10]. For the reaction

$$2 H_2(g) + O_2(g) \rightarrow 2 H_2O(g)$$

$$\Delta G_T^\circ = -118{,}000 + 26.75T \text{ cal (in the range 373–2500°K)}$$

and for the reaction

$$2 CO(g) + O_2(g) \rightarrow 2 CO_2(g)$$

$$\Delta G_T^\circ = -135{,}100 + 41.50T \text{ cal (in the range 298–2500°K).}$$

Accuracy is claimed to be $\pm 1$ kcal, which is equivalent to an error of $\pm 0.01$ volt in the calculated value of $V_T^\circ$.

Either of these two methods allows the standard e.m.f. of a cell reaction to be calculated at any temperature. When the reactants and products are not present at unit activity then the Nernst equation (2) must be used.

## 2. EFFICIENCY

Four aspects of the efficiency of a fuel cell must be considered:
(1) voltage efficiency
(2) current (or Faradaic) efficiency

(3) free energy efficiency

(4) comparative thermal efficiency.

If a hydrogen–oxygen fuel cell were to give a potential of 1.23 volt when producing current, then all the free energy of the reaction would be completely converted to electric power and the cell would be running at a *voltage efficiency of 100%*. In practice, most hydrogen–oxygen cells run at potentials in the range 0.6–0.8 volt and if efficiency is defined by

$$\frac{\text{operating voltage}}{\text{theoretical voltage}} = \text{voltage efficiency } (\varepsilon_v)$$

such cells are running at about 50–65% efficiency. The voltage efficiency is simply measured during the operation of a fuel cell or fuel cell battery and, provided the current efficiency ($\varepsilon_c$) (defined below) is 100%, it has the same value as the free energy efficiency ($\varepsilon_G$). (*q.v.*)

*Current efficiency* is best illustrated by means of an example. Considering the reaction

$$C_3H_8 + 6\,H_2O \rightarrow 3\,CO_2 + 20\,H^+ + 20\,e$$

if the *sole* product is $CO_2$ then all the current produced from a fuel cell consuming propane (or the current passed in the case of the anodic oxidation of propane by an electrolytic technique) will be used in forming $CO_2$ and the current efficiency is 100%. If any side products or intermediates are formed, then the end product is formed at a lower efficiency. The current efficiency, based on an assumed stoichiometric equation is therefore defined in the following ways:

$$\varepsilon_c = \frac{\text{number of electrons obtained per mole of reactant } (n')}{\text{number of electrons theoretically available per mole of reactant } (n)}$$

$$\varepsilon_c = \frac{\text{observed current}}{\text{current calculated from rate of consumption of reactant}}$$

$$\varepsilon_c = \frac{\text{number of coulombs equivalent to the amount of end product formed}}{\text{number of coulombs passed during electrolysis}}.$$

It has been implied that the current efficiency may be less than 100%. There are several reasons for this; ignoring mechanical faults such as leakage or evaporation of reactants, there are several chemical reasons, as follows:

(1) Side reactions may occur which yield *fewer* electron equivalents per mole than the required reaction.

(2) When a reaction proceeds through a series of consecutive reactions to the final end product, some loss or build-up of intermediates may occur.

(3) Non-electrochemical decomposition of the reactant may occur.

(4) Chemical reaction may occur between the fuel and oxidant. This is particularly likely in the type of fuel cell in which the fuel is dissolved in the electrolyte.

Most practical fuel cells are likely to use air as an oxidant and here there is only a secondary need to have a high current efficiency. If the air is to be supplied under pressure or circulated mechanically, then the more air that is required, the greater the power that is needed to supply it. Current efficiencies of 80–90% may be quite adequate for air electrodes but in the case of expensive fuels $\varepsilon_c$ should approach 100%.

The current efficiency may be different at each electrode of a cell and hence to calculate the *free energy efficiency* from $\varepsilon_c$ and $\varepsilon_v$, the potential of each electrode should be related directly to the standard hydrogen electrode; $\varepsilon_G$ of the individual electrodes can then be determined separately. Since $\Delta G = -nFE$ and $\Delta G' = -n'FE'$ it follows that

$$\varepsilon_G = \frac{\Delta G'}{\Delta G} = \varepsilon_v \cdot \varepsilon_c \tag{12}$$

(where $\Delta G'$ is the quantity of the free energy change for the reaction which appears as a voltage) and $\varepsilon_G$—the free energy efficiency of a single electrode—can be calculated. Free energy efficiency may be defined as the fraction of the available free energy that is converted to electric power. It is always preferable to use free energy efficiency rather than voltage efficiency since $\varepsilon_G$ gives a better measure of the chemical energy that is being converted to electrical energy. $\varepsilon_G$ should always be quoted with respect to the power being obtained since $\varepsilon_G$ varies with the current supplied to an external circuit.

One further aspect of efficiency must be mentioned. In order to facilitate comparison of fuel cells and heat engines the *ideal* or *comparative thermal efficiency* ($\varepsilon_T$) may be used. This is defined as

$$\varepsilon_T = \frac{\Delta G'}{\Delta H} = \varepsilon_G \cdot \frac{\Delta G}{\Delta H}$$

and may (even when $\varepsilon_G = 100\%$) be less than 100%. As an example for the reaction

$$H_2 + \tfrac{1}{2} O_2 \rightleftharpoons H_2O_{(l)}$$

for which $\Delta G° = -56.69$ kcal and $\Delta H° = -68.32$ kcal at 298°K, it follows that a fuel cell with a free energy efficiency of 60% is as efficient as a device burning hydrogen at a thermal efficiency of $60 \times (56.69/68.32) = 50\%$. This point must be remembered when comparisons are made between heat engines and fuel cells. It should also be realized that, if electrical power is required from a particular fuel, then the efficiency of the fuel cell should be compared with the overall efficiency of the heat engine burning the fuel and the generator converting mechanical energy to electricity.

### 3. MEASUREMENT OF CURRENT EFFICIENCY

In section 2 it was noted that the current efficiency of a process may be less than 100% for a number of reasons and that it is desirable that it should be as near 100% as possible. When screening a fuel for use in a fuel cell it is desirable to measure the current efficiency with which the reactant is converted to the final reaction product.

The measurement of current efficiency may be carried out either in a suitable half-cell by an electrolysis method or in a complete fuel cell (see Chapter 3). If gaseous products such as nitrogen are formed it is necessary to attach gas measuring equipment to the cell. When carbon dioxide is formed the effluent gas from the cell is passed through suitable drying tubes and $CO_2$ absorption equipment. If the products are liquid, samples of the electrolyte may be analysed by standard methods. The number of coulombs passed during electrolysis may be measured with a suitable coulometer; silver, copper or gas coulometers are usually employed. Alternatively, if a source of constant current is used for the electrolysis the number of coulombs is easily calculated from the product of the current and the duration of the electrolysis.

The potential of the electrode under study should be effectively constant during operation to ensure that the mechanism of the electrode reaction does not vary. A rigorous method of achieving this is by means of a potentiostat (see Chapter 4) whereby the electrode potential is automatically maintained at a constant value.

Many examples of current efficiency studies are described in the literature. Katan and Galiotto[11] have studied the anodic oxidation of ammonia in potassium hydroxide electrolyte confirming Wynveen's[12] findings that nitrogen is produced with high efficiency. Pavela[13] has measured the current efficiency for the anodic oxidation of methanol both in sulphuric acid, where the end product is carbon dioxide, and in sodium hydroxide, where the end product is formate (see Chapter 6). Schlatter[14] has found that propane and butane are oxidized to $CO_2$ with about 100% current efficiency in a complete cell, whilst Wroblowa, Piersma and Bockris[15] have found that ethylene is oxidized with high efficiency in both acidic and alkaline electrolytes.

## 4. REFERENCE ELECTRODES

The potentials of individual fuel cell electrodes are measured against suitable reference electrodes which have accurately known potentials on the standard hydrogen scale. Whilst it is beyond the scope of this book to discuss reference electrode systems in detail, brief mention will be made of reference electrodes which have been commonly used in studying the characteristics of fuel cell electrodes. For a more detailed discussion the reader is referred to a recent treatise on reference electrodes by Ives and Janz[16].

### (1) The calomel electrode

The calomel electrode has been widely used in fuel cell studies over a wide temperature range. It consists of a pool of mercury covered with a thin layer of mercurous chloride in contact with a solution of potassium chloride. Electrical contact to the mercury is made by means of a platinum wire. The potential of the electrode on the standard hydrogen scale is determined by the chloride ion concentration and by the temperature according to

$$E_{cal} = E^{\circ}_{cal} - 2.303 \frac{RT}{F} \log_{10} a_{Cl^-} \tag{13}$$

where $a_{Cl^-}$ is the activity of the chloride ion in solution and $E^{\circ}_{cal}$ is 0.268 volt. The potentials, on the standard hydrogen scale, of calomel electrodes containing 0.1N, N and saturated KCl solutions at $t°C$ are:

|  | E, volt (t°C) |
|---|---|
| $Hg/Hg_2Cl_2/KCl$ (0.1N) | $+0.334 - 9 \times 10^{-5}(t-25)$ |
| $Hg/Hg_2Cl_2/KCl$ (1.0N) | $+0.280 - 28 \times 10^{-5}(t-25)$ |
| $Hg/Hg_2Cl_2/KCl$ (sat.) | $+0.241 - 66 \times 10^{-5}(t-25)$ |

### (2) The mercury–mercuric oxide electrode

The mercury–mercuric oxide electrode is useful as a reference electrode in alkaline solutions. Donnan and Allmand[17] give the following values for the potential of the Hg–HgO electrode on the standard hydrogen scale in various alkaline solutions.

$$E, volt \ (t°C)$$

| | |
|---|---|
| Hg/HgO/$N$ KOH | $+0.1100 - 11 \times 10^{-5}(t-25)$ |
| Hg/HgO/$N$ NaOH | $+0.1135 - 11 \times 10^{-5}(t-25)$ |
| Hg/HgO/0.1$N$ NaOH | $+0.1690 - 7 \times 10^{-5}(t-25)$ |

where $t$ is the operating temperature in °C. No special precautions are necessary with this electrode, apart from the use of components of reasonable purity. Donnan and Allmand found that the electrode was stable for several days and its potential was reproducible to $\pm 0.1$ mV and was independent of the form of mercuric oxide used.

*(3) The hydrogen electrode*

The hydrogen electrode has found wide use in the study of fuel cell electrodes because of its applicability over a wide range of pH and temperature. It is also attractive in that it is a clean system and no extraneous ions such as chloride or mercury ions are introduced into the solution. The reversible hydrogen electrode consists essentially of a platinized platinum electrode partially immersed in a solution containing hydrogen ions and also in contact with hydrogen gas. Various methods of preparation and design of hydrogen electrodes are discussed by Ives and Janz[16]. The equilibrium which is set up at the platinized platinum electrode is

$$2 \ H^+ + 2 \ e \rightleftharpoons H_2 \ .$$

The potential of this reversible equilibrium is given by the expression

$$E = E° + \frac{RT}{2F} \ln \frac{a_{H^+}^2}{p_{H_2}} \tag{14}$$

where $a$ is the activity of the hydrogen ions in solution and $p_{H_2}$ is the pressure in atmospheres of the hydrogen gas above the electrode. When $a_H = 1$ and $p_{H_2} = 1$, $E = E°$. $E°$ is, by convention, zero at all temperatures.

Thus from eqn. (14)

$$E = 2.303 \frac{RT}{2F} \log_{10} \frac{a_{H^+}^2}{p_{H_2}}$$

and if $p_{H_2} = 1$
then

$$E = 2.303 \frac{RT}{F} \log_{10} a_{H^+}$$

or

$$E = -2.303 \frac{RT}{F} pH \qquad (15)$$

This defines the potential of a hydrogen electrode at any pH.

*(4) Reference electrodes for use with molten carbonate electrolytes*

These electrodes are dealt with in Chapter 7.

## REFERENCES

[1] For example, J. A. V. BUTLER, *Chemical Thermodynamics*, MacMillan, London, 1951.

[2] W. NERNST, *Z. Physik. Chem.*, **4** (1889) 129.

[3] J. O'M. BOCKRIS AND A. K. M. S. HUQ, *Proc. Roy. Soc. (London)*, A **237** (1956) 277.

[4] J. P. HOARE, *J. Electrochem. Soc.*, **109** (1962) 858.

[5] J. P. HOARE, *J. Electrochem. Soc.*, **110** (1963) 1019.

[6] S. SCHULDINER AND R. M. ROE, *J. Electrochem. Soc.*, **110** (1963) 1142.

[7] W. G. BERL, *Trans. Electrochem. Soc.*, **83** (1943) 252.

[8] J. M. LEE, *U.S. Army Signal R & D Lab.*, *2nd Semi-ann. Rept.* (1 Jan.–30 June 1960), Contract DA 36–039–SC–85259.

[9] For example, C. D. HODGMAN, *Handbook of Chemistry and Physics*, Chemical Rubber Publ. Co., Cleveland, Ohio.

[10] F. D. RICHARDSON AND J. H. E. JEFFES, *J. Iron and Steel Inst. (London)*, **160** III (1948) 261.

[11] T. KATAN AND R. J. GALIOTTO, *J. Electrochem. Soc.*, **110** (1963) 1022.

[12] R. A. WYNVEEN, Chap. 12, *Fuel Cells*, (ed. by G. J. YOUNG), Vol. 2, Reinhold, New York, 1963, p. 153.

[13] T. O. PAVELA, *Ann. Acad. Sci. Fennicae*, A II, **59** (1954) 7.

[14] M. J. SCHLATTER, *Preprints\* 145th Natl. Meeting Am. Chem. Soc., New York, Sept. 1963, Vol. 7: Div. Fuel. Chem., No. 4: Symp. Fuel Cell Systems*, p. 234.

[15] H. WROBLOWA, B.J. PIERSMA AND J. O'M. BOCKRIS, *J. Electroanal. Chem.*, **6** (1963) 401.

[16] D. J. G. IVES AND G. J. JANZ, *Reference Electrodes*, Academic Press, New York, London, 1961.

[17] F. G. DONNAN AND A. J. ALLMAND, *J. Chem. Soc.*, (1911) 845.

---

\* Proceedings to be published by American Chemical Society as *Fuel Cell Systems* (Advan. Chem. Ser. No. 47).

# Chapter 3

# KINETIC EFFECTS—PART 1

In Chapter 1 it was noted that the voltage of a fuel cell falls with increasing cell current. The reason for this declining efficiency with increasing output must now be examined.

## 1. ACTIVATION POLARIZATION

Reversible electrode processes are considered to be in a state of reversible equilibrium (a state in which there is no net reaction) when the forward and backward reactions occur at equal rates and the currents associated with these reactions are equal and opposite. When a current, no matter how small, flows in an external circuit connecting the two electrodes of a cell, this state of reversible equilibrium is no longer maintained. For current to flow, a net reaction must be occurring at each electrode and the forward and backward reaction rates (or currents) at each electrode cannot be equal. If the electrode processes are rapid, or if the current is small enough, the departure from equilibrium will be small and the difference between the theoretical cell voltage and the voltage when current is flowing will also be small.

With many electrode processes this is not the case and large deviations from the theoretical potentials occur even at small current densities. Furthermore, since fuel cells, to be compact, must operate at high current densities, an understanding of the properties of electrodes under these conditions is essential.

### (a) Slow electron transfer

In nearly all chemical reactions the reacting species have to overcome an energy barrier. Figure 5 is a schematic representation of this principle showing that, in this case, the energy barrier for the process A → B is lower than that for the reaction B → A. This concept of reactions proceeding through a

transition state is applicable to any type of reaction but in the case of electrode processes it is necessary to take into account the effect of the electric
field at the electrode solution interface. The effect of this field is twofold, it
favours the reaction in one direction and also hinders the reverse reaction.

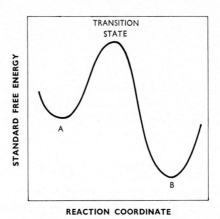

Fig. 5. Standard free energy diagram for a reaction.

When these considerations are applied to the electrode process

$$O + n e \xrightleftharpoons[k_b]{k_f} R$$

and it is assumed that the process occurs in a single step, it can be shown[1]
that the heterogeneous rate constants $k_f$ and $k_b$ can be expressed as

$$k_f = k \exp \frac{-\Delta G_f^* - \alpha nFE}{RT} \tag{1}$$

$$k_b = k \exp \frac{-\Delta G_b^* + (1-\alpha)nFE}{RT} \tag{2}$$

where $\Delta G^*$ is the standard free energy of activation and $\alpha$ is the transfer
coefficient, *i.e.* the fraction of the potential assisting the forward reaction,
the fraction $(1-\alpha)$ hindering the reverse process. The rates of the forward
and backward reactions, expressed as current densities $i_f$ and $i_b$, may now be
written

$$i_f = nFa_O k \exp \frac{-\Delta G_f^*}{RT} \exp \frac{-\alpha nFE}{RT} \tag{3}$$

$$i_b = nFa_R k \exp\frac{-\Delta G_b^*}{RT} \exp\frac{(1-\alpha)nFE}{RT}. \tag{4}$$

Note that, when $E = E_r$ (the reversible potential), $i_f = i_b$.

When current flows in an external circuit the electrode potential is usually considered to be the sum of the reversible potential and the *activation overpotential* or *polarization* $\eta_a$, and eqns. (3) and (4) may be written as

$$i_f = nFa_O k \exp\frac{-\Delta G_f^*}{RT} \exp\frac{-\alpha nFE_r}{RT} \exp\frac{-\alpha nF\eta_a}{RT} \tag{5}$$

and

$$i_b = nFa_R k \exp\frac{-\Delta G_b^*}{RT} \exp\frac{(1-\alpha)nFE_r}{RT} \exp\frac{(1-\alpha)nF\eta_a}{RT} \tag{6}$$

or as

$$i_f = nFC_O k_f \exp\frac{-\alpha nF\eta_a}{RT} \tag{5a}$$

and

$$i_b = nFC_R k_b \exp\frac{(1-\alpha)nF\eta_a}{RT} \tag{6a}$$

where the heterogeneous rate constants $k_f$ and $k_b$ have replaced the other terms, defined in eqns. (1) and (2), in eqns. (5) and (6). Since activity coefficients have been incorporated in $k_f$ and $k_b$, concentrations $C_O$ and $C_R$ are used instead of activities.

If $a_O$ and $a_R$ are unchanged by the current flowing, then by comparing eqns. (5) and (3), and eqns. (6) and (4) it follows that

$$i_f = i_0 \exp\frac{-\alpha nF\eta_a}{RT} \tag{7}$$

$$i_b = i_0 \exp\frac{(1-\alpha)nF\eta_a}{RT} \tag{8}$$

where $i_0$ is the value of both $i_f$ and $i_b$ when $E = E_r$. *The exchange current density*, $i_0$, is defined as the current density (in amp/sq.cm) flowing equally in each direction at the electrode when $\eta_a = 0$.

From eqns. (7) and (8) the net current density flowing in the forward direction when $\eta_a \neq 0$ is

$$i_c = i_f - i_b = i_0 \exp\frac{-\alpha nF\eta_a}{RT} - i_0 \exp\frac{(1-\alpha)nF\eta_a}{RT} \tag{9}$$

where the symbol $i_c$ is used to indicate that the net process is cathodic.

Alternatively, from eqns. (5a) and (6a) $i_c$ may be expressed as

$$i_c = nFC_O k_f \exp \frac{-\alpha nF\eta_a}{RT} - nFC_R k_b \exp \frac{(1-\alpha)nF\eta_a}{RT}. \tag{9a}$$

Both eqns. (9) and (9a) are used in the literature; they are, of course, equivalent.

Equation (9) can be simplified for high overpotentials ($\eta_a \ll -2.3RT/nF$, the overpotential being taken as negative for a net cathodic process). The backward reaction is now negligible and eqn. (9) becomes

$$i_c = i_0 \exp \frac{-\alpha nF\eta_a}{RT} \tag{10}$$

or

$$\eta_a = \frac{RT}{\alpha nF} (\ln i_0 - \ln i_c). \tag{11}$$

When the net process occurs in the reverse direction (when $R$ is oxidized) eqn. (9) becomes

$$i_a = i_0 \exp \frac{(1-\alpha)nF\eta_a}{RT} - i_0 \exp \frac{-\alpha nF\eta_a}{RT} \tag{12}$$

where $i_a$ is used to denote a net anodic current.

When $\eta_a \gg 2.3RT/nF$,

$$i_a = i_0 \exp \frac{(1-\alpha)nF\eta_a}{RT} \tag{10a}$$

or

$$\eta_a = \frac{RT}{(1-\alpha)nF} (\ln i_a - \ln i_0) \tag{13}$$

Equations (11) and (13) are both of the form of the equation discovered by Tafel[2] in 1905, viz.

$$\eta_a = a + b \log i. \tag{14}$$

Equation (14) is generally applicable for electrode reactions where the rate-determining step is a slow electron transfer process, provided that

$$|\eta_a| \gg \frac{2.3RT}{nF}$$

and that the activities (at the electrode) of the species involved in the reaction are not markedly changed by the current passing.

When $|\eta_a| \ll 2.3RT/nF$ eqn. (9) and its anodic counterpart, eqn. (12), simplify to

$$i_a = -i_c = \frac{ni_0 F\eta_a}{RT}.$$ (15)

Thus two simple eqns. (14) and (15) are available which satisfactorily explain the dependence of $i$ on $\eta_a$ for processes controlled by slow electron transfer. The use of these equations in determining $i_0$ and $\alpha n$ is described in section 5.

*Significance of the exchange current*

The exchange current has been defined as the current flowing equally in each direction at the reversible potential. Any difficulty in appreciating this concept should be overcome if the derivation of equilibrium conditions from the law of mass action be recalled. Equilibrium is established when the forward and backward rates are equal and, since current is defined by the rate of an electrochemical reaction, the concept of exchange current should be readily understood. Another way of describing $i_0$ is to consider eqns. (3) or (4). For example

$$i_0 = nFa_0 k \exp \frac{-\Delta G_f^*}{RT} \exp \frac{-\alpha nFE_r}{RT}.$$ (16)

It follows that $i_0$ gives a measure of $\Delta G_f^*$ and also of $\Delta G_b^*$. With efficient catalysis $\Delta G_f^*$ and $\Delta G_b^*$ are small, $i_0$ is large and, in view of eqn. (10), $\eta_a$ is relatively small. For example, for an electrode polarized by 0.01 volt at a given current density the value of $i_0$ is 34-times that for an electrode polarized by 0.1 volt at the same current density. Depending on the electrode material used, $i_0$ values in the range $10^{-3}–10^{-16}$ amp/sq.cm have been observed for the evolution of hydrogen; thus from eqns. (11) and (13) it is clear that $\eta_a$ can vary very widely at a constant current. Similar behaviour is observed for other reactions.

Another important aspect of the magnitude of $i_0$ is the ease with which the equilibrium potential is established. If $i_0$ is low (say $< 10^{-7}$ amp/sq.cm) it is unlikely that the equilibrium potential can be obtained. This is so since, even in conventionally pure systems, enough impurities remain to sustain a current greater than $10^{-7}$ amp/sq.cm. Thus the potential established is due to impurities rather than to the required equilibrium. The use of prolonged pre-electrolysis with a secondary electrode will remove impurities and aid in the establishment of the required equilibrium.

*References pp. 63–64*

In conclusion, it is worth noting that exchange currents are usually high ($\sim 10^{-3}$ amp/sq.cm) for single electron processes involving no structural rearrangements. For multi-electron changes, particularly where either more than one reactant ion or molecule is involved in the reaction, or where there are significant structural differences between reactant and product, then $i_0$ is usually low.

*Effect of surface roughness*

It has been stated that $i_0$ is expressed in amp/sq.cm. The area used must be the real area of the electrode and not the geometrical area, which does not take into account the roughness of the surface of the electrode. Surface roughness factors (the ratio of real to apparent surface areas) vary from one for a clean, undisturbed mercury surface to about 2000 for platinized platinum and to even higher values for thick porous carbon electrodes. The experimental techniques for measuring surface roughness factors are fairly complicated and when an accurate value of the true exchange current for a reaction is required it may be preferable to fabricate the electrode to have a roughness factor close to unity. This is not always possible but with drawn metal wires the true area is close to the geometrical area.

*Consecutive electrochemical reactions*

In the foregoing discussion the reaction

$$O + n\,e \rightleftharpoons R$$

was assumed to occur in a single step. In reality the reaction may go through several intermediate steps, each with an associated energy barrier. It is usually possible to assume that the step with the highest energy barrier will be rate-determining and that the other steps will be in an equilibrium state. However, if the rate-determining step involves fewer electrons than the overall reaction then the equations derived above must be modified. Equations (1) to (13) and also eqn. (15) are modified by the incorporation of "$n_a$" instead of "$n$", where $n_a$ is the number of electrons involved in the rate-determining step and must be $\leqslant n$. Equations (5a) and (6a) then become

$$i_f = nFC_O k_f \exp \frac{-\alpha n_a F \eta_a}{RT} \tag{5b}$$

$$i_b = nFC_R k_b \exp \frac{(1-\alpha)n_a F \eta_a}{RT} \tag{6b}$$

and eqn. (9a) may be modified similarly to give

$$i_c = nFC_O k_f \exp \frac{-\alpha n_a F \eta_a}{RT} - nFC_R k_b \exp \frac{(1-\alpha)n_a F \eta_a}{RT}. \tag{9b}$$

It should be noted that, since the current must be proportional to the rate of the overall reaction, the pre-exponential terms do not contain $n_a$.

*Summary*

The effects of slow electron transfer may be summed up as follows:

(1) A low free energy of activation (or a high exchange current) means that catalysis is efficient and that equilibrium is readily established.

(2) The lower the free energy of activation, the lower the polarization.

(3) As the effective area of an electrode is increased the polarization at a given current decreases.

In this section a simple approach to the problem of slow electron transfer has been used. More general treatments with more rigorous examination of the concepts used have been made by Bockris[3] and by Parsons[4]. Interested readers should consult these works.

*(b) Slow chemisorption*

The previous section was confined to a discussion of slow electron transfer processes. Before electron transfer can take place adsorption of the reactant must occur and this step may have a high activation energy associated with it.

A simple approach is to consider the sequence of reactions

$$A + \text{unoccupied site} \underset{k_{-1}}{\overset{k_1}{\rightleftharpoons}} A_{ads} \tag{17}$$

$$A_{ads} \xrightarrow{k'_f} B + e. \tag{18}$$

If Langmuir type adsorption is assumed to occur,

$$\frac{d\theta}{dt} = k_1 p(1-\theta) - k_{-1}\theta - k'_f \theta$$

where $\theta$ is the fraction of the available surface covered by adsorbed A and $p$ is the pressure of A at the electrode. The reverse electrochemical reaction has been neglected (this is valid if $\eta_a > 0.1$ volt) and B is assumed not to interfere with the area available to A.

Under steady state conditions, $d\theta/dt=0$ and, since $i=Fk'_f\theta$ and $k'_f=k_f$ exp $[(1-\alpha)F\eta_a/RT]$ it follows that

$$\eta_a = \frac{RT}{(1-\alpha)F} \ln \frac{i_a}{Fk_1 p - i_a} + \frac{RT}{(1-\alpha)F} \ln \frac{k_{-1}+k_1 p}{k_f}. \tag{19}$$

Comparison of eqns. (19) and (13) shows that $\eta_a$ will increase more rapidly with the current for slow chemisorption than for slow electron transfer. This treatment is not particularly satisfactory since

(a) the assumption of Langmuir adsorption is probably not valid in the majority of cases, and

(b) no account is taken of the possible variations of $k_1$ and $k_{-1}$ with potential.

There is, however, no simple, satisfactory treatment of this type of system.

That slow chemisorption can be a factor affecting the rates of electrode processes is well known, and mention may be made here of the work of Gilman and Breiter who have studied the anodic oxidation of methanol by a low speed potentiostatic sweep technique. They have shown that for $0.3 \leqslant \theta_M < 0.9$, $\theta_M$ being the fraction of the surface covered by methanol, adsorption and the subsequent discharge step are rate-determining[5]. Breiter[7] has also shown that the rate of adsorption of methanol may be expressed as $k_1 C_M (1-\theta_M)^p$ where $k_1$ is a potential dependent adsorption rate constant, $(1-\theta_M)$ is the free surface, $C_M$ is the concentration of methanol in solution and $p$ is a constant with a value close to 2. This suggests a Langmuir-type adsorption on two sites, though in a previous paper[6] the adsorption of methanol was shown to follow a Temkin isotherm, the rate reaching a maximum at 0.65 volt. Further discussion of this work will be found in Chapter 6.

### (c) Slow surface reactions and complex mechanisms

In addition to slow electron transfer and slow chemisorption it is possible that the reactions of adsorbed intermediates may be slow. This type of polarization is unlikely to occur when hydrogen is oxidized but may be important with more complex fuels and even with oxygen.

The usual approach to the situation, when it can be shown that electron transfer and chemisorption are not rate-controlling, is to write down a series of possible reaction sequences. Intermediates are assumed to be at the steady state and the equations are solved to give the current in terms of the overpotential. A series of values of "$b$" (the slope of the Tafel line, eqn. (14)) are obtained, each corresponding to a different reaction mechanism, although the same value of $b$ may be obtained for two or more schemes. The effect of the addition of a neutral salt on the Tafel slope gives additional evidence and it is often possible to decide on the most likely mechanism. It should be noted that the existence of an apparent transfer coefficient greater than unity can be deduced and also occurs in practice.

Bockris[8] has used this method to consider the processes occurring during the evolution of oxygen and Conway and Dzieciuch[9] used the same approach when studying the oxidation of formic acid and of trifluoracetic acid. Parsons[10] has considered the electrolytic evolution of hydrogen with three possible rate-controlling steps:

(1) the discharge reaction

$$H^+ + e - M \rightleftharpoons H - M$$

(2) the ion + atom reaction

$$H^+ + H - M + e - M \rightleftharpoons H_2 - M + M$$

(3) the combination reaction

$$2 H - M \rightleftharpoons H_2 - M + M .$$

When the combination reaction is the rate-controlling step the value of $b$ ranges from 2.303 $RT/2F$ to infinity, depending on the value of the standard free energy change, $\Delta G^\circ_{ads}$, for the reaction

$$H_2 + 2 M \rightleftharpoons 2 H - M .$$

With metals for which $\Delta G^\circ_{ads} > \sim 3$ kcal, hydrogen is weakly adsorbed and $b$ equals 2.303 $RT/2F$; with $\Delta G^\circ_{ads} < \sim -3$ kcal, hydrogen is strongly adsorbed and $b \to \infty$. With platinum metals for which $\Delta G^\circ_{ads} \approx 0$, $b = 2.303$ $RT/2\gamma F$, where $\gamma$ is a constant similar in type to $\alpha$. The cases when (1) and (2) are rate-controlling lead to different values of $b$; furthermore at different polarizations different steps become rate-determining and the Tafel plot may exhibit changes of slope.

### (d) Catalysis

The role of a catalyst is to speed up the overall reaction and if one step in the reaction sequence is much slower than the others the catalyst need only accelerate this, the rate-controlling step. Thus, as discussed in section 1(a), if the electron transfer step is the slowest reaction, a catalyst giving a higher value of the exchange current density $i_0$ is required. However, as a result of changing the catalyst some other step may become rate-controlling and this step may not be sufficiently fast. So, whilst in some cases it may be necessary to speed up only one step, in other cases the catalyst may be required to accelerate all the steps of the overall reaction. In section 1(c) some aspects of Parsons' work were discussed; further conclusions may be stated as follows.

Whichever reaction is rate-controlling for the electrolytic evolution of hydrogen the highest value of $i_0$ is obtained for metals for which $\Delta G_{ads}^\circ \approx 0$. With metals (such as Hg, Pb, Tl, Zn and Cd) for which $\Delta G_{ads}^\circ$ is positive and large, hydrogen is weakly adsorbed and low values of $i_0$ ($\sim 10^{-12}$ amp/ sq.cm) are observed. With metals (such as Mo, Ta, W) for which $\Delta G_{ads}^\circ$ is negative and large, hydrogen is so strongly adsorbed that further reaction is restricted and $i_0$ is again low ($\sim 10^{-6}$ amp/sq.cm). Only in a fairly narrow band of values of $\Delta G_{ads}^\circ$ close to zero ($\pm 3.5$ kcal) is the exchange current high ($\sim 10^{-3}$ amp/sq.cm). This region corresponds to the platinum group metals. Conway and Bockris[11] have shown that log $i_0$ for the evolution of hydrogen increases linearly with increasing values of the thermionic work function (the energy required to remove an electron from the atom to infinity) and that log $i_0$ also increases linearly with increasing $d$-band character of many metals.

Thus there are relationships between $i_0$ and three physical properties of the catalysts (although thermionic work function and $d$-band character are interrelated and it is probable that $\Delta G_{ads}^\circ$ is also related to them). At present these relationships are of little value to the fuel cell chemist since they are an explanation of observed facts and help little in the choice of "tailor-made" catalysts and, in any case, the correlations have only been demonstrated for the evolution of hydrogen. Only by intelligent guess-work have catalysts been made with the required properties, and this state of affairs is likely to continue until the theory of catalysis becomes better established.

## 2. CONCENTRATION POLARIZATION

In the derivation of eqns. (7) and (8) it was assumed that the activities of the reactant and product at the electrode were constant and independent of the rates of the processes involved. This cannot be strictly true since the reactant is being used and the product formed. In order that the electrochemical reaction may continue, reactant must continue to arrive at the electrode to replace that used and the product must leave the vicinity of the electrode.

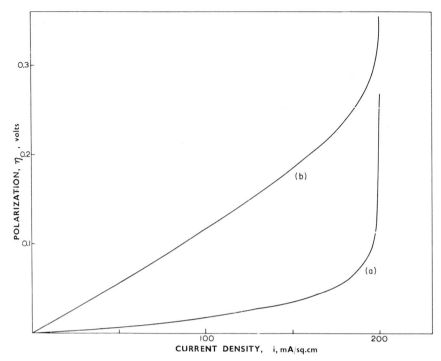

Fig. 6. $i$–$\eta$ curves showing concentration polarization. (a) Concentration polarization only; calculated from eqn. (26) for $n = 1$, $i_L = 200$ mA/sq.cm. (b) Concentration and ohmic polarization; calculated from eqns. (26) and (28) for $n = 1$, $i_L = 200$ mA/sq.cm, $l/\kappa = 1$ ohm · cm².

Reactant arrives at the electrode either by diffusion, by being supplied directly to the electrode or, in the case of an ionic reactant, by ionic transport. The rate at which a diffusing species arrives at the electrode may be increased by agitation (either thermal or mechanical) of the solution; direct supply of reactant to the electrode is controlled by external factors (and also in certain cases, by diffusion) and ionic transport is related to the current flowing. If the rates of arrival of reactants and the rates of departure of products are inadequate, serious concentration polarization may occur and this will manifest itself in a sharp change of potential as shown in Fig. 6. The current at which this sharp change in potential occurs is *the limiting current* for the process taking place at the electrode and in the case of a complete fuel cell the effect will be that the cell potential falls to about zero.

### (a) Mass transfer by diffusion only

Many limiting currents are controlled by diffusion, *i.e.* when the rate of electrochemical reaction equals the rate of diffusion of reactant no further increase in current can occur without the onset of a second electrode process. The potential changes sharply to a value at which some other process is possible. This is, of course, the basis of polarography where a high concentration of supporting electrolyte is used so that a small unknown concentration of an ionic species is not transported.

If the supply of reactant, whether ionic or neutral, to the electrode is controlled by diffusion only, then Fick's law of diffusion can be solved to give useable though complicated expressions. Some aspects of these equations are considered in Chapter 4 and for further details readers are referred to the work of Delahay[12].

A simple approach for *stirred* solutions is to consider that in the vicinity of the electrode there is a thin, stagnant layer of electrolyte and that a linear concentration gradient exists across this diffusion layer. If the concentration of species $O$ at the electrode is $C_e$ and the bulk concentration is $C_0$, then the rate of diffusion to the electrode can be written as

$$\text{rate/unit area} = \frac{D}{\delta}(C_0 - C_e) = \frac{I}{nFA} \qquad (20)$$

where $I$ is the current in amp, $D$ is the diffusion coefficient of $O$ in sq.cm/sec, $\delta$ is the thickness of the diffusion layer in cm, $A$ is the area of the electrode in sq.cm, and the units of $C_0$ and $C_e$ are moles/cu.cm. $\delta$ is usually taken to be about 0.03 cm for unstirred solutions, decreasing to 0.001 cm for vigorously stirred systems. Bircumshaw and Riddiford[13] have reviewed the subject of transport control and consider that the scientific basis for taking these values is negligible, but it is significant that $\delta$ is similar for reactions of very different chemical character. The justification for using this approach is that it is simple and the answers obtained are of the right magnitude.

From eqn. (20) it follows that when $C_e = 0$, *i.e.* when the limiting current is reached,

$$\frac{I_L}{A} = nF\frac{D}{\delta}C_0 \qquad (21)$$

or if $i_L$ is the limiting current density in amp/sq.cm (the area considered being the apparent area of the electrode, and surface roughness factors not being involved)

$$i_L = \frac{nFD}{\delta} C_0 . \qquad (22)$$

$D$ and $\delta$ appear to be little affected by concentration and, providing the reaction takes the same course at different concentrations (*i.e.*, providing $n$ does not change), for a diffusion controlled process $i_L$ is proportional to the bulk concentration of reactant.

In view of eqns. (20) and (21) it is easily shown that

$$\frac{C_e}{C_0} = 1 - \frac{I}{I_L} \qquad (23)$$

and if activities may be used instead of concentrations

$$a_e = a_0 \left( 1 - \frac{I}{I_L} \right) . \qquad (24)$$

When slow electron transfer was discussed in section 1(a), depletion of the reactant was not considered. Some concentration change must occur and, at high currents or low reactant concentrations, significant depletion may occur in the vicinity of the electrode. The equations derived previously must be modified, for example, eqn. (7) becoming

$$i_f = i_0 \left( 1 - \frac{I}{I_L} \right) \exp \frac{-\alpha nF\eta_{ac}}{RT} \qquad (25)$$

where $\eta_{ac}$ is the combined activation and concentration polarizations. However, provided $I/I_L < 1/10$, the error in $\eta_a$ is only about 0.003 volt. Since $I_L$ is proportional to $C_0$ the use of fairly concentrated solutions increases the validity of the equations derived in section (1a).

From the Nernst equation, using eqns. (20) and (21) and the assumption that $a_R$ is constant, it is easily shown that

$$\eta_c = \frac{RT}{nF} \ln \frac{I_L}{I_L - I} \qquad (26)$$

(where the suffix $c$ is used to indicate that the overpotential is due to concentration polarization) and the relationship between concentration overpotential and current is clear.

This specific type of polarization is likely to occur in fuel cells in which the reactant is dissolved in the electrolyte. To achieve high current densities the bulk concentration of reactant must be high. This also means that a large concentration of fuel may exist near the oxygen electrode, the performance of which may be affected and the current efficiency with respect to the fuel may be low.

On the credit side, an increase in the temperature increases $D$ and an increase in the agitation decreases $\delta$. Both effects increase $I_L$ and hence decrease $\eta_c$ for a given current. By suitable control of temperature, electrolyte–reactant circulation and concentration of reactant the current efficiency may be kept quite high and the effect of the fuel on the oxygen electrode kept to a minimum. Choice of catalyst for the oxygen electrode may also give some flexibility.

In the case where the reactant is a gas fed to one face of a porous electrode with the reaction zone (*i.e.* the gas/solid/liquid interface) close to the other face of the porous structure, *gas transport polarization* may occur. The pressure, $p_e$, of a gas at the active catalytic sites will be lower than the supply pressure, $p_0$, and, if diffusion through the pores occurs with an effective coefficient of $D_e$, the rate of diffusion to the reaction zone will be $(D_e/d) \cdot (p_0 - p_e)$ where $d$ is the thickness of the electrode. It follows that $\eta_c$ can again be expressed in the form of eqn. (26).

If the gaseous reactant used with an electrode of this type is oxygen in the air the situation becomes more complex. As oxygen is used at the reaction zone the partial pressure of nitrogen increases and, not only must oxygen diffuse to the reaction zone, but nitrogen must diffuse away. Blanketing of the reaction zone by nitrogen can occur relatively easily since $p_e(N_2) - p_0(N_2)$ can only be small. Thus the limiting current will be much smaller than if the electrode is used with pure oxygen, and considerable difficulty has been encountered when some porous carbon electrodes are used as air electrodes.

### (b) Mass transfer by diffusion and ionic transport

When the reacting species reaches the electrode by diffusion and ionic migration, eqn. (21) may be modified to

$$\frac{I_L}{A} = \frac{nFD}{(1-t_0)\delta} C_0 \tag{27}$$

for the case where species $O$ is an ion of transport number $t_0$.

Williams and Gregory[14] have discussed the case of *electrolyte concentration polarization* in hydrogen–oxygen fuel cells. They have shown that the predicted values of the limiting currents agree fairly well with theoretical values when the electrolyte is strong acid, strong alkali or potassium carbonate, the agreement being better for strong acid or potassium carbonate than for strong alkali. Because of the porous structure of the electrodes used by these workers the thickness of the diffusion layer was considerably increased (to about 0.1 cm) and with a normal value of $\delta$ the limiting currents would have been much greater.

In strong acid electrolytes hydrogen ions formed at the hydrogen electrode are used at the oxygen electrode and it was the oxygen electrode that exhibited electrolyte concentration polarization and a limiting current. In electrolytes of strong alkali or potassium carbonate the hydrogen electrode process was limited by the supply of hydroxyl ions. Williams and Gregory concluded that to achieve high operating current densities at low polarizations it is necessary to use either strong acid or strong alkali electrolytes.

### (c) Currents limited by other processes

So far currents limited only by the rate of mass transfer have been considered. It is of interest to discuss briefly what other factors can give rise to limiting currents. Consider the simple general scheme below:

$$A_0 \xrightarrow{(1)} A_e \xrightarrow{(2)} A_{ads} \xrightarrow{(3)} \begin{cases} B_{ads} \xrightarrow{(4)} B_e \xrightarrow{(5)} B_0 \\ + \\ H^+_{ads} \xrightarrow{(6)} H^+_e \xrightarrow{(7)} H^+_0 \end{cases}$$

where the suffix 0 indicates concentration in the bulk of solution, $e$ indicates concentration in the vicinity of the electrode and "ads" indicates concentration of adsorbed material.

Steps (1) and (7) have been discussed in sections 2(a) and 2(b) respectively. The effect that would be exhibited by step (5) is similar to that with porous electrodes running on air which have been considered previously. If either the adsorption of A or the desorption of B are slow a limiting current would be observed. Step (3) cannot give rise to a limiting current and step (6) is a rapid reaction.

Thus when a limiting current is observed it should not be assumed that the cause of the limiting current is slow mass transfer. For example, Pavela[15], studying the anodic oxidation of methanol in an electrolyte of sulphuric acid, found limiting currents which varied with methanol concentration in a manner which could not be ascribed to slow mass transfer.

### 3. OHMIC POLARIZATION

The effects at the electrodes and in the vicinity of the electrodes when a current is produced by a cell (or when electrolysis takes place) have been discussed and the effects occurring in the bulk of solution must now be considered. When electrons move in an external circuit there must be an associated movement of ions to carry the current through the electrolyte. Since the electrolyte has a finite resistance an internal loss of potential, $\eta_r$, occurs. Ohm's Law applies to $\eta_r$ so that

$$\eta_r = Ir .$$

$r$, the resistance of the electrolyte, may be expressed in terms of the distance $l$ between the two electrodes of geometrical area $A$ and the specific conductance $\kappa$ of the electrolyte, whence

$$\eta_r = I \frac{l}{A\kappa} . \tag{28}$$

$\kappa$ varies widely with the nature, the concentration and the temperature of the electrolyte. Some rough values of $\kappa$ for sulphuric acid and potassium hydroxide at 18°C are given in Table 2.

From eqn. (28) it is obvious that, for a given geometrical arrangement, as $\kappa$ increases $\eta_r$ decreases, and to keep ohmic polarization to a minimum the specific conductance should be as high as feasible. By careful design of fuel cells $l$ can be kept to quite a small value, probably about 0.5–2 mm. With the values, $\kappa = 0.4$ mho/cm and $l = 0.2$ cm an electrode operating at a current density of 200 mA/sq.cm ($\simeq 200$ amp/sq.ft) would have an ohmic polariza-

TABLE 2

SPECIFIC CONDUCTANCE, $\kappa$ AT 18 °C

| Molarity M | $\kappa(mho/cm)$ | |
|---|---|---|
| | $H_2SO_4$ | KOH |
| 1 | 0.37 | |
| 2 | 0.60 | 0.32 |
| 3 | 0.72 | 0.42 |
| 4 | 0.72 | 0.49 |
| 5 | 0.70 | 0.53 |
| 6 | | 0.55 |
| 7 | | 0.54 |

tion of 0.1 volt. Since most fuel cells are likely to have open circuit voltage of about 1 volt, ohmic polarization can cause an appreciable voltage drop at high current densities.

In addition to the ohmic polarization arising from the resistance of the bulk electrolyte there will be an additional ohmic polarization in the vicinity of each electrode caused by an increase or decrease of electrolyte concentration due to ion formation or discharge. Since the bulk electrolyte will probably be chosen with a concentration corresponding to its maximum specific conductance, an increase or decrease of electrolyte concentration near the electrodes will result in a lower value of $\kappa$. Thus ohmic polarization will be somewhat higher than in the calculated example above.

In the case where the electrolyte is maintained within a matrix (for example, when electrolytes of molten carbonate are used) the porosity and the tortuosity of the matrix must be taken into account, and

$$\kappa_{eff} = \frac{\sigma}{q} \kappa \qquad (29)$$

where $\kappa_{eff}$ is the effective specific conductance, $\sigma$ is the porosity and $q$ is a tortuosity factor. $\sigma$ usually ranges from about 0.3 to 0.7, whilst $q$ may be high; it is commonly about 2 or 3. Thus $\kappa_{eff}$ may be as low as 0.1 $\kappa$.

## 4. POLARIZATION IN POROUS ELECTRODES

Up to now only the polarization occurring at "plane" electrodes, with variable degrees of surface roughness, has been considered. Electrodes at which gases react usually have a porous structure; gas is fed to one side of the electrode and gas/solid/electrolyte contact is stabilized within the pores. One of the problems of fuel cell research is to understand the behaviour of this type of electrode.

Urbach[16] has considered the rate of decay of overpotential after current interruption that is to be expected with a specific theoretical pore structure. The hypothetical pore is considered to possess the following properties:

(1) The pore is in the form of a constricted tube.

(2) All the ohmic potential drop occurs at the constriction.

(3) The electrochemical reaction occurs only at a diffuse three-phase zone where gas/electrolyte/solid contact exists.

(4) The area available for reaction is small by comparison with the total surface of the pore.

The equations for the rate of change of overpotentials with time are solved on an analogue computer for various values of the parameters involved. The theoretical rates of decay of overpotential with time agree only moderately with the experimental values but if concentration polarization within the pores is also taken into account better agreement is achieved.

Austin[17] has treated the steady state polarization of porous electrodes and has defined four zones of polarization.

*Zone 1* At low currents, eqn. (9) applies.

*Zone 2* At higher currents, the normal Tafel equation (eqn. (14)) applies.

*Zone 3* When concentration polarization within the pores becomes significant, the slope of the Tafel line is doubled.

*Zone 4* When mass transport through a stagnant film *outside the porous electrode* becomes important, $i \rightarrow i_L$.

Again the theory is not completely satisfactory and, furthermore, the transition between the separate regions may be so extended that the zones may be unrecognisable. The theory is deficient in that ohmic polarization within the pores is not considered because of the mathematical difficulty.

It is clear that at present there is no adequate theory that can predict the exact behaviour of porous electrodes. This is hardly surprising since most of the porous materials used for practical electrodes are of ill-defined structure. Advances in both mathematics and the fabrication of porous electrodes will probably be needed before the behaviour of porous electrodes is clarified.

Another aspect of porous electrodes is that if an electrically conducting layer is applied on top of a non-conducting porous support there will be discontinuities in the electrical conductor. These discontinuities are necessary for the gaseous reactant to come into contact with the electrolyte.

Discontinuous electrical contact gives rise to increased cell resistance and a number of workers have been concerned with how the resistances of cells with electrodes of this type compare with the resistances of cells of the same geometry but with continuous electrodes. Gorin and Recht[18] have considered the case where the electrode material consists of screen electrodes having square areas of contact. Eisenberg and Fick[19] have extended this treatment to situations involving screen electrodes making circular areas of contact, and to perforated sheets with square and circular holes. The geometry is idealized to obtain a mathematical solution. Solutions are worked out for a series of values of the parameters involved. Results of these treatments are expressed in the form of a resistance ratio, $R_{eff}/R$, where $R_{eff}$ is the effective cell resistance and $R$ is the resistance of a cell of identical dimensions with two continuous plane electrodes. $R_{eff}/R$ is plotted against percentage area of contact in Fig. 7. It can be seen that above 40% contact area the values of the resistance ratio are similar for all the models considered, being between 1 and 1.5.

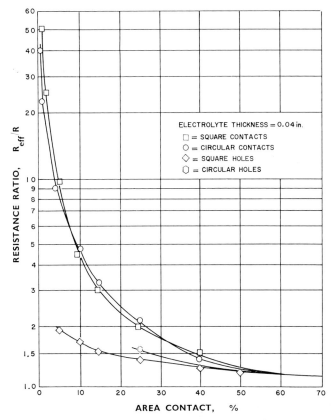

Fig. 7. Resistance effects in porous electrodes.

The mathematical solution also gives the additional information that for a given electrolyte thickness and a given percentage area contact, the distribution of contact should be as large as possible. This treatment is generally applicable to electrodes with discontinuous contacts of the type that may be used in low or high temperature cells.

*References pp. 63–64*

### 5. CURRENT/VOLTAGE CURVES

As a result of the simple theoretical treatment developed in this chapter the shapes of the current/voltage ($i/\eta$) curves can be discussed. The shape of such curves in the vicinity of the limiting current was considered in section 2 and the present section deals with the regions before the limiting current is reached. Current/voltage curves may be roughly classed as either reversible or irreversible depending on the characteristics of the reaction studied. Since the shapes of the curves depend on contributions from all types of polarization they may be difficult to interpret. The ohmic effect is easily eliminated and in the following discussion it is assumed that, except where indicated, the ohmic contribution is trivial.

#### (a) Current/voltage curves for reversible reactions

The term "reversible" is best considered by remembering that a reversible

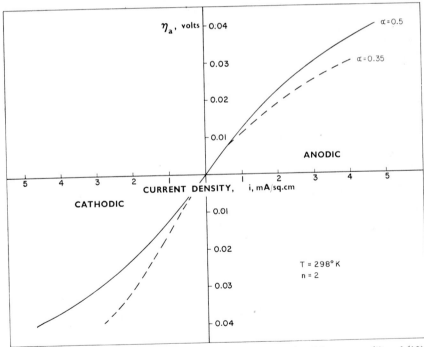

Fig. 8. Anodic and cathodic branches of an $i$–$\eta_a$ curve; calculated from eqns. (9) and (12) for $i_0 = 1$ mA/sq.cm.

reaction is one which rapidly reaches equilibrium, *i.e.* a reaction having a high exchange current ($\sim 10^{-3}$ amp/sq.cm). For this type of reaction eqn. (15) will apply if the current is not too high. The plot of $\eta_a$ against $i$ will be linear and will be symmetrical, *i.e.* there will be no change of slope when the direction of the net current is reversed. The reversible potential will be sharply defined when $i_{net} = 0$ and the value of the exchange current density $i_0$ can be determined from the slope of the $i/\eta_a$ curve. A word of warning is necessary here for, if the measured value of $\eta$ contains any significant ohmic contribution, then the calculated value of $i_0$ will be too low.

As the current increases the plot of $\eta_a$ against $i$ becomes curved owing either to a depletion of the reacting species in the vicinity of the electrode or to the invalidity of the approximation used in deriving eqn. (15). Most probably the departure from linearity will be due to $\eta_a \rightarrow RT/nF$ and eqn. (9) will now be operative for the cathodic section. The curved parts of the separate sections will only be symmetrical if $\alpha = 0.5$. These types of current/

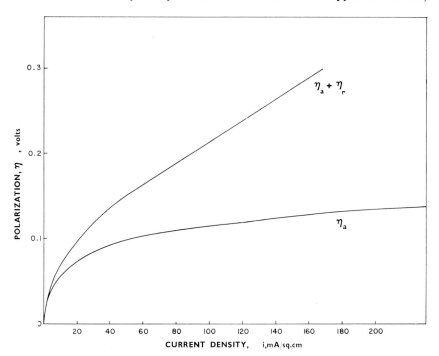

Fig. 9. *i–η* curves for process controlled by slow electron transfer; calculated from eqns. (10a) and (28) for an anodic process with $i_0 = 1$ mA/sq.cm, $n = 2$, $\alpha = 0.5$, $l = 0.2$ cm, $\kappa = 0.2$ mho/cm.

voltage curves are illustrated in Figs. 8 and 9 and it can be seen in Fig. 9 that the polarization curve is straightened somewhat when the ohmic component is not eliminated.

If the curvature of the $i/\eta$ plot is due to depletion of the reactant then, in view of eqn. (24), eqn. (15) becomes

$$i_c = \frac{-ni_0 F\eta_{ac}}{RT}\left\{\left(\frac{i_c}{i'_L} - \frac{i_c}{i_L}\right)\alpha + \left(1 - \frac{i_c}{i'_L}\right)\right\} \tag{30}$$

where the limiting current density for the forward reaction is $i_L$ and the limiting current density for the backward reaction is $i'_L$. Also, if $i'_L = i_L$, and $\eta_{ac}$ is the combined concentration and activation polarizations, eqn. (30) may be written as

$$\frac{i_c}{i_L - i_c} = \frac{i_0}{i_L}\frac{nF\eta_{ac}}{RT} \tag{31}$$

and $i_0$ can be determined from a plot of $i_c/(i_L - i_c)$ against $\eta_{ac}$.

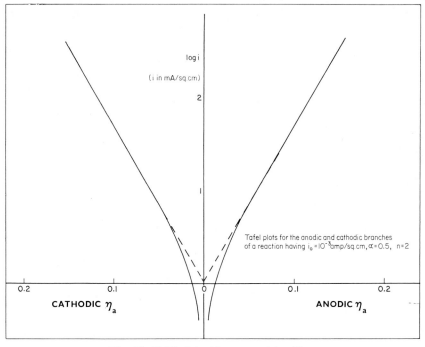

log i

(i in mA/sq.cm)

2

1

Tafel plots for the anodic and cathodic branches
of a reaction having $i_0 = 10^{-3}$amp/sq.cm, $\alpha = 0.5$, n=2

0.2          0.1          0          0.1          0.2

CATHODIC $\eta_a$                    ANODIC $\eta_a$

Fig. 10. Tafel plots at low current densities.

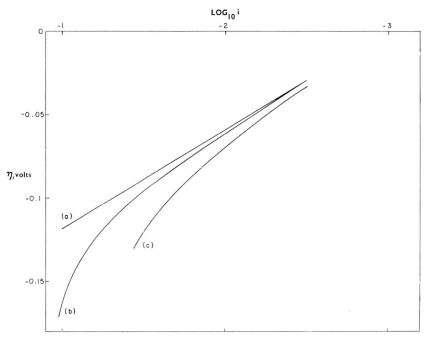

Fig. 11. Effect of $\eta_c$ and $\eta_r$ on the slopes of Tafel plots. (a) Activation polarization only calculated from eqn. (10); (b) activation and concentration polarization calculated from eqn. (25); (c) activation and ohmic polarization calculated from eqns. (10) and (28). The values $\alpha = 0.5$, $n = 2$, $i_L = 120$ mA/sq.cm, $i_0 = 1$ mA/sq.cm, $l/\kappa = 1$ ohm $\cdot$ cm$^2$ were used for a cathodic process.

### (b) Current/voltage curves for slow reactions

For slow (irreversible) reactions $i_0$ is small. Consequently, unless the current is very small, $\eta_a$ is high and the Tafel equation will probably hold*. The current/voltage curves are now markedly curved (and symmetrical only if $\alpha = 0.5$) and the reversible potential is obscure. If eqns. (11) and (13) apply, the plots of $\eta_a$ against log $i_a$ and log $i_c$ (the Tafel lines) are linear and when extrapolated intersect at the reversible potential. (If there is significant ohmic polarization in the measured $\eta$ the Tafel lines will tend to be curved.) $\alpha n_a$ can be determined from the slope of the Tafel plots and $i_0$ can be found by extrapolation to $\eta_a = 0$. Typical Tafel plots are shown in Figs. 10 and 11 and

---

* The same situation applies to rapid reactions under sufficiently high current conditions when $|\eta_a| > 2.3RT/nF$.

in Fig. 10 the linear portions of the anodic and cathodic Tafel lines are extrapolated to their intersection. The intersection of these lines gives the values of $E$ at $\eta_a = 0$ and of $i_0$. It should be noted that the curvature of the Tafel lines at low overpotential is due to the approximation used in deriving eqns. (10) and (10a) from eqns. (9) and (12) respectively. Figure 11 shows the effects of significant ohmic and concentration polarization on the Tafel line; in both cases the $\eta/\log i$ plot becomes curved and it is obviously necessary to eliminate $\eta_c$ and $\eta_r$ to obtain accurate values of $i_0$ and $\alpha n_a$.

When concentration polarization becomes important with processes controlled by slow electron transfer, eqn. (25) may be rewritten as

$$\frac{RT}{\alpha n_a F} \ln \frac{i_c}{i_L - i_c} + \ln \frac{i_L}{i_0} = -\eta_{ac} \qquad (32)$$

and, if $i_L$ is known, $\alpha n_a$ and $i_0$ may be determined by a suitable plot. Usually, however, results are obtained under conditions where $i_c \ll i_L$ and the simple plot gives $\alpha n_a$ and $i_0$. Unless the experimenter is particularly interested in the values of limiting currents under different conditions, studies should be designed so that the contribution of concentration effects to $\eta$ is minimized.

When the mechanism of the process is more complex and when the Tafel slope is very different from the expected (since $0 < \alpha < 1$ and $\alpha$ is usually 0.4–0.6, only a limited variation in the slope is possible) the amount of information available from current/voltage curves is limited. If the sole purpose of a study is the comparison of various catalysts, current/voltage curves give a simple comparative basis; when mechanistic studies are necessary more powerful techniques are required and some of these are discussed in Chapter 4.

### 6. APPARATUS AND MEASUREMENT

#### (a) Cells and half-cells

This section deals with simple apparatus which is used for the preliminary screening of catalysts, fuels, oxidants and electrolytes for fuel cells. A common form of test equipment used is known as a "half-cell" in which only one of the electrodes ultimately to be used in the fuel cell is studied. Half-cells may be of different types depending upon whether the fuel or oxidant is a gas or liquid. Complete cells, although sometimes used for initial screening, are more often used for life-testing, that is for studying the combined performance of fuel and oxidant electrodes over extended periods. The potential of a fuel cell electrode is measured against a suitable reference electrode of the type described in section 4 of Chapter 2.

*Half-cells for use with gas electrodes*

Figure 12 is a diagrammatic representation of a half-cell for use with a gas electrode. The cell must be constructed of a material, for example plastic or metal, which will withstand the electrolyte and the operating temperature.

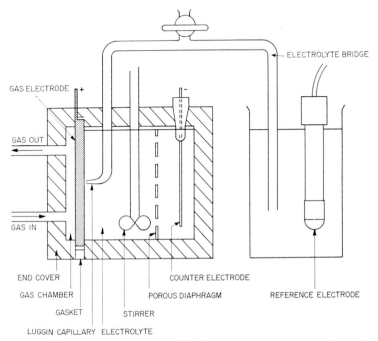

Fig. 12. Half-cell assembly for polarization measurements on gas electrodes.

With a metal construction, care must be taken to ensure that effective electrical insulation is used to prevent short circuiting the cell. A variety of electrode materials have been used such as porous carbon, sintered metals, meshes, or thin films of metal deposited on inert microporous substrates. The electrolyte may be a strong acid, strong base, an anion or cation exchange membrane. The test electrode and its associated terminal are clamped tightly between the end-plate, which is recessed to provide a gas chamber, and the cell body. A suitable gasket is provided to prevent edge leakage from the electrode. The cell is provided with an electrolyte bridge which is drawn out into a Luggin capillary, a stirrer, a counter electrode which may be a sheet of platinized platinum, and a porous diaphragm to separate the anode and cathode compartments. The electrolyte bridge is connected to a beaker containing a reference electrode and the whole apparatus is placed in a thermostated bath. When electrodes are studied in a half-cell it is necessary to supply current from an external source. The polarity of the test electrode is made positive if a fuel electrode is being studied (anodic oxidation) or negative if an oxidant electrode is being tested (cathodic reduction). The counter electrode is used merely to complete the electrical circuit within the cell. By arranging that the electrode being studied has the correct polarity, it is possible to simulate conditions which exist at either the anode or cathode of a fuel cell without the necessity of making a complete cell. The electrode potential is measured against a suitable reference electrode using either a Luggin capillary or an interrupter method (section 6(c)). The electrical circuit to be used in conjunction with the test cell will depend on the type of measurement to be made on the electrode; for instance it may be desired to follow the variation of current density as the electrode potential is increased, or to study the variation of current density with time when the potential of the

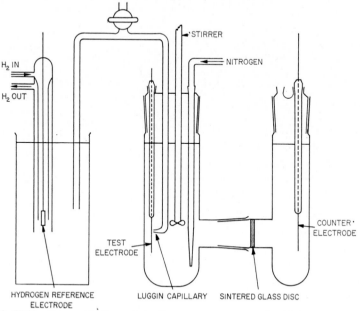

Fig. 13. Half-cell assembly for polarization measurements on liquid fuels and oxidants.

working electrode is held constant with respect to a reference electrode. Useful circuits for carrying out these and other measurements are discussed later in this section and in Chapter 4.

*Half-cells for use with liquid fuels or oxidants*

Figure 13 is a diagrammatic representation of a half-cell which is used for studying reactions involving a liquid fuel or oxidant. Test cells in this category are usually fitted with a stirrer, a nitrogen or argon bubbler and the electrode under test. Current is passed through the test and counter electrodes and corresponding potential measurements are made between the test and reference electrodes.

*Complete cells*

Figure 14 is a diagram of a complete fuel cell of the general type used by many workers when both fuel and oxidant are gaseous. When aqueous

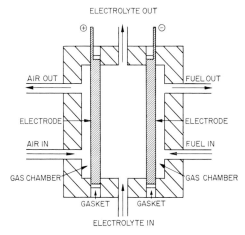

Fig. 14. A complete fuel cell for use with gaseous reactants.

electrolytes are used it is advisable to cause the electrolyte to flow through the cell, otherwise the electrolyte would become diluted over a long period of operation. When an electrolyte-soluble liquid fuel is used in a complete cell it is normally added to the circulating electrolyte. The polarization of the individual electrodes in the complete cell may be taken provided the cell dimensions allow the introduction of a suitable reference system.

### (b) Simple circuits

Figure 15 shows a simple electrical circuit suitable for the determination of current/voltage curves in a half-cell during electrolysis. $C$ is the electrochemical cell, $A$ is an ammeter, $B$ is a battery, $R$ a rheostat and $P$ a potentiometer. The required battery voltage will be determined by the resistance of cell $C$, and $R$ should have a resistance of about the same value as $C$. The ammeter should be a multirange meter so that all the current readings are of comparable accuracy. The potentiometer should be capable of measuring the potential to within at least a millivolt.

For measurements on complete fuel cells no external source of current is necessary and the circuit may be modified to that shown in Fig. 16 where the potentiometer is shown in alternative positions so that measurements can be made on either electrode. With either circuit the potentiometer connection to the electrode being studied is made directly to the electrode. This is necessary since if the connection is made at some point on the power lead there may be an appreciable ohmic drop between the connection and the electrode when high currents flow. These two circuits will give satisfactory results when used with suitable cells, Luggin capillaries and reference elec-

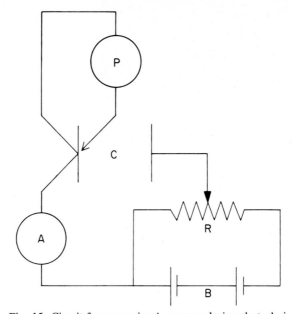

Fig. 15. Circuit for measuring $i$–$\eta$ curves during electrolysis.

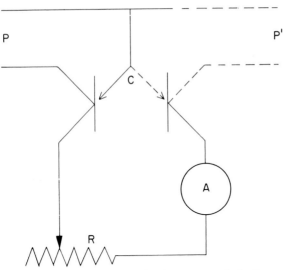

Fig. 16. Circuit for measuring $i$–$\eta$ curves on fuel cells.

trodes. At high currents, even when a Luggin capillary is used, some ohmic polarization is included in the measured voltage.

### (c) Elimination of ohmic polarization from total electrode polarization

It has been mentioned in section 5 that analysis of the polarization curve of an electrode requires the removal of any contribution of ohmic polarization to the observed electrode potential. Also, when outputs of complete fuel cells are being compared it may be necessary to eliminate any voltage losses due to internal resistance effects caused by differences in cell geometry.

    There are two principal methods of eliminating ohmic resistance; firstly by a direct method involving the use of a Luggin capillary and secondly by means of an indirect or interrupter method.

### Luggin capillary method

In this method, the electrode under examination is connected to a reference electrode by means of an electrolyte bridge which is drawn out to a capillary of small diameter at the end near the test electrode (Fig. 12). At low current densities and in solutions of high conductivity there is little potential difference between the end of the capillary and the electrode under study which is very close to it. Hence the measured electrode potential is virtually the true electrode potential. At high current densities the ohmic overpotential can be appreciable even though the Luggin capillary is nearly in contact with the electrode, and methods of correcting for this additional voltage drop have been described.

Bockris and Azzam[20] made measurements with a Luggin capillary held at measured short distances from the electrode. The greater the distance of the Luggin tip from the electrode the greater was the resistance error included in the measured potentials. Measured potentials were plotted against the distance of the capillary tip from the electrode surface and the resultant curve extrapolated to zero distance where the overpotential was assumed to be free of a resistive component. Bockris and Azzam found that at high current densities (>1 amp/sq.cm) the potential/distance curves showed a distinct change of slope when the Luggin tip was at a distance of about 0.05 cm from the electrode surface. In order to extrapolate to zero distance at high current densities they found it necessary to make measurements with the capillary tip at distances less than 0.05 cm from the electrode surface.

Barnartt[21] has recently described a method of determining the magnitude of the corrections for ohmic drop in electrode polarization measurements made with Luggin capillaries. Figure 17 shows a capillary tip of outer diameter $d$ placed at a distance $2d$ from the electrode surface. Barnartt found that the measured potential is that at a distance $d/3$ closer to the electrode than the position of the capillary tip, that is at a distance $L = 5d/3$ from the electrode. The ohmic potential drop between the Luggin capillary and the test electrode, which is one of a pair of parallel plane electrodes, is given by

$$\eta_r = \frac{iL}{\kappa} \tag{33}$$

where $L$ is defined above and $\kappa$ is the specific conductivity of the electrolyte. It is assumed that the specific conductivity of the electrolyte remains constant between the test electrode and the Luggin tip. Barnartt concluded that large capillaries (diameter >0.1 cm) were useful only when used at relatively low current densities in solutions of high conductivity. Even with the smallest convenient capillary of about 0.02 cm diameter placed as close to the electrode as possible the magnitude of the $IR$ drop correction limits the range of current densities and electrolyte conductivities over which accurate polarization measurements can be made. Barnartt found that small wires or spheres might be used advantageously as test electrodes in polarization studies since the $IR$ drop correction decreased as the electrode was made smaller.

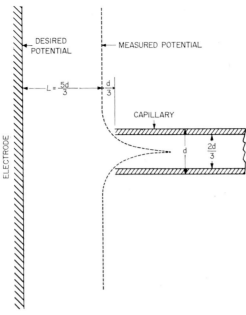

Fig. 17. Schematic diagram of *IR* drop in the electrolyte between capillary tip and electrode.

It may be concluded therefore that the Luggin capillary method for the elimination of the ohmic component of electrode polarization is both convenient and sufficiently accurate when used at low current densities in solutions of fairly high conductivity.

### Interrupter methods

The use of a Luggin capillary to eliminate the ohmic component of electrode polarization is not always convenient for a number of reasons. Firstly, when a complete cell is being studied, the geometry of the cell may preclude the use of a Luggin capillary. Secondly, it is often necessary to make fairly large corrections when Luggin capillaries are used at high current densities or in solutions of low conductivity. Methods of correction are tedious and may involve the uncertain assumption that the conductivity of the electrolyte near the electrode is the same as the bulk conductivity. Consequently, it has been found necessary to adopt some other means of measuring the potential of an electrode in its polarized state but with the resistive component of the polarization removed. The interrupter or commutator method has been developed to do this.

The basis of the interrupter method is that the current from the fuel cell or the electrolysing current supplied to a half-cell is periodically interrupted by means of a mechanical or electronic cummutator. The resistive component of the total electrode or cell polarization may be distinguished by the fact that when the circuit is either opened or closed the resistive polarization decays or builds up almost instantaneously whereas the activation and concentration polarization take an appreciable time. Consider the case where it is desired to obtain the resistance-free voltage of a complete cell in its polarized state. Figure 18 shows the basic principles of the circuit used. The cell is placed in series with a standard resistor, an ammeter and a variable resistor that enables different currents to be drawn from the cell. A means of interrupting the current is incorporated into the circuit. The current from the cell is thus switched on and off rapidly and the standard resistor and the cell are connected in turn across the Y-plates of a cathode ray oscillograph so that the voltage response across each may be monitored as the current is interrupted. Figure 19(a) shows the square wave form of current pulse obtained with equal "on"–"off" periods. The oscillograph is connected first across the standard resistor and the voltage/time trace obtained is as shown in Fig. 19(b). Since the impedance responsible for the voltage drop $\Delta V_s$ across

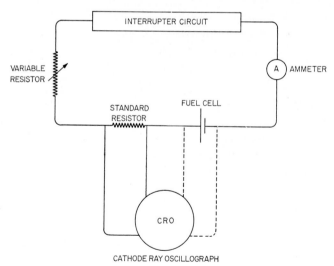

Fig. 18. Schematic diagram of interrupter circuit.

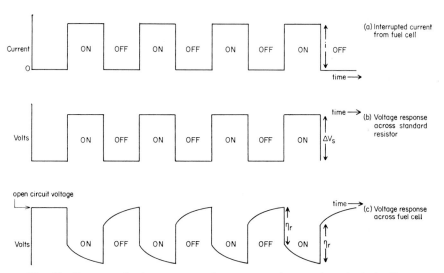

Fig. 19. Current and voltage response due to current interruption of a fuel cell.

the standard resistor is purely resistive in character, the wave form is also square and $\Delta V_s$ is easily measured with the calibrated Y-shift of the oscillograph. As the value of the standard resistor, $R_s$, is known, the value of the current, $I$, in the "on" period of the pulse can be calculated from Ohm's Law.

With the same current the oscillograph is next placed across the cell when the trace is of the form shown in Fig. 19(c). The curvature displayed in the trace depends on the amount of concentration and activation polarization present in the total electrode polarization. As the current pulse is switched on, the ohmic component of the polarization builds up almost instantaneously whilst the other components of the polarization indicated by the curved portions of the trace take a small but finite time to build up. The reverse occurs when the current pulse is switched off; the ohmic component decays immediately and the activation and concentration polarization decay more slowly. The ohmic component, $\eta_r$, of the polarization, represented by the vertical portion of the trace in Fig. 19(c) is measured using the calibrated Y-shift. Since the current, $I$, in the pulse was previously measured from the potential drop across the standard resistor and the same current passes through the cell, the internal resistance of the cell, $R_I$ may also be calculated and is given by

$$R_I = \frac{\eta_r}{I}. \tag{34}$$

*References pp. 63–64*

In order to determine the resistance-free voltage of the cell, it is arranged that the cell gives a continuous (non-interrupted) current equal to the current, $I$, in the "on" portion of the pulse. The corresponding terminal voltage $V_T$ is recorded on a voltmeter and the resistance-free voltage $V_F$ is then given by

$$V_F = V_T + \eta_r . \tag{35}$$

A series of readings are taken for different values of the current, $I$, and a current/voltage curve free of ohmic polarization can be constructed. Typical curves of terminal voltage and resistance-free voltage against current density are shown in Fig. 20.

The interrupter method when used in half-cell studies is much the same except that the oscillograph is placed between the anode (or cathode) and the reference electrode. The precise position of the electrolyte bridge relative

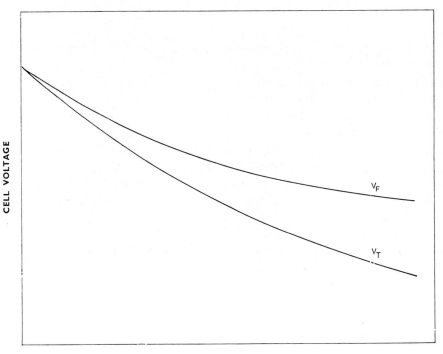

CURRENT DENSITY

Fig. 20. Typical curves for terminal voltage ($V_T$) and resistance free voltage ($V_F$) of a fuel cell.

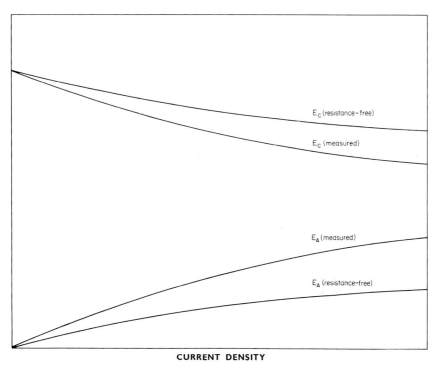

Fig. 21. Typical curves for measured and resistance free voltages of anode and cathode of a fuel cell.

to the working electrode is now unimportant since any voltage drop due to the resistance of the electrolyte will be automatically measured by this method. The resistance-free polarization of the cathode is given by the expression

$$E_C \text{ (res.-free)} = E_C + \eta_r \text{ (between cathode and reference electrode)} \quad (36)$$

whilst that of the anode is given by

$$E_A \text{ (res.-free)} = E_A - \eta_r \text{ (between anode and reference electrode)} \quad (37)$$

where $E_C$ and $E_A$ are measured voltages between the cathode and reference electrode and between the anode and reference electrode respectively.

Typical curves for measured and resistance-free voltages of anode and cathode are shown in Fig. 21.

Numerous workers have developed interrupter circuits based on principles similar to those described in the preceding paragraphs. Some of the circuits will be mentioned briefly but the reader is referred to the original texts for detailed circuit diagrams.

The first electronic interrupter was developed by Hickling[22] who used a thyratron as the basis both of the interrupter circuit and of the measuring potentiometer circuit. Because of the decay of polarization with time, Hickling used successively longer interruption periods in the range $10^{-5}$ to $2 \times 10^{-4}$ second and measured the electrode potential at the end of each "off" period. Curves of electrode potential against the duration of the "off" period were extrapolated to zero time to obtain a value of the potential immediately after interrupting the current. Hickling studied the overpotentials associated with both hydrogen evolution and oxygen evolution on smooth platinum in sulphuric acid and compared the results by his interrupter method with those obtained directly using a reference electrode and Luggin capillary. The resistance error introduced into the measured voltage when the direct method was used at high current densities was clearly shown. At 0.01 amp the direct and interrupter methods gave the same value of the hydrogen overpotential, whilst at 0.3 amp the overpotential given by the direct method was twice that given by the interrupter method.

A method similar to that used by Hickling was developed by Staicopoulos, Yeager and Hovorka[23]. With their apparatus, the current could be interrupted for periods as short as $5 \times 10^{-6}$ second. Potential measurements could be made with an accuracy of $\pm 5$ millivolts at any time whilst the current was on or off. Glicksman and Morehouse[24], and Brodd[25], used an interrupter method based on the general principles previously outlined to measure the internal resistance during discharge of a number of types of dry cell.

Kordesch and Marko[26] in 1960 described an interrupter working on a half-wave rectified, 60 c/s sine-wave pulse. The instrument was simple and robust and gave direct meter readings instead of displaying the results on an oscilloscope and it could easily be adapted to handle any current or voltage requirements. Pollnow and Kay[27] have recently described a transistorized version of the Kordesch–Marko interrupter. They claim that the use of a transistor imparts greater electrical stability to the apparatus and allows the ohmic component of the electrode polarization to be measured with a precision of $\pm 1$ millivolt compared with $\pm 5$ millivolts claimed for the Kordesch–Marko apparatus. The transistorized apparatus of Pollnow and Kay handled currents up to 9–10 amp and the maximum current could be raised still further by providing for increased heat dissipation from the transistor and by lowering the value of the current-limiting resistor.

Richeson and Eisenberg[28] have also described a current interrupter capable of handling up to 5 amp. Interruption periods as low as $1.6 \times 10^{-6}$ second were possible and the switching rate was from 500 c/s to any longer period. Trachtenberg[29], working with molten carbonate cells, has described a circuit by means of which the current is subjected to a single interruption and the decay of voltage followed as a function of time. The three types of polarization are distinguished from the voltage/time trace after interrupting the current. Ohmic polarization decays in less than a microsecond; decay of activation polarization is estimated to take from $10^{-6}$ to $10^{-4}$ second, whereas decay of polarization caused by concentration effects requires times greater than $10^{-4}$ second since mass transport must occur. Results obtained with this method are described in Chapter 7.

A single current interruption method has been found convenient for determining the internal resistance of large fuel cells. A cathode ray oscillograph fitted with a Polaroid Land Camera is connected across the cell and the trace is photographed when a load is applied or removed by a switch. From knowledge of the voltage drop on applying the load and the magnitude of the current the internal resistance of the cell may be calculated.

## REFERENCES

1 S. GLASSTONE, K. J. LAIDLER AND H. EYRING, *The Theory of Rate Processes*, McGraw-Hill, New York, 1941.
2 J. TAFEL, *Z. Phys. Chem.*, **50** (1905) 641.
3 J. O'M. BOCKRIS, *Modern Aspects of Electrochemistry*, Butterworths, London, 1954, Chap. 4.
4 R. PARSONS, *Trans. Faraday Soc.*, **47** (1951) 1332.
5 S. GILMAN AND M. W. BREITER, *J. Electrochem. Soc.*, **109** (1962) 1099.
6 S. GILMAN AND M. W. BREITER, *J. Electrochem. Soc.*, **109** (1962) 622.
7 M. W. BREITER, *J. Electrochem. Soc.*, **110** (1963) 449.
8 J. O'M. BOCKRIS, *J. Chem. Phys.*, **24** (1956) 817.
9 B. E. CONWAY AND M. DZIECIUCH, *Can. J. Chem.*, **41** (1963) 21.
10 R. PARSONS, *Trans. Faraday Soc.*, **54** (1958) 1053.
11 B. E. CONWAY AND J. O'M. BOCKRIS, *J. Chem. Phys.*, **26** (1957) 532.
12 P. DELAHAY, *New Instrumental Methods in Electrochemistry*, Interscience, New York, 1954.
13 L. L. BIRCUMSHAW AND A. C. RIDDIFORD, *Quart. Rev.* (*London*), **6** (1952) 157.
14 K. R. WILLIAMS AND D. P. GREGORY, *J. Electrochem. Soc.*, **110** (1963) 209.
15 T. O. PAVELA, *Ann. Acad. Sci. Fennicae, A II*, **59** (1954) 7.
16 H. B. URBACH, Chap. 7 in *Fuel Cells*, (ed. by G. J. YOUNG), Vol. 2, Reinhold, New York, 1963.
17 L. G. AUSTIN, Chap. 8 in *Fuel Cells*, (ed. by G. J. YOUNG), Vol. 2, Reinhold, New York, 1963.

[18] E. GORIN AND H. L. RECHT, Chap. 8 in *Fuel Cells*, (ed. by G. J. YOUNG), Vol. 1, Reinhold, New York, 1960.

[19] M. EISENBERG AND L. FICK, Chap. 9 in *Fuel Cells*, (ed. by G. J. YOUNG), Vol. 2, Reinhold, New York, 1963.

[20] J. O'M. BOCKRIS AND A. M. AZZAM, *Trans. Faraday Soc.*, **48** (1952) 145.

[21] S. BARNARTT, *J. Electrochem. Soc.*, **108** (1961) 102.

[22] A. HICKLING, *Trans. Faraday Soc.*, **33** (1937) 1540.

[23] D. STAICOPOULOS, E. YEAGER AND F. HOVORKA, *J. Electrochem. Soc.*, **98** (1951) 68.

[24] R. GLICKSMAN AND C. K. MOREHOUSE, *J. Electrochem. Soc.*, **102** (1955) 273.

[25] R. J. BRODD, *J. Electrochem. Soc.*, **106** (1959) 471.

[26] K. KORDESCH AND A. MARKO, *J. Electrochem. Soc.*, **107** (1960) 480.

[27] G. F. POLLNOW AND R. M. KAY, *J. Electrochem. Soc.*, **109** (1962) 648.

[28] W. E. RICHESON AND M. EISENBERG, *J. Electrochem. Soc.*, **107** (1960) 642.

[29] I. TRACHTENBERG, *Preprints\* 145th Natl. Meeting Am. Chem. Soc., New York, Sept., 1963, Vol. 7: Div. Fuel Chem., No. 4: Symp. Fuel Cell Systems*, p. 196.

Proceedings to be published by American Chemical Society as *Fuel Cell Systems* (Advan. Chem. Ser. No. 47).

*Chapter 4*

# KINETIC EFFECTS—PART 2

Chapter 3 dealt with current/voltage curves and it was assumed that they represent the steady state, *i.e.* the state such that the current and voltage are independent of time. In section 6(c) of that chapter the elimination of ohmic polarization was discussed and use was made of the fact that ohmic polarization builds up and decays almost instantaneously. Other forms of polarization take a finite time to build up or decay and whilst in some cases the time required is only a few milliseconds, in other cases the steady state may not be reached for several seconds. The study of the rate of change of the characteristics of the electrode processes can often give helpful information about the mechanism of the reactions. Two approaches are obvious: the current may be controlled and the potential monitored with time or the variation of current at constant potential may be measured. The first method—chronopotentiometry—requires simpler apparatus and will be discussed first. Only single electrode studies will be considered in this chapter.

## 1. PRINCIPLES OF CHRONOPOTENTIOMETRY

*Simple electrochemical reactions*

If a constant current is passed through an electrolytic cell which is not stirred and which has stationary electrodes then the concentrations of the electroactive substances in the vicinity of the electrodes vary with time. Since the current is constant the electrolysis proceeds at a constant rate and, for the reaction $O + n\,e \to R$, if $O$ arrives at the electrode sufficiently rapidly the concentration gradient and hence the electrode potential will soon settle to a steady value. However, in the absence of any convection or migration the species involved in the electrode reactions arrive solely by diffusion. Rigorous solution of Fick's first law of diffusion[1] for these conditions shows that a true steady state is never reached. The concept of a diffusion layer of constant thickness $\delta$ (with linear concentration gradient) as used in Chapter 3, section 2, is not valid and with increasing time $\delta$ the distance over which a non-linear concentration gradient exists increases and the concentration of the active species at the electrode decreases. When the concentration of $O$ at the electrode drops to zero an abrupt change of potential occurs and some second reaction occurs simultaneously with the first. The time that has elapsed from the start of electrolysis to the change in potential is called the *transition time*, $\tau$. It is obvious that the transition time will increase with increasing concentration of reactant, will decrease as the electrolysis current increases and will depend on the diffusion coefficient of the reactant, and it may be shown[2] that the relationship

$$\tau^{\frac{1}{2}} = \frac{\pi^{\frac{1}{2}} n F C_0 D^{\frac{1}{2}}}{2 i} \tag{1}$$

holds for both reversible and irreversible reactions. (Note that $i$ is the current density.) Equation (1), often referred to as *the Sand[2] equation*, shows that, when the supply of reactant is controlled by the rate of semi-infinite linear diffusion, the product $i\tau^{\frac{1}{2}}$ is independent of current density. Convection must be eliminated by having a stationary electrolyte and, in the case of an ionic reactant, an excess of indifferent electrolyte must be used to eliminate ionic migration.

It may also be shown that, for a reversible process, the electrode potential is related to time $t$, by the relationship

$$E = E^\circ + \frac{RT}{nF} \ln \left\{ \frac{\tau^{\frac{1}{2}} - t^{\frac{1}{2}}}{t^{\frac{1}{2}}} \right\} \tag{2}$$

and for a totally irreversible* process

$$E = E_i + \frac{RT}{\alpha n_a F} \ln \left\{ 1 - \left( \frac{t}{\tau} \right)^{\frac{1}{2}} \right\}. \tag{3}$$

$E_i$ in eqn. (3) is the potential immediately after the start of the electrolysis and depends on the rate constant of the reaction and the electrolysis current. Thus, for irreversible processes a displacement of the potential/time curve along the potential axis will occur when the electrolysis current is varied.

---

* A reversible process becomes irreversible under high overpotential conditions ($|\eta| \gg 0.1$ volt). This consideration was used in Chapter 3 in deriving the Tafel equation from eqns. (9) and (12).

Equation (1) has been used in analytical applications but for the fuel cell worker a more important application is likely to be the determination of diffusion coefficients. When the concentration of the reacting species is known and when $i\tau^{\frac{1}{2}}$ is independent of $i$, the diffusion coefficient of the reactant is readily calculated.

*Electrochemical reactions occurring in steps*

Chronopotentiometry at constant current can sometimes be used to study reactions occurring by a stepwise mechanism. If the reaction $O + n\,e \rightarrow R$ occurs by the mechanism

$$O \xrightarrow{\ n_1\,e\ } P \xrightarrow{\ n_2\,e\ } R$$

and $P$ is reduced at potentials markedly more cathodic than $O$, two transition times, $\tau_1$ and $\tau_2$, will be observed and it can be shown[3] that

$$\tau_2 = \tau_1 \left\{ 2\left(\frac{n_2}{n_1}\right) + \left(\frac{n_2}{n_1}\right)^2 \right\}. \tag{4}$$

Berzins and Delahay[3] showed that the reduction of oxygen in $1M$ lithium chloride on a mercury pool electrode gave $\tau_2/\tau_1 = 2.97$, which is in excellent agreement with the theoretical value of 3 for $n_1 = n_2$, and indicates that the Berl process is likely to be operative.

In a fuel cell the requirements of a catalyst are that it should enable the overall reaction to take place rapidly at a useful potential and, consequently, if the process is by a stepwise mechanism the steps should occur at very similar potentials. However, in evaluating catalysts this approach may be valuable.

*Electrochemical reactions preceded by a non-electrochemical step*

Often $i\tau^{\frac{1}{2}}$ is not independent of $i$ as predicted by the Sand equation, and this may sometimes be associated with a chemical step preceding the electrochemical step. If A is not reducible, but is in equilibrium with $O$ which is reduced to $R$, then for the reaction scheme

$$A \underset{k_b}{\overset{k_f}{\rightleftharpoons}} O \xrightarrow{\ n\,e\ } R$$

it can be shown[4] that

*References pp. 83–85*

$$i\tau^{\frac{1}{2}} \simeq \frac{\pi^{\frac{1}{2}}nFC_0D^{\frac{1}{2}}}{2} - \frac{\pi^{\frac{1}{2}}i}{2K(k_f+k_b)^{\frac{1}{2}}} \tag{5}$$

where $K$ is the equilibrium constant of the reaction between A and $O$ ($=k_f/k_b$). Equation (5) is an approximate relationship which holds well when $(k_f+k_b)^{\frac{1}{2}}\tau^{\frac{1}{2}} > 2$, but if $k_f$ and $k_b$ are small the value of $\tau$ required to ensure this condition may be impracticably high. The exact equation is beyond the scope of this book and interested readers should consult the work of Delahay[5]. If eqn. (5) is valid a plot of $i\tau^{\frac{1}{2}}$ against $i$ will be linear and, if the equilibrium constant $K$ is known, $k_f$ and $k_b$ can be calculated.

If use of eqn. (5) proves impossible, it can be shown[4] for high current densities that

$$\left(i\tau^{\frac{1}{2}}\right)_{i\to\infty} = \frac{\pi^{\frac{1}{2}}nFC_0D^{\frac{1}{2}}}{2(1+1/K)} \tag{6}$$

and $i\tau^{\frac{1}{2}}$ is again independent of current density. The equilibrium constant can be calculated from eqn. (6) if the limiting value of $i\tau^{\frac{1}{2}}$ is measurable at the available current densities.

Equation (5) was used by Buck and Griffith[6] when studying the anodic oxidation of methanol in basic solution. They considered that the pre-electrochemical reaction

$$CH_3OH+OH^- \rightleftarrows CH_3O^-+H_2O$$

might be important but they found that the calculated value of $k_f$ was much lower than expected and they concluded that adsorption of methanol or $CH_3O^-$ caused $k_f$ to be too low. When slow adsorption–desorption phenomena occur at electrodes, Munson[7] has shown that a plot of $i\tau^{\frac{1}{2}}$ against $i$ is linear for *long* transition times and has a negative slope, which is, however, different from that predicted by eqn. (5).

### Study of electrode surfaces

Under suitable conditions interactions of the electrode with the solvent can be examined, and Hickling[8–12] has used this feature to study the formation of hydride and oxide films on various metals. As an example the case of platinum[8] in normal sulphuric acid may be considered. A constant current is passed through the electrolytic cell and through a large capacitance in series with the cell. The circuit is so designed that when the working electrode has reached a preset potential the current is interrupted and the capacitance is discharged through the cell. An equal quantity of electricity is therefore passed through the cell in each direction and the working electrode is returned to its original condition. Either a single pulse or repetitive pulses may be used and high currents are used so that little diffusion to or from the electrode can occur. The voltage/time (or quantity of electricity, since the current is constant) curve is displayed on an oscilloscope. The results for platinum are shown in Fig. 22 and the more important sections are described in Table 3. Similar results have been obtained by Hickling for other metals[9-12].

Two interesting points emerge from a study of Fig. 22, *viz.*

(1) The reversibility of the hydrogen deposition and consumption as indicated by the closely similar potentials at which these processes occur.

(2) The irreversibility of the formation and removal of the surface oxide.

The reproducibility of the amount of hydride deposited on platinum has been used to study the adsorption of other materials on platinum. Thus Gilman and Breiter[13] have studied the adsorption of methanol by measuring the difference in the amounts of hydride formed on platinum with and without

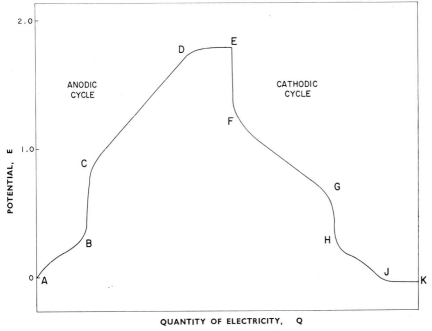

Fig. 22. Variation of the potential of a platinum electrode at constant current in sulphuric acid electrolyte.

TABLE 3

PROCESSES OCCURRING DURING CHRONOPOTENTIOMETRIC SWEEPS OF PLATINUM IN
SULPHURIC ACID

| Section of Fig. 22 | Process occurring | Quantity of electricity involved (coulombs/sq.cm) |
|---|---|---|
| AB | Ionization of adsorbed hydrogen | $\simeq 0.4 \times 10^{-3}$ |
| BC | Charging of the double layer | |
| CD | Formation of a surface oxide of platinum | $\simeq 0.8 \times 10^{-3}$ |
| DE | Evolution of oxygen from an oxide-covered surface | |
| FG | Reduction of the surface oxide | $\simeq 0.8 \times 10^{-3}$ |
| HJ | Deposition of hydrogen on the platinum surface | $\simeq 0.4 \times 10^{-3}$ |
| JK | Evolution of hydrogen | |

methanol in the perchloric acid electrolyte. The same technique has been applied by Breiter[14] to a study of the coverage of platinum by formic acid and the method seems generally applicable to the adsorption of many species on different catalysts, provided hydrogen does not diffuse into the electrode.

*Determination of the capacity of the double layer and surface roughness factors*

A further use of chronopotentiometry is in the determination of the *differential double layer capacitance*, $C_d$. This is defined as

$$C_d = - \frac{dQ}{dE}$$

whence

$$C_d = - \frac{dQ}{dt} \cdot \frac{dt}{dE} = -i \frac{dt}{dE}. \tag{7}$$

With $i$ constant, and provided that $C_d$ is independent of potential, the double layer capacitance can readily be calculated from a known current and the rate of change of potential. Such a calculation can readily be carried out for section BC in Fig. 22 and Hickling[8] has calculated a value of about 200–300 $\mu$F per apparent sq.cm for the double layer capacitance of the platinum–sulphuric acid system. In the sections AB and CD an electrochemical reaction is occurring and in addition to the double layer capacity (which is considered as a spatial distribution of charges at the electrode/

electrolyte interface) there is also a *pseudo-capacity* associated with the electrochemical reactions.

The use of eqn. (7) has been advocated as a method of determining true surface areas. Since $i$ is the current density, $C_d$ is the differential double layer capacity per unit area and by comparing the capacitance of electrodes of known and unknown true area it is possible to determine the unknown area. Brodd and Hackerman[15] have measured $C_d$ for electrodes with various surface roughness factors (determined by measurements of krypton adsorption at low temperatures) and have concluded that the determination of true surface areas by this method is applicable to Pt, Ni, Fe, Ta and possibly to Cr, Cu and Pb but is inapplicable to Al. It appears from this work that provided the measured capacity may be unequivocally related to double layer charging only (*i.e.* provided there is no pseudocapacity), surface areas can be determined moderately accurately. However, because of irregularities in materials with high surface roughness factors there must be a non-uniform current distribution and the metal/electrolyte interface can hardly behave as a pure capacity. Thus whilst the method is much more rapid than the usual B.E.T. gas adsorption techniques it is not altogether satisfactory.

In principle there appears to be no reason why surface roughness factors cannot be determined by comparing the lengths of section AB of Fig. 22 for electrodes of known and unknown surface area. The transitions at points A and B are quite sharp, and by this means the total area of the electrode available to hydrogen can be determined. By using a repetitive pulse technique the adsorption of impurities should be kept to a minimum because they are likely to be oxidized in section CD. However, some dissolution of the electrode material may occur at high potentials and the true area of the electrode may change with time, so that a single pulse technique in a high purity electrolyte may be the most satisfactory approach.

Schuldiner and Roe[16] have used section CD of Fig. 22 for the determination of the surface area of smooth platinum. The quantity of electricity passed as the potential rose from 0.88 to 1.76 volt was corrected for the double layer capacitance by using the average measured value of $C_d$ in this potential range, and was used then to calculate the true surface area.

Another method of measuring double layer capacitance is to use a square-wave charging technique in which a constant current, $I_1$, is passed through the cell until the steady state is achieved. The current is then switched abruptly to some other value $I_2$ for a predetermined time before being returned abruptly to $I_1$. Very short pulses (about 10 $\mu$sec) are used and from the potential/time trace the differential double layer capacitance may be calculated. Provided the time allowed at current $I_1$ is long enough for restoration of the initial equilibrium, a multipulse method may be used. Riney, Schmid and Hackerman[17] have used this technique and have shown that the differential capacity potential curves obtained on platinum and mercury agree well with those obtained with a capacitance bridge.

### (a) Experimental techniques

The apparatus required for chronopotentiometric measurements can be quite simple if great accuracy is not required. A fairly steady current may be obtained by using a source of high voltage, and a high resistance, $R_1$, in series with a low resistance electrolytic cell. If the electrode potential

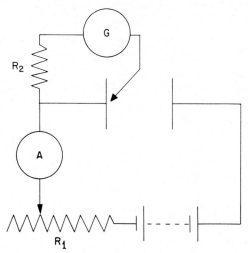

Fig. 23. Simple circuit for chronopotentiometry.

(relative to a reference electrode) is monitored on a sensitive mirror galvanometer with a large series resistance, $R_2$, then the transition time may be measured roughly with a stop watch. Figure 23 shows a suitable arrangement.

A simple transistor circuit for providing a constant current is shown in Fig. 24; by suitable selection of the components a wide variation in current can be achieved. With a Mullard OC-76 transistor and resistances $R_1 = 100$ ohms and $R_2 = 25$ kiloohms a current in the range 30 $\mu$A to about 10 mA can be selected. Owing to thermal effects in the transistor the current may vary slightly over the first few milliseconds but thereafter will be constant. With short transition times more stable currents are required and suitable circuits are described in the literature[8,18-21].

Because of the charging of the double layer, transition times shorter than a millisecond cannot be measured with any accuracy, and because convection is likely to interfere at times longer than a few minutes, the preferred range of transition times is about 5 milliseconds to one minute. The currents required to give transition times in this range are accordingly selected.

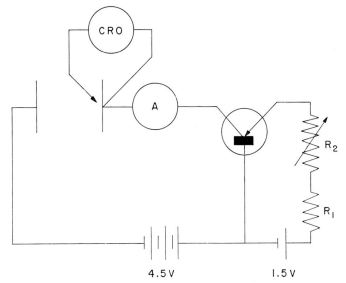

Fig. 24. A transistorized circuit for chronopotentiometry.

To obtain an accurate measure of the transition time a high resistance voltage recorder or a cathode ray oscillograph should be used. A high speed chart drive and rapid response recorder will cover the range above about 5 seconds and for shorter transition times photographing the oscillograph trace will enable $\tau$ to be determined accurately.

It should always be borne in mind that the current drawn in the circuit between working electrode and reference electrode must be negligible compared to the current flowing through the cell. Thus the voltage measuring equipment must have a sufficiently high input impedance and with low electrolysis currents a preamplifier with an electrometer tube input may be required. For an accurate potential/time curve the preamplifier must be highly stable and of good linearity, but if a measurement only of the transition time is required these factors are less important.

## 2. PRINCIPLES OF CHRONOAMPEROMETRY

Instead of the current being controlled, the potential of the electrode is now controlled and the variation of the current with time is recorded. In unstirred solutions with stationary electrodes the current decreases with time owing to a depletion of the electroactive substance at the electrode surface. For a reversible process, if the electrode reaction is carried out at such a rate that the concentration of reactant drops to zero as soon as electrolysis is started, the current–time relationship may be shown[22] to be

$$I_r = \frac{nFAD^{\frac{1}{2}}C_0}{\pi^{\frac{1}{2}}t^{\frac{1}{2}}} \qquad (8)$$

where $I_r$ is the current corresponding to the reversible reaction at a time $t$ seconds after the start of electrolysis.

For a totally irreversible process ($|\eta| \geqslant 0.1$ volt), Delahay and Strassner[23] and also Evans and Hush[24] have shown that

$$I = nFAC_0 k_f \exp Q^2 t \cdot \text{erfc } Qt^{\frac{1}{2}}$$

where                                                                         (9)

$$Q = \frac{k_f}{D^{\frac{1}{2}}}.$$

Tables of values of the function [$\exp x^2 \text{ erfc } x$] are available in the literature[25–26] and when $x=0$, [$\exp x^2 \text{ erfc } x$]$=1$, the function decreasing as $x$ increases.

Equation (9) can be rearranged and by substitution from eqn. (8) the relationship

$$\frac{I}{I_r} = \frac{\pi^{\frac{1}{2}} k_f t^{\frac{1}{2}}}{D^{\frac{1}{2}}} \exp \frac{k_f^2 t}{D} \text{ erfc } \frac{k_f t^{\frac{1}{2}}}{D^{\frac{1}{2}}} \qquad (10)$$

can be obtained. For large values of $k_f t^{\frac{1}{2}}/D^{\frac{1}{2}}$ (when $k_f$ is large enough or the time of the electrolysis is sufficiently long) then $I=I_r$. From experiments of short duration the rate constant $k_f$ can be calculated.

To fulfil the condition of total irreversibility the overpotential must be raised to more than 0.1 volt. Apart from this limitation the method may be used to calculate $k_f$ at a series of different potentials, provided the reactant arrives at the electrode solely by linear diffusion. At present, the method has only been applied in polarographic work but there seems to be no reason why the technique should not be used to gain information of direct use to the fuel cell chemist. Similar equations can be derived when a chemical reaction precedes the electrochemical stage and Delahay[3] has reviewed these treatments, which are beyond the scope of this book.

In stirred solutions the approximate relationship introduced when discussing concentration polarization in Chapter 3, section 2, may be used to derive

$$I = nFAD \frac{C_0}{\delta} \exp \frac{-DAt}{V\delta} \qquad (11)$$

Equation (11), in which $V$ is the volume of solution in the electrolytic cell, was derived and verified by Lingane[27] and shows how the current at constant potential drops due to consumption of the reactant. The equation may be used to calculate $D$ and $\delta$.

There is a further reason for currents declining with time at constant potential, which may be of greater importance to the fuel cell research worker. If the product, an intermediate or a side-product of an electrochemical reaction is adsorbed on the electrode to an appreciable extent then the reaction will be hindered by a poisoning of the electrode. Effectively the area of the electrode available for reaction will decrease and, at constant electrode potential, the current will diminish with time. Giner[28] has recently reported declining currents of this type during the anodic oxidation of formic acid on platinum and he ascribes the current decline to the formation of a strongly adsorbed "reduced $CO_2$" the nature of which is not clear. CO or a radical such as "COOH" is tentatively suggested as the poisoning species.

At present no mathematical treatment applicable to this type of situation is available and it seems unlikely that a general treatment is possible. By considering various mechanisms it may be possible to predict the shape of the current/time curves and so elucidate the actual mechanism. Until satisfactory mathematical treatments are available the amount of information obtainable from this type of experiment is rather limited but it does provide a rapid means of assessing the "self-poisoning" characteristics of a system. Thus a comparison of a series of catalysts from this point of view may be carried out qualitatively.

Many systems in which the catalysis is imperfect or in which the end product is polar may be expected to show this type of behaviour. For example, Prigent, Bloch and Balaceanu[29] have shown that acetone inhibits the anodic oxidation of isopropanol, and the oxidation of isopropanol at constant potential would be expected to show a declining current.

## (a) Experimental techniques

Figure 25 shows a suitable circuit for chronoamperometry. PS is a potentiostat—an apparatus for maintaining the electrode potential at a constant value. The electrode potential is sensed by the potentiostat, which has an inbuilt

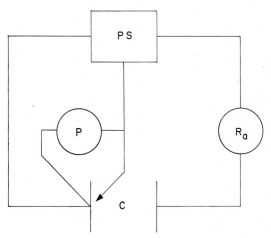

Fig. 25. Circuit for chronoamperometry.

standard voltage adjustable to any required value. The two potentials are electronically compared and the current flowing in the power circuit is automatically adjusted so that the electrode potential is maintained at the same value as the standard. A small current is required to flow in the reference electrode—working electrode—potentiostat circuit and the instrument should be designed so that this signal is kept to the smallest practicable value. Many designs of potentiostat have been published in the literature[30-37] ranging from the original circuit of Hickling[30] to the specialized designs of Bewick and Fleischmann[47]. In addition models based on some of these designs are commercially available.

Because some small current must be taken from it care should be taken that the reference electrode does not become polarized and it should be sufficiently large for its potential to be hardly altered by the current required to operate the potentiostat.

In Fig. 25 $P$ is a potentiometer and $R_a$ is a recording ammeter, which may be either an oscillograph measuring the change in potential across a standard resistance or a suitable current recorder. The recorder should be of sufficiently fast response, should not be of too high a resistance and should be in the circuit between the potentiostat and the counter electrode.

If the total circuit resistance is too high the available driving voltage of the potentiostat may be inadequate for correct functioning of the apparatus. In these circumstances the current will be controlled by Ohm's Law and will not be a true function of the electrode processes. With high currents or potentiostats with small driving voltages this effect may be observed and must be eliminated by one of several methods, *e.g.* by reducing the cell resistance or by reducing the area of the working electrode.

### 3. OTHER ELECTROCHEMICAL TECHNIQUES USED IN FUEL CELL RESEARCH

#### (a) Linear chronoamperometry

*Single sweep methods*

In this method the potential of the electrode is a linear function of time and the current/time (or voltage) curve is recorded. Either a single pulse or multiple pulses may be used and in the latter case the potential is repeatedly swept to some required polarization and then back to the starting potential.

If the steady state at the electrode is rapidly established or if the electrode potential is altered sufficiently slowly, then the recorded curve will be almost identical with current/voltage curves obtained by any other method. If the electrode potential is swept so rapidly that the steady state is not established the curve obtained will show a maximum. Figure 26 shows this type of behaviour, which can be interpreted qualitatively as follows. As the electrode potential is increased the rate of the electrochemical reaction increases and the concentration of the reacting species at the electrode decreases. Above some potential the decrease in the rate of diffusion becomes greater than the increase in the rate of the reaction. The current then decreases and a maximum is observed. Theoretical treatment of the single sweep method applied to reversible processes was carried out by both Randles[38] and Sevcik[39], who showed that the peak current at 25°C may be expressed as

$$I_p = 2.72 \times 10^5 \ A \ n^{\frac{3}{2}} D^{\frac{1}{2}} v^{\frac{1}{2}} C_0 \tag{12}$$

where $v$ is the potential sweep rate in volts/sec and $k$ is a constant which incorporates gas constant, the temperature and the Faraday and has the value $2.72 \times 10^5$ at 25°C. For totally irreversible processes ($|\eta| \gg 0.1$ volt) Delahay[40] has shown that the peak current at 25°C may be written as

$$I_p = 3.01 \times 10^5 n (\alpha n_a)^{\frac{1}{2}} A \ D^{\frac{1}{2}} C_0 v^{\frac{1}{2}} \tag{13}$$

where $n_a$ is the number of electrons in the rate-controlling step, $n$ is the total number of electrons involved in the overall reaction and $\alpha$ is the transfer coefficient. From eqn. (13) $\alpha n_a$ is readily calculated and it is also possible to deduce the rate constant from the shape of the current voltage curve.

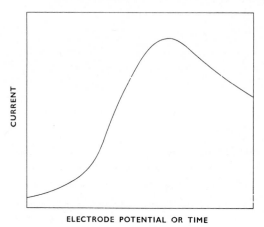

Fig. 26. Shape of current/voltage curves obtained under linear chronoamperometric conditions.

*Multisweep methods (triangular potential sweeps)*

When the linearly changing potential applied to the electrode is reversed at some required overpotential rather different results are obtained. As an example, potential sweeps on a platinum electrode in sulphuric acid electrolyte may be considered. Figure 27 shows (a) the applied potential/time function and (b) the resulting current/potential curve. The various steps, which are similar to those for Fig. 22, are given in Table 4. The marked change in current in section JA (and to lesser extent in section EK) is due to the electrode potential changing from its maximum (or minimum) value causing a sudden reversal of the capacity current.

For any reversible reaction it may be shown that the potential at which

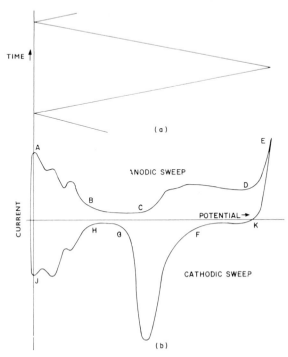

Fig. 27. Current/potential relationship obtained under linear chronoamperometric conditions for a platinum electrode in sulphuric acid.

TABLE 4

PROCESSES OCCURRING DURING LINEAR CHRONOAMPEROMETRIC SWEEPS OF PLATINUM IN SULPHURIC ACID

| Section in Fig. 27 | Process occurring |
|---|---|
| AB | Oxidation of adsorbed hydrogen |
| BC | Double layer charging |
| CD | Formation of an oxide layer |
| E | Oxygen evolution |
| FG | Reduction of the oxide layer |
| HJ | Formation of an adsorbed hydrogen layer |

the anodic peak current is observed will differ from the potential at which the cathodic peak current occurs by $0.056/n$ volt at $25°C$. The greater the irreversibility of a process the more marked will be the potential displacement and this gives a test of reversibility. From Fig. 27 the reversibility of the process

$$H_{ads} \rightleftharpoons H^+ + e$$

is clear, as is the irreversibility of the oxide formation and reduction. These same conclusions were deduced previously from Fig. 22.

A triangular potential sweep technique has been used in much research which is of interest in connection with fuel cells. Will and Knorr have studied the formation of hydrogen and oxygen films on platinum[41] and also on rhodium, iridium, palladium and gold[42]. Breiter[43] has used linear chronoamperometry to study the oxidation of hydrogen inhibited by the formation of oxide films on platinum and has studied the anodic oxidation of formic acid on platinum[14]. Kutschker and Vielstich[44] have studied the oxidation of formic acid on several metals. Buck and Griffith[6] and also Gilman and Breiter[13] have applied the method to the electro-oxidation of methanol, and Gilman[45] has used the same technique for a study of the oxidation of carbon monoxide. A modified apparatus, in which a fast anodic or cathodic sweep can be superimposed on the triangular sweep, has been used by Gilman[46] for further studies. The results of some of this work is discussed in other chapters and the experimental technique has been considered by Delahay[5].

Will and Knorr[41] have also used the technique to determine the effective surface areas of smooth platinum electrodes. The quantity of electricity $\int i dt$ corresponding to the anodic oxidation of a hydride film is found by integrating the appropriate part of the $i/V$ curves obtained at known sweep rates. From the quantity of electricity passed, and with the assumption that each atom of hydrogen corresponds to one surface atom of platinum, the surface roughness factor is readily calculated. Juliard and Shalit[47] have advocated the same method for determining the areas of platinized surfaces. The remarks made in section 1 of this chapter about repetitive pulse techniques should also apply to this method.

### (b) Non-linearly changing potential

In principle the electrode potential may be made to vary in any known manner with time. In practice it is usual to superimpose a varying potential on a d.c. component, the varying component being either a sinusoidal or a square wave function. Up to the present, research using these techniques has been little applied in connection with fuel cells. It seems likely that such methods may be used in the future since they enable the rate constants of very rapid reactions to be measured. The methods have been reviewed by Delahay[5] and the literature on the subject is considerable.

One aspect of this type of work worth considering in more detail is its application to the determination of surface coverages from capacitance values. Breiter[48] has studied the adsorption of amyl alcohol on platinum by measuring the amplitude of the a.c. component of current through the cell ($\tilde{I}$), the amplitude of the applied alternating voltage ($\tilde{V}$) and the phase shift ($\Phi$). If the electrical analogue of the electrode can be considered as a resistance $R$ in series with a capacitance $C$ then

$$\cot \Phi = \omega R C \tag{14}$$

and

$$\tilde{I} = \frac{\tilde{V}}{\left[ R^2 + \dfrac{1}{\omega^2 C^2} \right]^{\frac{1}{2}}} \tag{15}$$

where

$$\omega = 2\pi f \tag{16}$$

$f$ being the frequency. From the known values of $f$, $\Phi$, $\tilde{I}$ and $\tilde{V}$ the capacitance $C$ can be evaluated.

Frumkin[49] has proposed a model of the double layer which can lead to the simplified equation

$$C_{d_\theta} = C_{d_0}(1 - \theta) + C_{d_1} \tag{17}$$

where $C_{d_\theta}$ is the capacitance at some fractional coverage $\theta$ and $C_{d_0}$ and $C_{d_1}$ are the capacitances at zero and complete coverage respectively. From eqns. (13)–(16) $\theta$ can be calculated, and Breiter[50] has shown how the coverage of platinum by methanol depends on potential and concentration. When the results derived for methanol are compared with those obtained by the method outlined in section 1, the agreement is satisfactory at high coverages but not particularly good at low and intermediate coverages. Since Breiter claims an accuracy of about 5% for the measurements, the disparity between the two methods is due either to the use of eqn. (17) or to the use of a series combination of resistance and capacitance as the electrical analogue of the electrode. In fact, eqn. (16) only applies at the potential of maximum adsorption and must be modified for use at other potentials. Using a modified version of eqn. (17) that takes into account the potential dependence of the interaction between adsorbed molecules and the variation of the adsorption equilibrium constant with potential, Damaskin[51] has recently found excellent agreement between the calculated and measured differential capacity–potential curves.

The calculation of capacitance by the use of eqns. (14)–(16) depends on the validity of the assumed electrical analogue, and if this is invalid the calculation leads to a value of $C$ which is a composite function of double-layer capacity and pseudo-capacity. The use of the exact version of eqn. (17) requires differential double-layer capacities, and such values are obtained by the superimposed a.c. method only at very high frequencies.

For a detailed discussion of the properties of electrodes under a.c. conditions the works of Dolin and Erschler[52], Randles[53], Erschler[54], Delahay[5] and a recent review by Frumkin[55-56] should be consulted. The properties of the electrical double layer and its influence on the rates of electrode reactions have been recently reviewed by Parsons[57].

### (c) Rotating disc electrodes

Only a little research of interest to the fuel cell worker has been carried out with rotating disc electrodes but it seems likely that they may be used more widely in connection with fuel cell problems, and a brief mention in this book seems worthwhile.

A horizontal disc immersed in an electrolyte is rotated at a constant angular velocity $\omega$, about a vertical axis through its centre. If there is no precession or vertical movement of the electrode, there is no turbulence in the solution and if the volume of the solution is large then the rate of supply of reactant to the electrode can be obtained by solving the hydrodynamic equations. For a reaction which is *solely controlled by the rate of mass transfer* Levich[58] has shown that the limiting current density can be expressed as

$$i_L = 0.62 \, nFC_0 D^{\frac{2}{3}} \omega^{\frac{1}{2}} v^{-\frac{1}{6}} \tag{18}$$

where $v$ is the kinematic viscosity of the solution. According to eqn. (18) $i_L$ is proportional to $\omega^{\frac{1}{2}}$ and this has been verified by Siver and Kabanov[59] for the reduction of oxygen to $H_2O_2$ on an amalgamated copper disc.

Equation (18) predicts that when $\omega=0$, $i_L=0$, and this cannot be true. Departures from eqn. (18) at stirring speeds below about 140 r.p.m. have been observed by Gregory and Riddiford[60] and more recently by Kholpanov[61], who has published a modified equation which predicts a finite limiting current with stationary discs. It is apparent that eqn. (18) can only hold at intermediate stirring speeds; departures are observed at low stirring speeds due to the inadequacy of the simple theory, and if the stirring speed is so rapid as to cause turbulence the theory again does not apply.

Gregory and Riddiford have examined eqn. (18) in detail and have concluded that better agreement with experiment is obtained if the equation

$$i_L = 0.554\, nFC_0 D^{\frac{2}{3}}\omega^{\frac{1}{2}} v^{-\frac{1}{6}} J_\infty^{-1} \tag{19}$$

where

$$J_\infty = 0.8934 + 0.316\left(\frac{D}{v}\right)^{0.36} \tag{20}$$

is used.

The use of a rotating disc electrode permits corrections for concentration effects to be made when activation-controlled reactions are studied. By applying eqn. (20) concentration polarization may be eliminated from the experimental results and, provided ohmic polarization is eliminated, the resulting overpotential will be purely activation-controlled.

A modification to the rotating disc technique which has been advocated is the use of an outer concentric ring. A separate polarizing circuit is used and, in suitable circumstances, intermediates formed on the disc may be detected on the ring. The method requires that the intermediates should not be too unstable or too strongly adsorbed and, under these conditions, it may prove valuable. As an example of this technique the reduction of oxygen[62] where hydrogen peroxide was detected on the outer ring, may be cited.

Only an outline of some recent electrochemical techniques has been given in this chapter; a more detailed discussion of both the theoretical and practical aspects is given by Delahay[3] and is recommended to readers interested in the field.

## REFERENCES

[1] A. FICK, *Pogg. Ann.*, **94** (1855) 59.
[2] H. J. S. SAND, *Phil. Mag.*, **1** (1901) 45.
[3] T. BERZINS AND P. DELAHAY, *J. Am. Chem. Soc.*, **75** (1953) 4205.
[4] T. BERZINS AND P. DELAHAY, *J. Am. Chem. Soc.*, **75** (1953) 2486.

5  P. DELAHAY, *New Instrumental Methods in Electrochemistry*, Interscience, New York, 1954.
6  R. P. BUCK AND L. R. GRIFFITH, *J. Electrochem. Soc.*, **109** (1962) 1005.
7  R. A. MUNSON, *J. Phys. Chem.*, **66** (1962) 727.
8  A. HICKLING, *Trans. Faraday Soc.*, **41** (1945) 333.
9  A. HICKLING, *Trans. Faraday Soc.*, **42** (1946) 518.
10  A. HICKLING AND D. TAYLOR, *Discussions Faraday Soc.*, **1** (1947) 277.
11  A. HICKLING AND J. E. SPICE, *Trans. Faraday Soc.*, **43** (1947) 762.
12  A. HICKLING AND G. G. VRJOSEK, *Trans. Faraday Soc.*, **57** (1964) 123.
13  S. GILMAN AND M. W. BREITER, *J. Electrochem. Soc.*, **109** (1962) 622.
14  M. W. BREITER, *Electrochim. Acta*, **8** (1963) 447.
15  R. J. BRODD AND N. HACKERMAN, *J. Electrochem. Soc.*, **104** (1957) 705.
16  S. SCHULDINER AND R. M. ROE, *J. Electrochem. Soc.*, **110** (1963) 332.
17  J. S. RINEY, G. M. SCHMID AND N. HACKERMAN, *Rev. Sci. Instr.*, **32** (1961) 588.
18  D. J. MEIER, R. J. MEYERS AND E. H. SWIFT, *J. Am. Chem. Soc.*, **71** (1949) 2340.
19  W. N. CARSON, *Anal. Chem.*, **22** (1950) 1565.
20  C. N. REILLEY, W. D. COOKE AND N. H. FURMAN, *Anal. Chem.*, **23** (1951) 1030.
21  D. D. DeFORD, C. J. JOHNS AND J. N. PITTS, *Anal. Chem.*, **23** (1951) 941.
22  F. G. COTTRELL, *Z. Physik. Chem.*, **42** (1902) 385.
23  P. DELAHAY AND J. E. STRASSNER, *J. Am. Chem. Soc.*, **73** (1951) 5219.
24  M. G. EVANS AND N. S. HUSH, *J. Chim. Phys.*, **49** (1952) c159.
25  H. S. CARSLAW AND J. C. JAEGER, *Conduction of Heat in Solids*, Oxford University Press, London, 1947.
26  B. O. PIERCE, *A Short Table of Integrals*, Ginn, Boston, 3rd edn., 1929.
27  J. J. LINGANE, *J. Am. Chem. Soc.*, **67** (1945) 1916; *Anal. Chim. Acta*, **2** (1948) 584.
28  J. GINER, *Electrochim. Acta*, **9** (1963) 63.
29  M. PRIGENT, O. BLOCH AND J. C. BALACEANU, *Bull. Soc. Chim. (France)*, (1963) 368.
30  A. HICKLING, *Trans. Faraday Soc.*, **38** (1942) 27.
31  A. L. HODGKIN, A. F. HUXLEY AND B. KATZ, *J. Physiol.*, **116** (1952) 424.
32  M. FLEISCHMANN AND H. R. THIRSK, *Trans. Faraday Soc.*, **51** (1955) 71.
33  M. FLEISCHMANN, J. SOWERBY AND H. R. THIRSK, *Trans. Faraday Soc.*, **53** (1957) 91.
34  M. BREITER AND F. G. WILL, *Z. Elektrochem.*, **61** (1957) 1177.
35  ALAN BEWICK, ARTHUR BEWICK, M. FLEISCHMANN AND M. LILER, *Electrochim. Acta*, **1** (1959) 83.
36  A. HICKLING, *Electrochim. Acta*, **5** (1961) 161.
37  ALAN BEWICK AND M. FLEISCHMANN, *Electrochim. Acta*, **8** (1963) 89.
38  J. E. B. RANDLES, *Trans. Faraday Soc.*, **44** (1948) 327.
39  A. SEVCIK, *Collection Czech. Chem. Commun.*, **13** (1948) 349.
40  P. DELAHAY, *J. Am. Chem. Soc.*, **75** (1953) 1190.
41  F. G. WILL AND C. A. KNORR, *Z. Elektrochem.*, **64** (1960) 258.
42  F. G. WILL AND C. A. KNORR, *Z. Elektrochem.*, **64** (1960) 270.
43  M. W. BREITER, *J. Electrochem. Soc.*, **109** (1962) 425.
44  A. KUTSCHKER AND W. VIELSTICH, *Electrochim. Acta*, **8** (1963) 985.
45  S. GILMAN, *J. Am. Chem. Soc.*, **66** (1962) 2657.
46  S. GILMAN, *J. Am. Chem. Soc.*, **67** (1963) 78.
47  A. L. JULIARD AND H. SHALIT, *J. Electrochem. Soc.*, **110** (1963) 1003.
48  M. W. BREITER, *J. Electrochem. Soc.*, **109** (1962) 42.
49  A. N. FRUMKIN, *Z. Physik.*, **35** (1926) 792.
50  M. W. BREITER, *Electrochim. Acta*, **7** (1962) 533.
51  B. B. DAMASKIN, *Electrochim. Acta*, **9** (1964) 231.

52 P. DOLIN AND B. ERSCHLER, *Acta. Physicochim. U.R.S.S.*, **13** (1940) 747.
53 J. E. B. RANDLES, *Discussions Faraday Soc.*, **1** (1947) 11.
54 B. ERSCHLER, *Discussions Faraday Soc.*, **1** (1947) 269.
55 A. N. FRUMKIN, Chap. 2 in *Advances in Electrochemistry and Electrochemical Engineering*, (ed. by P. DELAHAY AND C. W. TOBIAS), Vol. 1, Interscience, New York, 1961.
56 A. N. FRUMKIN, Chap. 5 in *Advances in Electrochemistry and Electrochemical Engineering*, (ed. by P. DELAHAY AND C. W. TOBIAS), Vol. 3, Interscience, New York, 1963.
57 R. PARSONS, Chap. 1 in *Advances in Electrochemistry and Electrochemical Engineering*, (ed. by P. DELAHAY AND C. W. TOBIAS), Vol. 1, Interscience, New York, 1961.
58 B. LEVICH, *Acta. Physicochim. U.R.S.S.*, **17** (1942) 257; **19** (1944) 117, 133.
59 Y. G. SIVER AND B. N. K. KABANOV, *Zh. Fiz. Khim.*, **22** (1948) 53; **23** (1949) 428.
60 D. P. GREGORY AND A. C. RIDDIFORD, *J. Chem. Soc.*, (1956) 3756.
61 L. P. KHOLPANOV, *Russ. J. Phys. Chem. (English Transl.)* **35** (1961) 1538.
62 A. FRUMKIN, L. NEKRASOV, B. LEVICH AND JU. IVANOV, *J. Electroanal. Chem.*, **1** (1959–60) 84.

# Chapter 5

# HYDROGEN–OXYGEN (AIR) FUEL CELLS

Hydrogen cells are the simplest of all fuel cells; they were the first to be made and at the time of writing are the most highly developed. Although the use of the hydrogen–oxygen cell will probably be limited to special applications, the oxygen or, more accurately, the air electrode must remain an important factor in the realization of any low temperature fuel cell for widespread use. This chapter is concerned primarily with the types of electrode used in the various hydrogen–oxygen cells which have been made. It is confined in scope to fuel cells that rely on hydrated ions for current transport, that is to say those that use aqueous or ion exchange electrolytes. In the first instance the electrode reactions are discussed together with the catalysts appropriate to them. This is followed by a description of the physical form of fuel cell electrodes.

## 1. TYPE OF ELECTRODE

### (a) The hydrogen electrode

The overall reaction for the anodic oxidation of hydrogen in acid electrolytes is

$$H_2 \rightleftharpoons 2\,H^+ + 2\,e \tag{1}$$

and in alkaline electrolytes is

$$H_2 + 2\,OH^- \rightleftharpoons 2\,H_2O + 2\,e\,. \tag{2}$$

Both of the equations above represent *overall* reactions and give no indication of the mechanisms involved, which not only vary with the medium but also with the electrode material. The hydrogen electrode process has been the subject of a great deal of study and the reader is referred to several excellent reviews[1-4]. Only a few remarks will be made here about the process when using solid electrodes.

With solid electrodes the results obtained are very greatly influenced by the manner of activation and generalizations become almost impossible. However, a characteristic which is commonly observed during the dissolution of hydrogen is a limiting current. The origin of these limiting currents varies with electrode material, activation of the electrode and with the medium.

Breiter, Knorr and Meggle[5] found strong evidence that the limiting currents observed with active platinum, rhodium and iridium electrodes were due to slow diffusion of hydrogen to the electrodes. Frumkin and Aikazian[6], using rotating platinum disc electrodes, found control by diffusion at low angular velocities, but at high angular velocities the process was controlled by the ionization reaction. Because three-phase electrodes, as described in section 2, are used in most fuel cells the problem of limiting currents due to slow transport of dissolved hydrogen is avoided and this aspect need not be considered further.

Horiuti and Okamoto[7] obtained results which indicated that, with nickel electrodes, the surface dissociation of hydrogen molecules to atoms was rate-limiting, and Schuldiner[8] has more recently interpreted his results on active platinum and rhodium electrodes in a similar manner. These findings are of interest in view of the identification of the probable rate-determining step for the evolution of hydrogen on smooth platinum as the slow combination of adsorbed hydrogen atoms. Using inactive platinum electrodes Vetter and Otto[9] obtained results that may be interpreted by slow adsorption of hydrogen on to the surface. In direct contrast with these findings is the galvanostatic work of Munson[10], who has shown that, with active platinum electrodes, the rate of adsorption is sufficiently rapid for equilibrium to be maintained between dissolved hydrogen at the electrode surface and the adsorbed species.

From the foregoing outline of some of the work that has been carried out with solid electrodes it is clear that the rate-limiting step is not unambiguously established. It seems certain that this step varies with the activity of the electrode and that different electrodes of the same material may have different rate-determining steps.

A further cause of limiting currents that can occur in alkaline solutions is the depletion of hydroxyl ions in the vicinity of the electrode. Thus, if the hydrogen dissolution reaction is represented by eqn. (2), a strong alkaline electrolyte should be used. Williams and Gregory[11] have dealt with this form of concentration polarization in fuel cells. A similar argument can be advanced for the oxygen electrode in acid electrolytes, and, for *high limiting currents*, the choice of electrolytes is restricted to either strongly acid or alkaline media. The catalysts and other constructional materials used must be able to withstand one or other of these environments. These cases of electrolyte concentration polarization have been considered in Chapter 3.

As far as the technology of fuel cells is concerned, the chief point about hydrogen electrodes is that it is a relatively straightforward matter to make electrodes from which substantial currents may be drawn at a potential close to that of the reversible hydrogen electrode in the same medium. This is because satisfactory catalysis of reactions (1) or (2) is readily achieved. The catalysis of the hydrogen electrode processes has been mentioned briefly in Chapter 3, and from a practical point of view a variety of approaches are possible. The platinum metals, platinum and palladium in particular, have relatively high exchange currents; that is to say they are intrinsically good catalysts for the desired electrode reaction. If used in finely divided form these metals are suitable catalysts for low temperature fuel cells using both alkaline and acid electrolytes. Platinum is less prone to oxidation than palladium[12] and for that reason is more widely, but by no means exclusively, used.

Hydrogen electrodes of a 75/25 palladium–silver alloy are described by Oswin and Chodosh[13]. Instead of one of the expensive platinum metals nickel is sometimes employed. As the hydrogen reaction on nickel has a much lower exchange current at a given temperature than on platinum, higher operating temperatures can be used to accelerate the reaction as in the Bacon cell[14]. The remarkable DSK hydrogen electrodes made by Justi[15] from Raney nickel–aluminium alloy probably owe their activity to their very high surface area and the larger number of surface defects introduced by the dissolution of aluminium. More recently, the semiconductor, nickel boride $Ni_2B$, has been reported[16] to be almost as active as palladium for the anodic oxidation of hydrogen.

Although all of the above catalysts may be used in alkaline electrolytes, platinum is used almost exclusively with strong acid electrolytes. For example, in the case of acid ion-exchange membrane fuel cells Cairns *et al.*[17] show that while platinum and palladium initially give similar performances, the life of the fuel cell is considerably shorter with the palladium catalyst.

The performance of hydrogen electrodes appears to be better in acid than in alkaline electrolytes; for example, Williams and Gregory[11] have developed a hydrogen electrode which operates in $5N$ sulphuric acid at room temperature close to the reversible hydrogen potential at current densities as high as 600 mA/sq.cm. On the other hand, similar electrodes in $5N$ potassium hydroxide polarize some 200 mV at a current density of 100 mA/sq.cm. Nevertheless, acceptable hydrogen electrodes can be made for use with both acid and alkaline electrolytes.

### (b) The oxygen electrode

Ideally, the reaction at the oxygen electrode in alkaline electrolyte would be

$$O_2 + 2 H_2O + 4 e \rightarrow 4 OH^-$$ (3)

and in acid electrolyte

$$4 e + O_2 + 4 H^+ \rightarrow 2 H_2O .$$ (4)

At 25°C both of these reactions should take place at a potential of 1.23 volt with respect to a reversible hydrogen electrode in the same medium but, as shown in Chapter 2, it is only possible to observe this potential by careful experimentation. Unfortunately, it is not yet possible to make electrodes that can sustain substantial currents at potentials near to the theoretical.

A good deal of controversy exists about the mechanism of the oxygen reduction reaction but, apart from specific details, only two substantially different courses have been proposed. Berl[18] showed that hydrogen peroxide was an intermediate in the reduction of oxygen on carbon electrodes in alkaline electrolytes and demonstrated that the potential was determined by the reaction

$$O_2 + H_2O + 2 e \rightleftharpoons HO_2^- + OH^- .$$ (5)

Application of the Nernst equation to this reaction gives

$$E = E^\circ - \frac{RT}{2F} \ln \frac{a_{OH^-} - a_{HO_2^-}}{a_{O_2} a_{H_2O}}$$ (6)

and eqn. (6) shows that, the lower the perhydroxyl ion concentration, the higher will be the potential. Berl's mechanism has been substantiated by the work of Weiss and Jaffe[19] and by isotope studies carried out by Davies, Clark, Yeager and Hovorka[20]. The isotope experiments showed that all of the oxygen in the perhydroxyl ion arises from oxygen gas and that the O–O bond is not broken during the electrochemical step. These findings led Davies et al.

to propose the mechanism:

$$O_2 \rightarrow O_2 \text{ (ads)}$$

$$O_2 \text{ (ads)} + 2\,e \rightarrow O_2^{2-} \text{ (ads)}$$

$$O_2^{2-} \text{ (ads)} + H_2O \rightarrow HO_2^- + OH^-$$

The alternative hypothesis which has received much support is that the electroreduction of oxygen proceeds by the formation and decomposition of surface oxides. Such mechanisms agree with those proposed by Bockris[21] for the anodic evolution of oxygen. Sawyer and Day[22] suggest that the following reactions occur with platinum, palladium and silver:

$$2\,M + O_2 + 2\,H_2O \rightarrow 2\,M\,(OH)_2 \tag{7}$$

$$M\,(OH)_2 + 2\,e \rightarrow M + 2\,OH^- \tag{8}$$

and Lingane[23] has shown that, with platinum electrodes, the oxygen reduction potential is controlled by the potential of the Pt/PtO couple. By analysing the results of Bockris and Huq[24] and of Hoar[25], Riddiford[26] has shown that the overall reaction occurs by a mechanism in which metal oxides are chemically formed and electrochemically reduced. The overall process may be written as

$$O_2 + 2\,M \rightarrow 2\,MO \tag{9}$$

$$H_2O + MO + e \rightarrow MOH + OH^- \tag{10}$$

$$MOH + e \rightarrow M + OH^- \tag{11}$$

the last step being rate-controlling when platinum electrodes are used.

It is clear from the above short discussion and also from the review of Yeager and Kozawa[27] that the mechanism of the oxygen electrode process is not firmly established. It appears that the reaction may take different routes dependent on parameters such as the electrolyte medium, temperature and electrode material.

An argument sometimes advanced for the direct reaction (3) which involves four electrons is that the current efficiency based on this reaction is 100%. However, unless any of the intermediates for the other routes decompose to yield oxygen which is lost from the electrode then the current efficiencies must also be 100%. Since peroxides, if formed, are likely to decompose on the surface to form oxygen which can react again the chance of a current efficiency less than 100% is small.

With such a nebulous scientific background the development of catalysts for the oxygen electrode has been largely empirical. Kordesch has developed porous carbon oxygen electrodes incorporating catalysts chosen for their ability to decompose peroxide. In particular, he favours various spinels formed on carbon electrodes by the thermal decomposition of solutions of various metal nitrates. Examples quoted from the relevant patents[28] include mixed cobalt and aluminium nitrates and also more complex mixtures containing for example, the nitrates of manganese, cobalt, copper, silver and aluminium. Alternatively to the spinels used by Kordesch the carbon may be impregnated with silver or one of the platinum metals; platinum and palladium are particularly favoured, but osmium[29] has been suggested as well as iridium. When oxygen electrodes are made of nickel, nickel oxide may be used as the catalyst but it is a very poor $p$-type semiconductor, with a resistivity of approximately $10^{13}$ ohm cm. $Ni^{3+}$ ions can, however, be introduced into the lattice by adding univalent cations such as $Li^+$ and this can reduce the resistivity to less than 10 ohm cm. This approach was first used by Bacon[14]. In general, this type of catalyst is used only in fuel cells operating at 200°C or higher. With nickel electrodes intended for use at temperatures closer to ambient it is necessary to use more active catalysts than nickel oxide. Silver, as used by Justi and Winsel[30] for example, is often chosen. At the potential of the oxygen electrode in strongly alkaline electrolytes, silver is likely to be present as the oxide. For this reason silver oxide is sometimes used directly in making oxygen electrodes. Ruetschi[31] also claims that a nickel–silver alloy containing from 10 to 50% wt. nickel is particularly good.

Gray and Eiss[32] have pointed out that silver oxide is soluble in strong solutions of potassium hydroxide. However, our own experience is that not even platinum is completely free from attack when used on oxygen electrodes in alkaline electrolytes. In these circumstances the catalyst chosen must be a compromise between effectiveness and cost, bearing in mind the life required.

In acid electrolytes platinum, used for the oxygen electrode by Grove in 1841, is still the most widely employed catalyst. Palladium can be used but is susceptible to oxidation and dissolution; the use of alloys such as platinum–gold[33] and platinum–iridium[34] has also been suggested. At present no alloys comprising cheaper metals have been found to be satisfactory catalysts for the oxygen electrode processes and, until such materials can be used, it is essential that the expensive metals be used as effectively as possible.

The role of surface roughness was discussed in Chapter 3 and any method of increasing this factor can be used either to enhance the electrode reactions or to reduce the amount of catalyst required to give a specified performance. For example, the dispersion of platinum on carbons of very high surface area may ensure optimum use of the precious metal. There is no doubt that the method of preparation of the catalyst as well as its chemical composition play a very important part in determining the performance of electrodes.

## 2. ELECTRODE STRUCTURE

*Three-phase contact*

In the hydrogen–oxygen cell two electrodes are used to promote either reactions (1) and (4) or (2) and (3). Three phases must come together for these reactions to occur, the reacting gas, a solid, electronically conducting electrocatalyst to promote the desired reaction and the electrolyte. This situation is illustrated in Fig. 28.

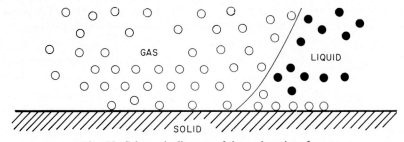

Fig. 28. Schematic diagram of three-phase interface.

As there can only be line contact between three phases, two phases must combine for the reaction to occur at a finite rate. The only practical possibility seems to be for gas molecules to diffuse through the liquid interface on to the catalyst surface. If Fick's Law is applied to mass transport of the gas molecule across a film of liquid, it is readily apparent that at one atmosphere of oxygen only very thin films of liquid can sustain a useful current density. Taking the diffusion coefficient of oxygen in the electrolyte at a temperature of 18°C to be $1.9 \times 10^{-5}$ sq.cm/sec and the solubility of oxygen as $3 \times 10^{-3}$ cu.cm gas/cu.cm of solution, a film of electrolyte 1 micron thick will sustain a current of only 2.5 mA/sq.cm. As the diffusion coefficient depends on the concentration and nature of the electrolyte, some electrolytes are more critical of electrode structure than others. For example, Williams and Gregory[11] give results showing a limiting current of 200 mA/sq.cm for a particular oxygen electrode with an electrolyte of $5N$ potassium hydroxide. When the electrolyte concentration was increased from $5N$ to $10N$, with a consequent reduction in the solubility of oxygen in the electrolyte, the limiting current due to gas transport was reduced to 20 mA/sq.cm. On the other hand, they found that there were no limitations due to gas transport from oxygen electrodes in sulphuric acid, in which oxygen is considerably more soluble than it is in potassium hydroxide.

While the picture of the gas/liquid/electrode interface given in Fig. 28 explains some characteristics of gas electrodes, it is probably grossly over-simplified; Liebhafsky, Cairns, Grubb, and Niedrach[35] have suggested that an extremely thin film of electrolyte covers the electrode on which a state of dynamic equilibrium exists on a microscopic scale. That is, areas of the electrode are alternately covered by liquid and gas. On this hypothesis, the gas transport process is very complex.

Whatever the true picture of the interface, the gas electrodes in a practical fuel cell must ensure adequate contact between gas, electrolyte and catalyst and usually, but not invariably, a stable gas/liquid interface is aimed at.

It is, of course, essential that electrodes should be suitable for assembly into practical fuel cells. Usually electrodes are in the form of flat plates which are then assembled so that hydrogen and oxygen electrodes are parallel to each other and as close together as convenient. By keeping the thickness of electrolyte separating the electrodes to a minimum, ohmic losses are reduced. Sometimes hydrogen and oxygen electrodes are made in the form of concentric cylinders with electrolyte retained in the annular space between them. The alternative of separate cylindrical electrodes is hardly ever employed because of resistive losses in the electrolyte. The various approaches to electrode design are considered in the following sections.

### (a) Biporous "Bacon" electrodes

Perhaps the most easily understood method of stabilizing the gas/liquid interface is that chosen by Bacon and illustrated in Fig. 29.

The electrode is formed of two porous layers of sintered nickel, a coarse-pored layer on the gas side and a fine-pored layer adjacent to the electrolyte. Gas is supplied at a pressure slightly higher than that of the electrolyte, the pore sizes being chosen such that the electrolyte is blown out of the coarse-pored layer but retained by surface tension in the finer layer. The interface is stable over a limited range of differential pressures between gas supply and electrolyte. Hydrogen electrodes of this type used by Bacon were made of sintered nickel. In order to improve the catalytic properties of the electrode, its surface area was increased by impregnation with nickel nitrate which was thermally decomposed and reduced with hydrogen[14]. Oxygen electrodes had the same structure, but the surface was oxidized and the oxide "lithiated" to improve its conductivity. The catalytic activities of Bacon's electrodes were not high and in order to obtain substantial outputs temperatures of 200°C and pressures of 300–600 lb./sq.in. were employed. However, the electrodes were

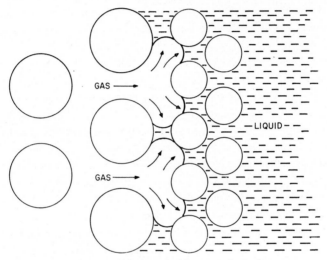

Fig. 29. Diagram of a biporous electrode.

capable of withstanding these conditions and the outputs obtained were the highest ever recorded for hydrogen–oxygen cells; Fig. 30 shows the outstanding performance of Bacon's electrodes.

These electrodes have been further developed by the Pratt and Whitney Division of United Aircraft in the U.S.A., who have adapted them for use at atmospheric pressure or thereabouts by the structure of the porous layers[36]. In order to keep the vapour pressure of the electrolyte below that of the gas supplies it is necessary to use very strong solutions of potassium hydroxide which are solid at room temperature. As this type of fuel cell is unable to be started at room temperature provision must be made to heat it to its operating temperature. It is thus primarily useful when power is required for long periods. An example of a task for which it is well suited is as a power supply for space vehicles and, in fact, the Pratt and Whitney cell has been developed for use in the Apollo lunar probe.

Although the current densities obtained from this type of fuel cell are very high indeed, the fuel cells are still comparatively large and heavy and the specific power in terms of weight or volume is disappointingly low. No doubt great improvements can be obtained with further development.

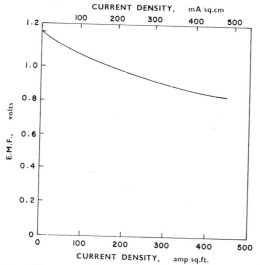

Fig. 30. Performance of Bacon-type hydrogen–oxygen cell (500°F; atmospheric pressure; electrolyte 83–85% KOH).

### (b) Homoporous sintered metal electrodes

Although the Bacon two-pore structure is an elegant solution to the problem of obtaining a workable three-phase system, it is by no means the only one. In order to make satisfactory two-pore electrodes extremely close control of the pore size is necessary but this difficulty may be eased if an electrode with pores of only one size is used and gas circulated through it. This approach has been described by Duddy, Ferrell and Ruetschi[37] and Plust[38], both of whom developed "bubbling electrodes". The oxygen electrodes of Duddy et al., although probably expensive, have excellent performance (Fig. 31) and a long life, but a pump is needed to circulate the gas. If a hydrogen electrode of this form is also used a diaphragm must be provided in the cell to prevent mixing of the gases.

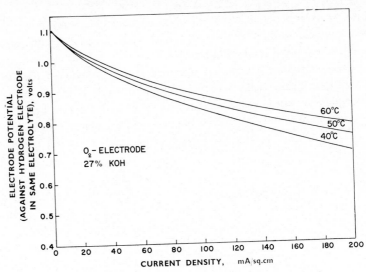

Fig. 31. Polarization of a single bubbling oxygen electrode.

The DSK (Doppelskelett-Katalysator) electrodes of Justi are usually homoporous. For a full description of the construction and performance of these electrodes the book by Justi and Winsel[15] may be consulted. Briefly the hydrogen electrode is formed from a sintered mass of nickel powder and Raney nickel–aluminium alloy powder. After fabrication the aluminium is removed from the alloy particles by anodic etching in potassium hydroxide solution. This leaves an extremely active nickel surface; in fact, the electrodes are so active that if exposed to air they become red hot. For the oxygen electrode, Justi favours silver as the catalyst. Either he replaces the Raney nickel alloy of the hydrogen electrode with an alloy of silver and zinc[15] or he causes silver to be deposited by electrolytic replacement on one of his nickel electrodes. It appears that by suitable control of the manufacturing technique, Justi is able to produce electrodes with a satisfactorily stable gas/liquid interface and excellent performance (Fig. 32).

An interesting method of stabilizing the gas/liquid interface in homoporous electrodes is used by the Allis-Chalmers Company and has been described by Wynveen and Kirkland[39]. This consists of retaining the potassium hydroxide electrolyte in asbestos between the hydrogen and oxygen electrodes, the volume and concentration of electrolyte being dependent upon operating conditions. These must be such that the volume of electrolyte remains sensibly constant so that the system neither dries out, nor floods the electrodes owing to inadequate removal of water from one or both of the gas streams. When used with porous nickel electrodes activated with platinum and palladium these cells have given the very creditable output of 340 amp/sq.ft. at 0.6 volt at a temperature of 65°C and 5 lb./sq.in. gauge pressure. (1 amp/sq.ft. is approximately equal to 1 mA/sq.cm.)

To summarize, porous metal electrodes are robust and capable of withstanding high operating temperatures and, under suitable conditions, they can give very high outputs and extended lives in hydrogen–oxygen cells. In general, because nickel is used in their construction, they are restricted to use with alkaline electrolytes, and for this reason they are not too well suited to operation on air, which normally contains carbon dioxide. This must be removed in some way or provision made for replenishing the electrolyte. Additionally, some of these electrode structures are prone to nitrogen blanketing; because of the tortuous path between the face of the electrode to which air is applied and the electrolyte interface nitrogen in the air has difficulty in diffusing out. Under these circumstances gas concentration polarization may give rise to a limiting current as discussed in Chapter 3.

### (c) Carbon gas-diffusion electrodes

One of the earlier types of electrode used in low temperature fuel cells was the gas-diffusion electrode of Schmid[40]. Since carbon bodies usually acquire a hydrophobic surface in the course of their manufacture, electrolyte will

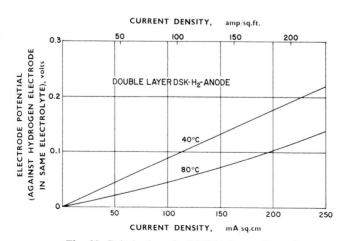

Fig. 32. Polarization of a DSK hydrogen electrode.

not penetrate their pores and a stable gas/liquid interface may be achieved where the electrolyte and carbon are in contact. In a typical form a tubular electrode is immersed in the electrolyte and gas supplied to the inside of the tube. The carbon from which these electrodes are made is "activated" in which process it acquires a large surface area (several hundred square metres per gram) and many interconnected pores. The gas, hydrogen or oxygen, is able to diffuse through the pores to the surface of the electrolyte. Because of the multiplicity of pores there is a very extensive line of contact between gas, solid and liquid. In alkaline electrolytes carbon itself is active as a catalyst for the oxygen electrode although it is usual to enhance its activity by use of silver, platinum or palladium or a spinel[28]. Carbon may be impregnated with the precious metals by being soaked in a solution of a suitable salt, which is then reduced to the metal on heating in a reducing atmosphere. The reducing atmosphere is of importance to avoid oxidation of the carbon. In acid electrolytes carbon alone is ineffective as an electrocatalyst for the oxygen electrode and platinum is often used to promote the desired reaction. It has also been claimed that a platinum–iridium combination is advantageous[34]. Carbon itself does not catalyse the electrolytic oxidation of hydrogen, so that the hydrogen electrode is normally impregnated with platinum or palladium.

Although carbon gas-diffusion electrodes are initially hydrophobic or "wet proof" this effect is short-lived and various proprietary processes are used to enhance this aspect of the electrode performance. Traditionally, paraffin wax is applied as a solution in a volatile solvent such as petroleum ether. However, with high current densities the oxidizing conditions on the oxygen electrode in alkaline electrolyte are extremely severe and the paraffin wax oxidizes. When this occurs the electrode "floods", that is, as the surface of the electrode loses its hydrophobic properties owing to oxidation, the electrolyte enters the very fine pores of the carbon. This renders the electrode ineffective. This type of electrode is particularly prone to flooding when attempts are made to evaporate the water of reaction into one of the gas streams. In order to reduce or eliminate flooding, alternatives to paraffin wax have been sought. Polyethylene[42] and polytetrafluoroethylene (PTFE)[41] are examples of waterproofing agents giving a low energy surface with greater resistance to oxidation, PTFE being outstandingly good in this respect.

An additional feature of the carbon gas-diffusion electrode is the poor performance of oxygen electrodes when used with air. This is caused by nitrogen blanketing as discussed previously.

Porous carbon fabricated from suitable coals is fragile and appropriate precautions must be observed in cell manufacture. Alternatively, better mechanical properties may be obtained by forming carbon electrodes on a wire or perforated metal screen, a suitable binder being used between the particles.

In spite of these many drawbacks, hydrogen–oxygen fuel cells using carbon electrodes giving high outputs have been brought to a comparatively high state of development, particularly by the Union Carbide Consumer Products Company.

### (d) Thin microporous electrodes

As has already been stated, the reaction zone for gas electrodes operating at or about atmospheric pressure is limited to areas in which the electrolyte film is very thin. It is therefore logical to make fuel cell electrodes in which the catalyst is confined to a thin layer.

Probably the first workers to adopt this approach were Mond and Langer[43] who used a perforated gold or platinum plate covered with pla-

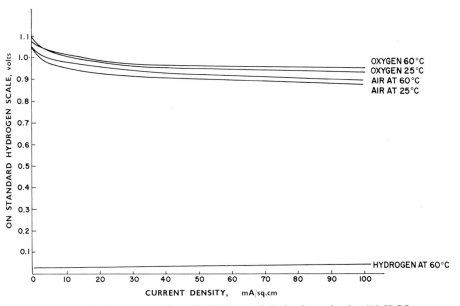

Fig. 33. Polarization curves for "Shell" Research Ltd. electrodes in $6N$ $H_2SO_4$.

tinum black. The sulphuric acid electrolyte was retained in a plaster of Paris diaphragm against which the hydrogen and oxygen electrodes were placed. Probably because of the unsatisfactory geometry of this system,the output was low. A much more successful approach was that of Williams and Gregory[44] ("Shell" Research Ltd.), who prepared fuel cell electrodes by evaporating a metal, usually silver or gold, on to a substrate of a microporous plastic. A catalyst was then applied by electrodeposition or in a binder system[33]. The gas was applied to the coated face of the electrode and the electrolyte interface maintained in the right place by a slight differential pressure applied between gas and electrolyte; typically, this differential pressure was between 1 and 3 lb./sq. in. "Porvic" microporous polyvinyl chloride with a thickness of 0.03 inch (0.76 mm) made in England by Porous Plastics Ltd. is a very suitable substrate for this type of electrode, which can be used in both acid and alkaline electrolytes. As is shown in Figs. 33 and 34, excellent performance is obtained from these electrodes, particularly noteworthy being the very good performance of the oxygen electrode on air.

Being very thin and largely composed of plastic, these electrodes are extremely light and yet reasonably robust as they can be flexed without damage. Fuel batteries with complete cells having a total thickness of 0.25 inch (0.68

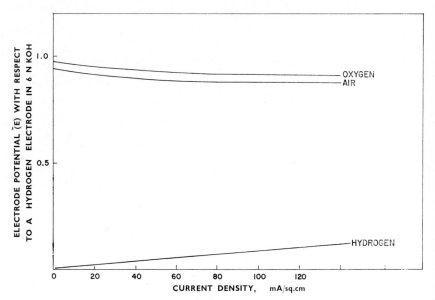

Fig. 34. Polarization curves for "Shell" Research Ltd. electrodes in 6$N$ KOH at 60°C.

mm) or less can readily be constructed. Catalyst loadings are relatively low and so the fuel cells are reasonably cheap.

Another form of thin electrode has been described by Haldeman *et al.* of American Cyanamid[45]. Although few details of these electrodes have been disclosed, it appears that they consist of a catalyst and binder spread uniformly on to a metal gauze. The electrolyte interface is maintained by absorbing the electrolyte on asbestos or glass fibres. With this system care must be taken to remove the water of reaction by evaporation in the gas system. The catalyst may be platinum black or platinum supported on carbon. Excellent performance is obtained with these electrodes. That other thin electrodes of good performance have been made is clear from reference 35 which refers to proprietary electrodes made by General Electric. These electrodes consist of a mixture of platinum black and PTFE pressed onto a suitable gauze. The non-wetting properties of PTFE allow a gas–liquid interface to be established without the need for a differential pressure, an advantage with air electrodes. Although expensive, these electrodes give outstanding performance.

### (e) Membrane diffusion electrodes

As hydrogen diffuses readily through palladium it is possible to use a thin palladium membrane as a hydrogen electrode. This was realized by Beutner[46] in 1911, although his fuel cell was unsound in principle. More recently, Oswin and Chodosh[13] have described such an electrode which uses a membrane of palladium–silver alloy which has superior mechanical properties to palladium itself. These electrodes elegantly solve the three-phase problem as hydrogen diffuses through the metal electrode and reacts on the face adjacent to the electrolyte. Because hydrogen alone diffuses through the electrode, the fuel gas is automatically purified and fuel cells with alkaline electrolytes can without difficulty consume fuel gases containing $CO_2$ and CO. These electrodes operate best at temperatures in the range 100–200°C (see Fig. 35).

### (f) Nitric acid redox electrodes

To complete this review of electrode structure and type, reference should be made to the nitric acid–nitrous acid redox electrode which has been proposed from time to time as an oxygen (air) electrode in fuel cells.

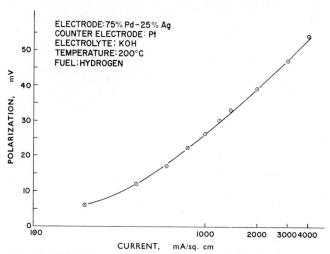

Fig. 35. Polarization of a hydrogen membrane diffusion electrode.

Jungner[47] proposed the use of a mixture of nitric and sulphuric acids through which air was bubbled. A carbon electrode was immersed in the catholyte, which was separated from the anolyte with a porous diaphragm. It was thought that the nitric acid would be reduced electrolytically at the cathode:

$$HNO_3 + 2\ H^+ + 2\ e \rightarrow HNO_2 + H_2O. \qquad (12)$$

Equation (12) represents a fast reaction which occurs at a potential ($+0.94$ volt) quite close to that of the oxygen electrode in acid. It was expected that oxygen from the air would then reoxidize the nitrous acid to nitric acid:

$$2\ HNO_2 + O_2 \rightarrow 2\ HNO_3. \qquad (13)$$

This same principle was used in fuel cells described by Garner and Williams[48] and Shropshire and Tarmy[49].

Unfortunately, whereas reaction (12) is fast, reaction (13) does not proceed very rapidly and, furthermore, both nitrous and nitric acids are relatively volatile and are gradually lost from the system. Additionally, the diaphragm necessary in the system adds to the internal resistance of the cell, while two electrolyte systems must be used. (If nitric acid were in contact with the fuel electrode it would be reduced and this would adversely affect the electrode potential.) This system is then neither invariant nor simple; nevertheless, high cell outputs have been achieved using this principle.

## (g) Structures incorporating ion exchange membrane

Although many of the features of fuel cells which use ion exchange membranes as the electrolyte bear a marked resemblance to those of cells with liquid electrolytes, it is convenient to consider this class of cell separately. The whole subject of ion exchange fuel cells has been reviewed in detail by Niedrach and Grubb[50] and in this chapter the general principles of operation only are considered.

The ion exchange membrane was first suggested as a fuel cell electrolyte by Grubb[51]. Figure 36 shows the essential features of a cell in which this type of electrode is used. The hydrogen and oxygen electrodes are held against opposite faces of the membrane and since the liquid capacity of the membrane is limited, any surplus water of reaction is automatically rejected. Care must be taken that the membrane is not completely dried out as water is required for the electrode reactions. Wicks are normally used to maintain the desired water balance. Usually cationic (hydrogen ion) exchange membranes are

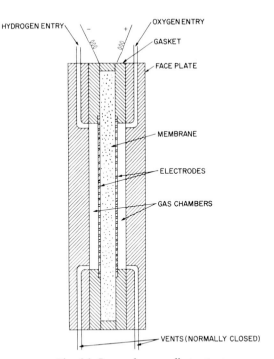

Fig. 36. Ion exchange cell structure.

used as they have better stability and conductivity than anionic exchange resins. Further, if air is used as the oxidant, the carbon dioxide present tends to replace the hydroxyl groups in an anionic exchange resin by carbonate ions, increasing the internal resistance of the cell and seriously reducing electrode performance. The cationic exchange resin is immune from this trouble. The earlier ion exchange membranes used as electrolytes were condensation polymers of phenolsulphonic acid and formaldehyde. Because of the low tensile strength, it was necessary to reinforce these polymers with fabric. The mem-

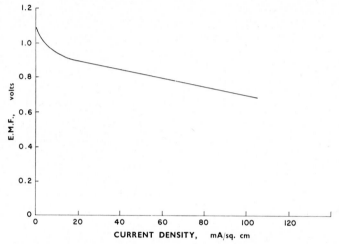

Fig. 37. Performance of an ion exchange membrane hydrogen–oxygen cell.

branes were also dimensionally unstable, their size altering with variation in water content, and they were liable to form pinholes and micro-cracks if allowed to dry. Also, relatively short operating lives were obtained because of the chemical instability of the polymers. Douglas and Oster[52] report that these problems can be overcome by using interpolymers of polyfluorocarbons and polystyrenesulphonic acid. With these membranes electrolyte resistances in the range 0.5–1.0 ohm/sq.cm are attained and the cell life is limited only by oxidative degradation of the polymer at higher operating temperatures.

In the first fuel cells with ion exchange membranes, the electrodes were of platinum or nickel gauze which had been coated with platinum black or palladium black by electrodeposition or other means. These gauzes were pressed against the membrane. Evidently the three-phase system so formed was not particularly effective as the performance of the electrodes was poor. Subsequently, greatly improved performance has been obtained from PTFE-bonded sheets of platinum black as the electrodes[52]. This type of electrode may be bonded directly to the fluorocarbon–polystyrenesulphonic acid type of membrane referred to above. As these electrodes have a relatively high resistance, in order to carry the current it is necessary to incorporate gauze screens external to the electrode or forming part of the electrode structure itself. Typical outputs from these cells are 50 amp/sq.ft. at 0.8 volt at 100°F operating temperature, with a peak power of over 100 watts/sq.ft. Current/ voltage curves for these cells are shown in Fig. 37.

Although the electrode structures described by Douglas and Oster are the most successful in fuel cells using ion exchange membranes, others have been proposed. Perry[53] has described the use of porous metal electrodes, and Hunger, porous carbon electrodes[54]. Packed layers of powders may also be used[50]. In acid systems platinum appears to be the preferred catalyst as it is more stable than palladium, although palladium can give very high levels of performance initially. For alkaline systems a wider range of catalysts is applicable but, as already stated, these systems are unattractive from other points of view.

Although ion exchange membranes are normally employed as the sole electrolyte, Juda *et al.*[55] have described the use of two membranes separated by a liquid electrolyte. One electrode is attached to each of the membranes. It is difficult to believe that this is an advantageous arrangement as it combines the bad features of both ion exchange cells and free electrolyte cells with no compensating advantages.

## 3. RELATIVE MERITS OF DIFFERENT HYDROGEN–OXYGEN CELLS

The subject of complete power units is discussed in a later chapter, but it is perhaps worthwhile at this point to consider the relative merits of the different hydrogen–oxygen fuel cells. In any given instance when the final choice has to be made a number of conflicting factors have to be borne in mind; some observations on these follow.

When operation on hydrogen and oxygen is contemplated, potassium hydroxide solutions are in many ways the best electrolytes. The wide choice of relatively cheap metals which may then be used to construct the cells eases the engineering problems. Sintered metal electrodes may be used over a wide range of operating temperatures and, from the point of view of longevity and robustness, have much to commend them but they are not particularly cheap and are difficult to manufacture in large sizes with adequate uniformity. Because of the simpler engineering involved, the writer prefers the Bacon biporous electrode with its stable interface to the gassing or bubbling porous metal electrode. Where operation at room temperature is required, activation of porous nickel electrodes with precious metals is desirable although it is often difficult to recover the precious metals from nickel when the electrode has reached the end of its useful life.

Porous carbon electrodes should be cheaper than porous metal electrodes. It is generally more difficult to remove the water of reaction from carbon electrodes owing to danger of flooding the electrode pores. The mechanical properties of carbon are poor and it is difficult to manufacture large uniform electrodes in this material. Maximum operating temperatures for carbon electrodes are lower than for metal electrodes. Microporous plastics electrodes are probably the cheapest and easiest porous electrodes to produce. The high degree of uniformity of the microporous polyvinyl chloride from which the electrodes are made makes it possible to produce large electrodes of uniform and repeatable performance; they are also very light. The performance of the oxygen electrodes on air is also very good. However, use of a substrate of polyvinyl chloride limits the operating temperature of these electrodes to 65°C. Much higher operating temperatures have been achieved with a substrate of microporous PTFE but this is expensive.

Although the microporous plastics electrodes are readily adapted for use in acid electrolytes, there is normally no great advantage in using such electrolytes in hydrogen–oxygen cells. The exception to this generalization is the General Electric fuel cell with acid ion exchange membrane; these cells can be made into light, compact, hydrogen–oxygen cells with simple means of water removal, without any moving parts.

When operation on air is considered, thin electrodes are preferred. Although alkaline electrolytes are now being used in air-breathing fuel cells, the problems of carbonate formation in the electrolyte are such that acid electrolytes are much to be preferred. If impure hydrogen containing $CO_2$ and CO is used as the fuel, acid electrolytes are essential unless a membrane diffusion electrode is used.

REFERENCES

1  M. W. BREITER, in *Trans. Symp. on Electrode Processes*, (ed. by E. YEAGER), Wiley, New York, 1961, p. 307.
2  A. N. FRUMKIN, Chap. 2 in *Advances in Electrochemistry and Electrochemical Engineering*, (ed. by P. DELAHAY), Vol. 1, Interscience, New York, 1961.
3  A. N. FRUMKIN, Chap. 5 in *Advances in Electrochemistry and Electrochemical Engineering*, (ed. by P. DELAHAY), Vol. 3, Interscience, New York, 1963.
4  M. BREITER, L. KANDLER, B. KENNEL AND H. FEIGL, *U.S. Dept. Comm. Tech. Rept. ASD–TR–61–475*, 1962.
5  M. BREITER, P. A. KNORR AND R. MEGGLE, *Z. Elektrochem.*, **59** (1955) 153.
6  A. N. FRUMKIN AND E. A. AIKAZIAN, *Dokl. Akad. Nauk. S.S.S.R.*, **100** (1955) 315.
7  J. HORIUTI AND G. OKAMOTO, *Bull. Chem. Soc. Japan*, **13** (1938) 216.
8  S. SCHULDINER, *NRL Rept. 5291*, April 1959; *NRL Rept. 5398*, November 1959.
9  K. J. VETTER AND D. OTTO, *Z. Elektrochem.*, **60** (1956) 1072.
10  R. A. MUNSON, *J. Phys. Chem.*, **66** (1962) 727.
11  K. R. WILLIAMS AND D. P. GREGORY, *J. Electrochem. Soc.*, **110** (1963) 209.
12  M. POURBAIX, *Atlas D'Equilibres Electrochimiques à 25°C*, Gauthier–Villars, Paris, 1963.
13  H. G. OSWIN AND S. M. CHODOSH, *Preprints\* 145th Natl. Meeting Am. Chem. Soc.*, New York, Sept. 1963, Vol. 7: *Div. Fuel Chem.*, No. 4: Symp. Fuel Cell Systems, p. 84.
14  F. T. BACON, in *Fuel Cells*, (Chem. Eng. Progr. Tech. Manual), Am. Inst. Chem. Engrs., New York, 1963, p. 66.
15  E. W. JUSTI AND A. W. WINSEL, *Kalte Verbrennung—Fuel Cells*, Franz Steiner Verlag, Wiesbaden, 1962.
16  R. JASINSKI, *Preprints\* 145th Natl. Meeting Am. Chem. Soc.*, New York, Sept. 1963, Vol. 7: *Div. Fuel Chem.*, No. 4: Symp. Fuel Cell Systems, p. 109.
17  E. J. CAIRNS, D. L. DOUGLAS, L. W. NIEDRACH AND W. T. GRUBB, *A.I.Ch.E. J.*, **7** (1961) 551.
18  W. BERL, *Trans. Electrochem. Soc.*, **83** (1943) 253.
19  R. S. WEISS AND S. S. JAFFE, *J. Electrochem. Soc.*, **93** (1948) 128.
20  M. DAVIES, M. CLARK, E. YEAGER AND F. HOVORKA, *J. Electrochem. Soc.*, **106** (1959) 56.
21  J. O'M. BOCKRIS, *J. Chem. Phys.*, **24** (1956) 817.
22  D. T. SAWYER AND R. J. DAY, *Electrochim. Acta*, **8** (1963) 589.
23  J. J. LINGANE, *J. Electroanal. Chem.*, **2** (1961) 296.
24  J. O'M. BOCKRIS AND A. K. M. S. HUQ, *Proc. Roy. Soc. (London)*, A **237** (1956) 277.
25  T. P. HOAR, in *Proc. 8th CITCE Meeting, Madrid, 1958*, (ed. by G. VALENSKI), Butterworths, London, 1958, p. 439.
26  A. C. RIDDIFORD, *Electrochim. Acta*, **4** (1961) 170.
27  E. YEAGER AND A. KOZAWA, *Combustion and Propulsion, 6th AGARD Colloquium*, Pergamon, Oxford, 1964.
28  A. MARKO AND K. KORDESCH, *U.S.Patents 2,615,932* (1952) *and 2,669,598* (1954).
29  ABEL, *Brit. Patent 732,022* (1955).
30  E. W. JUSTI AND A. W. WINSEL, *J. Electrochem. Soc.*, **108** (1961) 1073.
31  P. RUETSCHI, *Brit. Patent 939,238* (1963) *and U.S.Patent 3,020,327* (1962).
32  T. J. GRAY AND R. EISS, *Nature*, **194** (1962) 469.
33  K. R. WILLIAMS AND R. T. SHORT, *Brit. Patent 951,807* (1964).

* Proceedings to be published by American Chemical Society as *Fuel Cell Systems* (Advan. Chem. Ser. No. 47).

34 C. E. THOMPSON, Brit. Patent 946,367 (1964).
35 H. A. LIEBHAFSKY, E. J. CAIRNS, W. T. GRUBB AND L. W. NIEDRACH, Preprints* 145th Natl. Meeting Am. Chem. Soc., New York, Sept. 1963, Vol. 7: Div. Fuel Chem., No. 4: Symp. Fuel Cell Systems, p. 124.
36 H. G. OSWIN, Platinum Metals Rev. 8 (1964) 42.
37 J. C. DUDDY, D. T. FERRELL AND P. RUETSCHI, Proc. Ann. Power Sources Conf., 16 (1962) 9.
38 H. G. PLUST, Brown Boveri Rev., 49 (1962) 3.
39 R. A. WYNVEEN AND T. G. KIRKLAND, Proc. Ann. Power Sources Conf., 16 (1962) 24.
40 A. SCHMID, Helv. Chem. Acta, 7 (1924) 370.
41 W. G. TASCHEK, Preprints* 145th Natl. Meeting Am. Chem. Soc., New York, Sept. 1963, Vol. 7: Div. Fuel Chem., No. 4: Symp. Fuel Cell Systems, p. 5.
42 R. WITHERSPOON, H. URBACH, E. YEAGER AND F. HOVORKA, The oxygen electrode, Western Reserve Univ. Tech. Rept. 4, U.S. Office Naval Res. Contract Nonr. 581(00), Oct. 1954.
43 L. MOND AND C. LANGER, Proc. Roy. Soc. (London), 46 (1889) 296.
44 K. R. WILLIAMS AND D. P. GREGORY, Brit. Patent 874, 283 (1961).
45 R. G. HALDEMAN, W. P. COLMAN, S. H. LANGER AND W. A. BARBER, Preprints* 145th Natl. Meeting Am. Chem. Soc., New York, Sept. 1963, Vol. 7: Div. Fuel Chem., No. 4: Symp. Fuel Cell Systems, p. 118.
46 R. BEUTNER, Z. Elektrochem., 17 (1911) 91.
47 E. W. JUNGNER, U.S.Patent 884,664 (1908).
48 P. J. GARNER AND K. R. WILLIAMS, Brit. Patent 844, 584 (1960).
49 J. A. SHROPSHIRE AND B. L. TARMY, Preprints* 145th Natl. Meeting Am. Chem. Soc., New York, Sept. 1963, Vol. 7: Div. Fuel Chem., No. 4: Symp. Fuel Cell Systems, p. 158.
50 L. W. NIEDRACH AND W. T. GRUBB, Chap. 6 in Fuel Cells, (ed. by W. MITCHELL), Academic Press, New York, 1963.
51 W. T. GRUBB, U.S.Patent 2,913,511 (1959).
52 D. L. DOUGLAS AND E. A. OSTER, Abstr. 4th Intern. Symp. on Batteries, 1964.
53 J. PERRY JR., Proc. Ann. Power Sources Conf., 14 (1960) 50.
54 J. HUNGER, Proc. Ann. Power Sources Conf., 14 (1960) 55.
55 W. JUDA, C. E. TIRRELL AND R. M. LURIE, Progr. Astron. Rocketry, 3 (1961) 445.

* See note on p. 107.

# Chapter 6

# ELECTROLYTE-SOLUBLE FUELS

The design of a low-temperature, low-pressure fuel cell is governed by the kinds of fuel and oxidant the cell is intended to utilize. Gaseous fuels demand a porous electrode so constructed that the required electrochemical reaction takes place at gas/liquid/solid interfaces within the pores. Such electrodes are relatively expensive. If the fuel is soluble in the electrolyte, electrode construction is simpler; a thin conducting sheet, supporting catalytically active material if necessary, is basically all that is required. Liquid fuels are, moreover, advantageous as compared with their gaseous counterparts because of their greater ease of transport and storage, whilst the elimination of heavy gas cylinders and the high calorific value per unit volume of liquid fuels should permit of improvements in energy/weight and energy/volume ratios for the complete power unit. For these reasons, the development of fuel cells utilizing electrolyte-soluble fuels has become the object of much research within the past few years.

An ideal liquid fuel should have the following properties. It should be cheap and readily available. Its boiling point and freezing point should be such that it will remain liquid over a wide range of temperature. It should be chemically stable and soluble in, but inert towards, strong acids or bases. It should have a reasonably low viscosity and a high flash point. It should have a high calorific value and should yield inoffensive, preferably gaseous, reaction products. Finally, it should ionize rapidly at a suitable anode with a minimum of overvoltage and be converted into final oxidation products such as carbon dioxide and water. At the same time it should be inert at the cathode. Obviously no single substance is likely to fulfil all of these requirements, and in practice, few materials are worth considering.

Pavela[1] measured the anodic activity of a number of water-soluble organic compounds on a platinum electrode. His results (Table 5) showed that primary alcohols were the most reactive compounds studied. Schlatter[2] carried out a similar survey covering a larger number of compounds and

*References pp. 153–155*

TABLE 5

REACTIVITIES OF ORGANIC COMPOUNDS DURING ANODIC OXIDATION IN BASIC AND ACID
ELECTROLYTES (DATA FROM PAVELA[1])

| Reactivity | Electrolyte | |
|---|---|---|
| | N NaOH | N H₂SO₄ |
| High | Methanol | Methanol |
| | Ethanol | Ethanol |
| | Ethylene glycol | Formic acid |
| | | Formaldehyde |
| Medium | Benzyl alcohol | |
| | Propylene glycol | |
| | Sodium formate | |
| | Isopropanol | |
| | s-Butanol | |
| Low | Propanol | |
| | Butanol | |
| | α-Phenylethyl alcohol | |
| Unreactive | t-Butanol | Acetic acid |
| | Phenol | Benzoic acid |
| | Diethyl ether | |

reached conclusions similar to those of Pavela. He pointed out that the electrochemical activity of organic compounds was generally less in acid solution than in base. Wynn[3] studied methanol, formaldehyde, ethanol, isopropanol, acetaldehyde and potassium formate in a basic electrolyte and concluded that methanol and formaldehyde were the most reactive materials. Many of the substances investigated do not oxidize electrochemically to carbon dioxide and water, for example, ethanol yields acetic acid, and isopropanol yields acetone[4]. Glasstone and Hickling[5] discussed in some detail the electrolytic oxidation products formed from various classes of organic compounds. These reaction products can generally be oxidized only at high potentials and unless complete oxidation of the fuel at low potentials can be achieved the advantage of the fuel cell as a highly efficient energy converter will not be realized.

Methanol is a particularly promising organic substance for fuel cell research. It is not cheap, but it can be produced in bulk and in an expanded market the price is likely to fall substantially. Its physical properties approach the ideal, and it can be oxidized electrochemically to carbon dioxide and water. However, commercially attractive fuel cells using methanol have not yet been developed, primarily because no known electrocatalyst will yield a suitably high current density with methanol at an acceptable degree of polarization.

A large number of water-soluble inorganic compounds can readily be oxidized electrochemically, though only a few, in particular, ammonia and hydrazine, merit consideration for use in fuel cells. Ammonia is cheap and available in bulk, though its widespread use as a fuel would not be without hazard. Hydrazine is more reactive than ammonia but, at the same time, is much more expensive and is very toxic. Hydroxylamine is reactive but has no advantage over hydrazine, and is more expensive. The use of sodium borohydride as a liquid fuel has been proposed[6]. It is said to be stable in alkaline solutions and to react at a suitable electrode surface to give high current densities at reasonable cell voltages. Unfortunately, the current efficiency is below 50% of the theoretical value for the reaction

$$H_2BO_3^- + 5\,H_2O + 8\,e \rightleftharpoons BH_4^- + 8\,OH^- \qquad E° = -1.23 \text{ to } -1.24$$

owing to the evolution of hydrogen. Electrodes active enough to consume this hydrogen also catalyse chemical decomposition of the fuel. It is possible that these difficulties can be overcome but it seems unlikely that such an expensive material could ever be used economically as a fuel.

In this chapter we shall deal only with the most promising soluble fuels, namely methanol, ammonia and hydrazine. We shall, furthermore, discuss only direct conversion systems. Cells utilizing reformed methanol or cracked ammonia gases do not come within the scope of this chapter.

Complete cells require an oxidant as well as a fuel. Generally, oxygen is used although air is preferable for greater economy of operation. The use of a soluble oxidant, though permitting simpler electrode construction, may involve higher running costs. The possible adverse effect of the fuel on the potential of the cathode and of the oxidant (if electrolyte-soluble) on the potential of the anode must also be taken into account. However, the choice of oxidant is likely to be determined ultimately by economic considerations rather than technical ones. We shall therefore confine our detailed discussion to problems of the fuel electrode.

## 1. THE METHANOL FUEL CELL

### (a) Complete fuel cells

Despite a growing volume of literature on the use of methanol as a fuel in a direct-conversion fuel cell, very few complete power-producing cells or batteries (exclusive of laboratory test rigs not designed as power producers) have ever been constructed. Two units which use a soluble oxidant have been described. The first (Allis-Chalmers Manufacturing Company, 1961)[7] was based on an electrolyte comprising methanol and hydrogen peroxide dissolved in potassium hydroxide. The electrodes consisted of nickel sheets each platinized on one side and silvered on the other; when assembled in series in the fuel battery the platinized sides acted as anodes and the silvered sides as cathodes. Circulation of the electrolyte simplified the problems of heat removal, electrolyte sampling, and fuel and oxidant addition. A 100 sq.in. (645 sq.cm.) 40-cell unit provided 40 amp at 15 volts at an unspecified temperature. Some loss of hydrogen peroxide occurred by decomposition on the anode together with some non-electrochemical oxidation of methanol. This cell neatly demonstrated the compactness and simplicity of construction possible with both dissolved fuel and dissolved oxidant.

The second unit (Armour Research Foundation, 1963)[8] incorporated anode and cathode compartments separated by a dialysis membrane; methanol and potassium chlorate both in potassium hydroxide solution were used as anolyte and catholyte respectively. The anode was constructed by flame-spraying nickel–aluminium alloy onto a suitable base metal (nickel sheet or porous sintered nickel) followed by electrochemical leaching of the aluminium phase in potassium hydroxide solution. Platinum was finally electrodeposited onto the resultant Raney nickel. The cathode was similarly constructed of Raney nickel–silver without platinization. Operated at 55°C, the cell gave 100 mA/sq.cm at 0.7 volt. The chief advantage claimed for it was that its energy-to-weight ratio compared favourably with those obtainable from cells using stored gaseous reactants.

Of greater commercial interest are oxygen or, preferably, air-breathing fuel cells, an early example of which was described by Kordesch and Marko (1951)[9]. This cell utilized formaldehyde, ethanol or methanol, an alkaline electrolyte and a porous-carbon air electrode impregnated with suitable metallic catalysts. The nature of the fuel catalyst was not disclosed. The output from this cell was, however, very low (0.3 mA/sq.cm at 0.8–0.9 volt at room temperature with formaldehyde as fuel).

A later example described by Justi and Winsel (1955)[10] used the patented DSK electrodes described in Chapter 5. The anode was a sheet of porous nickel and the cathode was, in effect, a hollow sheet of porous nickel–silver to which oxygen was supplied. The fuel was dissolved in aqueous potassium hydroxide. It was claimed that the cathode showed no activity towards the fuel and hence separate anode and cathode compartments were not necessary. Performance figures for methanol were not given. Since the hollow cathode had no outlet this cell was patently incapable of operating on air.

A basically similar methanol cell has been described by Wynn (1960)[3]. This cell comprised a platinized porous carbon anode and a hollow porous carbon cathode impregnated with the mixed oxides of silver, cobalt and aluminium. With a potassium hydroxide electrolyte and running on air, it yielded 8 mA/sq.cm at 0.35 volt. Wynn also experimented with hydrochloric acid as the supporting electrolyte and reported that performance was poorer than in alkali. However, his choice of hydrochloric acid was unfortunate because it is well known that chloride ions adversely affect the catalytic activity of platinum[11].

To avoid fuel losses by direct oxidation on the cathode, Hunger (1960)[12]

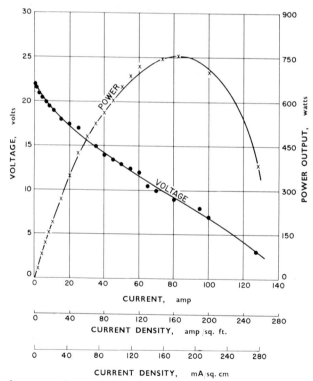

Fig. 38. Performance characteristics of a 40-module methanol–air fuel cell (Allis-Chalmers).

constructed a cell with porous metal electrodes sandwiching an anion exchange membrane. Fuel (methanol) and air or oxygen were fed to the appropriate electrode each of which was treated with an undisclosed catalyst. Outputs were very small, e.g. 1 mA/sq.cm at 0.5 volt with oxygen, or 1 mA/sq.cm at 0.25 volt with air (at room temperature). His choice of an *anion* exchange membrane was dictated by the better performance of the oxygen electrode in a basic medium. Complete oxidation to carbon dioxide caused depletion of the alkali and necessitated the addition of further alkali together with the fuel.

Another methanol cell with an alkaline electrolyte has been described by Murray and Grimes (Allis-Chalmers Manufacturing Co., 1963)[13]. The anode consisted of a sheet of nickel on which was deposited a platinum–palladium catalyst. The special advantage claimed for this catalyst is that, whereas on all previously known catalysts methanol is electrochemically oxidized in alkaline solution to formate, with this new material complete oxidation to carbonate and a consequent high current efficiency is achieved. The cathode was constructed from silver-impregnated porous nickel sheet, suitably waterproofed and attached to the reverse face of the anode in such a way as to leave a gas space for the supply of oxygen in between. The current voltage characteristics and power output of a 40-cell module using oxygen are shown in Fig. 38. Further operating details are given in Table 6. The data in Fig. 38 and Table 6 are typical of the outputs which are now reached with this system. It can be seen by reference to Fig. 38, however, that the cell polarizes considerably under load, so that only a low overall voltage efficiency is realized at acceptable current densities (100 mA/sq.cm or higher).

TABLE 6

OPERATING CHARACTERISTICS OF THE ALLIS-CHALMERS METHANOL–OXYGEN FUEL CELL MODULE

| Characteristics | Operating range | | Overload output |
|---|---|---|---|
| Power output (watts) | 440 | 570 | 750 |
| Total operating voltage (volts) | 16 | 14 | 10 |
| Total operating current (amp) | 27.5 | 41 | 73 |
| Operating voltage/cell (volts) | 0.4 | 0.35 | 0.25 |
| Current density (mA/sq.cm) | 57.0 | 84.8 | 151 |
| Power/volume ratio (kW/cu.ft.) | 0.365 | 0.46 | 0.605 |
| Power/weight ratio (watts/lb.) | 2.94 | 3.80 | 5.00 |
| Pressure (lb./sq.in.) | 0–5 | 0–5 | 0–5 |
| Temperature (°C) | 50 | 50 | 50 |

All the cells described above use an alkaline electrolyte. It has been pointed out by Williams and Gregory[14] that to avoid concentration polarization at one or other of the electrodes it is necessary to use either a strongly basic or a strongly acidic electrolyte. Both systems present problems. It has been generally observed that, in alkaline systems, methanol is anodically oxidized only to formate [2,4,15], which is resistant to further oxidation. However, it now seems that this difficulty has been overcome (see above). A further difficulty stems from the gradual conversion of the electrolyte to carbonate. This is objectionable for two reasons. Firstly, the cell efficiency decreases because of the increasing concentration polarization at the electrode surface and the decreasing conductivity of the electrolyte. Secondly, for economic utilization, it will be necessary to provide for the regeneration of the electrolyte[13]. Chemical processes, such as, for example, precipitation of carbonate by the addition of lime, might conceivably be used. Justi[16] claims to have developed an economic dialysis process but details have not been made public. It remains to be seen whether or not a practical economic system can be developed.

Acid electrolytes do not suffer from these disadvantages. Methanol can be converted with a high current efficiency to carbon dioxide[1,2,17] which is not retained by the electrolyte. Unfortunately, it is less readily oxidized in acid than in basic solution[2], in the sense that equivalent current densities are obtained only at increased polarization. Acid systems entail greater corrosion problems, although use of plastic materials for structural components will undoubtedly alleviate this problem. Finally, it should be mentioned that greater difficulties are generally experienced with the oxygen electrode in acid than in alkaline electrolytes, though, as shown in Chapter 5, these difficulties can be solved.

In the authors' laboratory an 8-cell methanol–air battery has been constructed utilizing sulphuric acid as the electrolyte. The electrodes were constructed from microporous polyvinyl chloride supporting either active platinum (cathodes) or platinum–ruthenium (anodes). This unit has given 30 mA/sq.cm at 0.25 volt per cell at 30°C over extended periods of time. No comparable unit is known, though the literature indicates no lack of interest in this aspect of fuel cell research[18–23].

Opinions are divided on the merits of these two distinct types of methanol fuel cell. Our own preference is for the acid type since it seems inconceivable that regeneration of an alkaline electrolyte can ever be achieved without sacrificing a substantial proportion of the power produced by the cell. However, both systems demand better and cheaper catalysts than those which are currently available. Experience with other types of fuel cell, notably the hydrogen–oxygen cell, illustrates the rapid development possible with systems largely free from electrochemical problems. It is pertinent, therefore, to consider the mechanism of the electrochemical oxidation of methanol and to assess the difficulties which, so far, preclude the practical use of methanol in fuel cells.

### (b) Open circuit potentials

The overall electrochemical oxidation of methanol in an acid medium takes the form of eqn. (1), which in conformity with the "European" sign convention, is written with the electrons on the left hand side:

$$CO_2 + 6\,H^+ + 6\,e \rightleftharpoons CH_3OH + H_2O\,. \tag{1}$$

The reaction isotherm corresponding to eqn. (1) is

$$-\Delta G = RT \ln K - RT \ln \frac{(a_{CH_3OH})(a_{H_2O})}{(a_{CO_2})(a_{H^+})^6} \tag{2}$$

where $K$ is the thermodynamic equilibrium constant, $a_x$ is the activity of species $x$ and $\Delta G$ is the free energy change.

Elimination of $\Delta G$ from eqn. (2) by means of Gibbs' equation

$$-\Delta G = nFE \tag{3}$$

where $n$ is the number of electrons associated with the reaction, $F$ is the Faraday and $E$ is the electrode potential referred to the standard hydrogen scale, gives

$$E = \frac{RT}{6F} \ln K - \frac{RT}{6F} \ln \frac{(a_{CH_3OH})(a_{H_2O})}{(a_{CO_2})(a_{H^+})^6}\,. \tag{4}$$

When all the reacting substances are at unit activity the second term on the right hand side of eqn. (2) vanishes, giving

$$-\Delta G^\circ = RT \ln K \tag{5}$$

where $\Delta G^\circ$ is the *standard* free energy of the reaction. By analogy with eqn. (5), eqn. (4) becomes

$$E^\circ = \frac{RT}{6F} \ln K \tag{6}$$

whence

$$E = E^\circ + \frac{RT}{6F} \ln \frac{(a_{CO_2})(a_{H^+})^6}{(a_{CH_3OH})(a_{H_2O})} \tag{7}$$

where $E^\circ$ is the *standard* electrode potential for the reaction. Equation (7) is the familiar Nernst equation. For liquid phase reactions activities can be expressed in the form

$$a_x = f_x C_x$$

where $f_x$ and $C_x$ are the activity coefficient and the concentration in moles/l of species $x$. For simplicity, ideal conditions will be assumed, *i.e.* $f_x = 1$ for all species involved in the reaction, although this approximation will, in fact, introduce appreciable errors when the concentrated electrolyte solutions commonly employed in fuel cell studies are considered. Equation (2) now becomes

$$-\Delta G = RT \ln K_c - RT \ln \frac{(C_{CH_3OH})(C_{H_2O})}{(C_{CO_2})(C_{H^+})^6} \tag{8}$$

and eqn. (5) becomes

$$-\Delta G^\circ = RT \ln K_c \tag{9}$$

where $K_c$ is the equilibrium constant expressed on the molarity scale (mole/l). Standard electrode potentials can be calculated from standard free energy data, provided that the selected data relate to the free energy of the species in aqueous solution at a concentration of one mole/l. It is advantageous, however, to use the standard free energy of formation of water generally found in standard texts, *i.e.* on the mole fraction scale. Terms involving water in expressions such as eqn. (7) can then be equated to unity and ignored, as is conventional for reactions involving the solvent. When this practice is adopted, the standard electrode potential $E^\circ$ can be defined as the equilibrium potential of the electrode when all the reacting species are at a concentration of one mole/l in water and the concentration (activity) of water is equated to unity. *Standard* electrode potentials should not be confused with *open circuit* potentials. Open circuit potentials can be readily computed via the Nernst equation (7) and, of course, vary with the experimental conditions.

In alkaline solution the equation for the electrochemical oxidation of methanol must take into account the formation of carbonate ion, *i.e.*,

$$CO_3^{2-} + 6 H_2O + 6 e \rightleftharpoons CH_3OH + 8 OH^- . \tag{10}$$

Application of the Nernst equation to eqn. (10) gives

$$E = E° + \frac{RT}{6F} \ln \frac{(C_{CO_3^=})(H_2O)^6}{(C_{CH_3OH})(OH^-)^8} .$$ (11)

Equations (1) and (11) suggest that the reaction takes place in a single electrochemical step, but this is improbable. It has been shown by Pavela[1], Schlatter[2], and others[4,24] that when methanol is anodically oxidized, either in acidic or basic solution, formaldehyde and formic acid are intermediate reaction products. A summary of probable intermediate steps, together with the appropriate standard electrode potentials, is given in Table 7. The anodic oxidation of methanol is likely to give, in the first instance, formaldehyde (reaction 1, Table 7). In aqueous solution formaldehyde is virtually completely hydrated to methylene glycol[25], eqn. (12), which is ionized in alkaline solution (eqn. (13)).

$$HCHO + H_2O \rightleftharpoons CH_2(OH)_2 \qquad K_c \simeq 10^3 \text{ at } 25°C$$ (12)

$$CH_2(OH)_2 \rightleftharpoons CH_2(OH)O^- + H^+ \quad K_c = 1.75 \times 10^{-13} \text{ at } 25°C$$ (13)

The value of the acid dissociation constant of methylene glycol suggests that the molecule can be regarded as fully ionized in basic solution (pH > 13) and undissociated in neutral or acid solution[26]. In these circumstances the second step in the anodic oxidation of methanol may, with some justification, be considered to involve either methylene glycol or its anion according to the pH of the electrolyte.

In basic solution both carbonate and bicarbonate anions will be formed in the final step, but we have for simplicity written reaction 10, Table 7 as involving carbonate anions only.

The free energy data given in Table 7 are mostly taken from standard texts[27], but some explanation is necessary in certain instances.

The standard free energy of aqueous formaldehyde is said to be about −32 kcal/mole[25] or −31 kcal/mole[27]. These values are misleading since they are based on equilibrium data relating to the formation of methylene glycol (eqn. (12)). The hydration of aqueous formaldehyde does not involve the transfer of electrons from the electrolyte to the electrode (or *vice-versa*) and is not part of the electrochemical process. The standard free energy of aqueous methylene glycol is correctly given by the addition of the appropriate contribution of water to the standard free energy of "aqueous formaldehyde" as is done in Table 7. From these data, and the dissociation constant for

STANDARD ELECTRODE POTENTIALS FOR METHANOL AND RELATED COMPOUNDS

| Reaction No. | Electrolyte | Reaction* | $\Delta G°$ kcal/mole; at 25°C | $E°$ volts; at 25°C |
|---|---|---|---|---|
| 1 | Acid | $HCHO_{(aq)} + 2\,H^+ + 2\,e \rightleftharpoons CH_3OH_{(aq)}$ <br> $-27.8 \qquad\qquad -41.7$ | $-13.9$ | $+0.30$ |
| 2 | Acid | $CH_2(OH)_{2(aq)} \rightleftharpoons HCHO_{(aq)} + H_2O_{(lq)}$ <br> $-88.6 \qquad -27.8 \quad -56.7$ | $+4.1$ | |
| 3 | Acid | $HCO_2H_{(aq)} + 2\,H^+ + 2\,e \rightleftharpoons CH_2(OH)_{2(aq)}$ <br> $-85.1 \qquad\qquad\qquad -88.6$ | $-3.5$ | $+0.076$ |
| 4 | Acid | $CO_{2(g)} + 2\,H^+ + 2\,e \rightleftharpoons HCO_2H_{(aq)}$ <br> $-94.3 \qquad\qquad\qquad -85.1$ | $+7.2$ | $-0.20$ |
| 5 | Basic | $HCHO_{(aq)} + 2\,H_2O_{(lq)} + 2\,e \rightleftharpoons CH_3OH_{(aq)} + 2\,OH^-_{(aq)}$ <br> $-27.8 \quad -2\times56.7 \qquad\qquad -41.7 \quad -2\times37.6$ | $+24.3$ | $-0.52$ |
| 6 | Basic | $CH_2(OH)O^-_{(aq)} \rightleftharpoons HCHO_{(aq)} + OH^-_{(aq)}$ <br> $-70.4 \qquad\qquad -27.8 \quad -37.6$ | $+5.0$ | |
| 7 | Basic | $HCO_2^-_{(aq)} + 2\,H_2O_{(lq)} + 2\,e \rightleftharpoons CH_2(OH)O^-_{(aq)} + 2\,OH^-_{(aq)}$ <br> $-80.0 \quad -2\times56.7 \qquad\qquad -70.4 \qquad -2\times37.6$ | $+47.8$ | $-1.02$ |
| 8 | Basic | $CO_3^-_{(aq)} + 2\,H_2O_{(lq)} + 2\,e \rightleftharpoons HCO_2^-_{(aq)} + 3\,OH^-_{(aq)}$ <br> $-126.2 \quad -2\times56.7 \qquad\qquad -80.0 \quad -3\times37.6$ | $+46.8$ | $-1.00$ |
| 9 | Acid | $CO_{2(aq)} + 6\,H^+ + 6\,e \rightleftharpoons CH_3OH_{(aq)} + H_2O_{(lq)}$ <br> $-92.3 \qquad\qquad\qquad -41.7 \qquad -56.7$ | $-6.1$ | $+0.043$ |
| 10 | Basic | $CO_3^=_{(aq)} + 6\,H_2O_{(lq)} + 6\,e \rightleftharpoons CH_3OH_{(aq)} + 8\,OH^-_{(aq)}$ <br> $-126.2 \quad -6\times56.7 \qquad\qquad -41.7 \quad -8\times37.6$ | $+123.9$ | $-0.88$ |

* The figures beneath reaction components are the standard free energies (in kcal/mole) used in the calculation of the standard electrode potentials.

reaction (12) ($K_c \simeq 10^3$ at 25°C)[28], the true standard free energy of aqueous formaldehyde can be derived (Table 7). Similarly, the standard free energy of the methylene glycol anion was derived from the dissociation constant for reaction (13) ($K_c = 1.75 \times 10^{-13}$ at 25°C) which was obtained by interpolation from the data of Wadano[26]. Because of the lack of precision in the data on which these values have been calculated, they must be regarded as only approximate.

In the preparation of Table 7 the standard state of gaseous substances has been taken to be 1 atmosphere pressure and that of dissolved substances 1 mole/l. The standard state of water is the pure liquid. Values of $E°$ derived in this way simplify the derivation of theoretical open circuit potentials via the Nernst equation.

The potentials of the various steps in the anodic oxidation of methanol may be compared with experimentally determined values with a view to identifying the potential-controlling step. That this object has not been achieved reflects the experimental difficulties in determining reliable open circuit potentials.

Electrode reactions are governed by the ordinary laws of chemical kinetics, and in a sequence of electrochemical reactions the net current, $i_c$, passing through the electrode is given by eqn. (9b) of Chapter 3 (see page 33).

At equilibrium $i_c = 0$, therefore

$$C_O k_f \exp \frac{-\alpha n_a F \eta_a}{RT} \rightleftharpoons C_R k_b \exp (1-\alpha) \frac{n_a F \eta_a}{RT}. \tag{14}$$

The two terms in eqn. (14) represent the equal anodic and cathodic currents flowing in opposite directions at the open circuit potential; when these are small the process will be slow, and unless conditions are rigorously controlled, the electrode potential may be governed by faster impurity processes. It appears that this is generally the case for methanol and related compounds such as formaldehyde and formic acid. Under the influence of the powerful catalysts necessary to increase the rate of the required anodic process, side reactions generally occur. For instance, Müller and Schwabe[29] observed that formic acid decomposes in the presence of finely divided platinum; Müller[30] also reported that formaldehyde decomposed violently on specially prepared rhodium with evolution of hydrogen and formic acid, and that osmium converted formaldehyde to methanol and carbon dioxide[31]. Boies and Dravnieks[32] noted that concentrated (20 %) solutions of formaldehyde decompose in the presence of finely divided platinum with liberation of hydrogen. This also occurs, apparently, during the anodic oxidation of formaldehyde[33,34].

Formaldehyde will also undergo the Cannizaro reaction (eqn. (15)) in alkaline solution:

$$2\,HCHO + OH^- \rightleftharpoons CH_3OH + HCO_2^- . \tag{15}$$

Complex situations seem unavoidable in any effort to establish open circuit potentials for methanol and related products. In any case, stable open-circuit potentials more negative than the reversible hydrogen potential cannot be realized in aqueous solutions except in the circumstance that the electrode surface has a high hydrogen-evolution overpotential, *e.g.*, mercury.

Unstable open circuit potentials have been frequently reported for methanol. Breiter and Gilman[18] found that the open circuit potential of methanol in acid solution on bright platinum drifted cathodically from 0.4 volt in a few minutes. They ascribed this either to a concurrent oxidation/reduction of methanol on the surface with the formation of a small amount of hydrogen, or to the dissociation of methanol into radicals and hydrogen atoms. In either case the adsorbed hydrogen atoms were believed to control the observed potential shift. After the electrode had remained in the electrolyte for an appreciable length of time, this absorbed hydrogen could be detected by the charging curve method. Similar open circuit potential shifts for methanol, formaldehyde and formic acid have been reported by Shlygin and co-workers[35,36], who proposed an electron-radical oxidation mechanism. Slott[37] studied the variation of the open circuit potential of aqueous formic acid with time and concluded that the minimum potential found could be attributed to the presence of hydrogen. After reaching the minimum value the open circuit potential rose, owing to the presence of an unidentified neutral organic compound formed by further decomposition of formic acid. Schwabe[38] has also reported an unstable formic acid open circuit potential, but claimed that the hydrogen which might have been formed was not potential-determining.

An observation that must be taken into account in considering open circuit potentials in aqueous systems in the region of the reversible hydrogen potential is that at potentials up to about 0.3 volt above the reversible hydrogen potential the surfaces of platinum, palladium and other noble metal catalysts contain adsorbed hydrogen atoms which can be readily detected by the methods of chronopotentiometry[39]. The structure and properties of this layer have attracted a good deal of attention[40] which does not concern us here. It is sufficient to suggest that the presence of this layer will influence the measured open circuit potentials of organic species which should lie within this region.

It is evident that the direct approach to the measurement of open circuit potentials is unlikely to be successful. An alternative approach is to study current–voltage relationships in the open circuit potential region. Equation (14) shows that, at the open circuit potential, an electrode is in a state of dynamic equilibrium, simultaneously passing equal and opposite currents. If the potential is displaced sufficiently, say anodically, the cathodic current will fall to a negligible value, whence

$$I_a = nFAC_R k_b \exp (1-\alpha)\frac{n_a F \eta_a}{RT} \tag{16}$$

and

$$\eta_a = \frac{2.3RT}{(1-\alpha)n_a F} \log nFAC_R k_b + 2.3 \frac{RT}{(1-\alpha)n_a F} \log I_a . \tag{17}$$

Equation (17) will be recognized as a form of the Tafel equation. A corresponding equation applies in the case of a cathodic potential displacement. A plot of $\log I_a$ and the corresponding $\log I_c$ vs. $E$ will be of the form shown in Fig. 10 (page 48) where both anodic and cathodic currents are regarded as positive.

The linear portions of the curve in Fig. 10 obey the Tafel equation as given by eqn. (17) and its corresponding cathodic counterpart. The curved portions of the plot correspond to eqn. (9b) of Chapter 3 (see page 33) but this region, around the open circuit potential, does not yield reliable data in the particular circumstances of interest. Projections of the linear portions of the curve in Fig. 10 intersect at the point where $I_a = I_c$, that is, at the true open circuit potential. This method is useful provided the electrode reaction is genuinely reversible and capable of permitting current to pass in each direction. Generally it seems that this is not true of methanol, formaldehyde or formic acid. Methanol is readily oxidized to formaldehyde but the reverse reaction may not be kinetically equivalent since it probably requires the preliminary dehydration of methylene glycol [41]. Methylene glycol is readily oxidized anodically to formic acid, but the reverse reaction, if it occurs at all, takes place only at an exceptionally high overvoltage [25]. Formic acid is readily oxidized anodically to carbon dioxide but the reverse reaction has been observed only on amalgamated zinc [42]. On platinum carbon dioxide is apparently not reduced to formic acid [43]. Apart from considerations of reversibility, the theoretical standard potentials of these systems are generally close to the reversible hydrogen potential. As a consequence cathodic polarization would inevitably cause hydrogen evolution, since known catalysts for the required reaction have a small overpotential for hydrogen evolution. Because of these difficulties, reliable open circuit potential measurements on methanol, formaldehyde and formic acid have not been made.

### (c) Current/voltage curves

From a practical point of view the most important characteristic of an electrode is its behaviour when current is drawn. The principal factors controlling the potential of a working electrode, *i.e.* activation polarization, concentration polarization and the "ohmic drop" have been discussed in Chapter 3. The "ohmic drop" is not intrinsically characteristic of the electrode and since it can be readily eliminated from current–voltage measurement by established methods it will not be considered here. Concentration and activation polarization are not always easy to distinguish.

If the electrode process is so fast that activation polarization is negligible the current will be controlled by the rate at which reactive material reaches the electrode surface (neglecting migration effects). In the case of stirred solutions Nernst's approximation of Fick's law leads to eqn. (20) in Chapter 3 (page 38). Application of the Nernst equation to this equation gives

$$\eta = \frac{RT}{nF} \ln \frac{C_0}{C_0 - \dfrac{I\delta}{nFAD}}.$$ (18)

If $D$ and $\delta$ are known, eqn. (18) may be used to compare theoretical and experimental current/voltage curves, though this procedure is unlikely to provide convincing evidence for or against concentration polarization.

The limiting current (diffusion control) is given by eqn. (22) in Chapter 3 (page 39), which provides a better test for concentration polarization, since it predicts that the limiting current will be proportional to the concentration of the reacting substance. Experimental tests of this relationship are easily carried out.

Principal characteristics of concentration polarization in unstirred solution are that the current (at a fixed potential) is (1) lower than in stirred solutions and (2) falls with time. A simple observation of the effects of stirring may therefore qualitatively indicate concentration polarization.

An indication of the conditions under which concentration polarization will apply to the methanol electrode in stirred solution can be given by substituting appropriate values for $D$ and $\delta$ in eqn. (20) of Chapter 3. The value of $\delta$ will depend (amongst other factors) on the rate of stirring but an average value of 0.003 cm may be assumed[44]. The diffusion coefficient of methanol in aqueous systems is not known precisely; for the present purpose a value of $10^{-5}$ cm$^2$/sec may be assumed. Substitution of these values in eqn. (20) of Chapter 3 gives

$$i \simeq 2000 \, (C_0 - C_e) \tag{19}$$

and

$$i_L \simeq 2000 \, C_0 \tag{20}$$

(where $i$ is in amp/sq.cm, $C_0$ and $C_e$ are in mole/cu.cm).

The relationship between concentration overpotential and limiting current is given by equation (26) in Chapter 3 (page 39) from which it may be calculated that, if the current passing is one-tenth of the limiting value, $\eta_c$ is 4.5 mV. If this value represents a negligible degree of polarization, then for methanol (and most organic compounds, since the same values of $D$ and $\delta$ generally apply) concentration polarization will be inappreciable when

$$i \leqslant 200 \, C_0 \quad \text{(room temperature, stirred solution).} \tag{21}$$

Very few published data on methanol are suitable for assessing the applicability of eqn. (20). Pavela[1] measured limiting currents as a function of methanol concentration and temperature in basic and acid electrolytes, but his results appear to relate to unstirred solutions. Although eqn. (20) does not apply to unstirred solutions, in practice a degree of agitation is unavoidable and under these circumstances eqn. (20) of Chapter 3 may be held to apply if $\delta$ is given a value of 0.03 cm[45]. Equation (20) then becomes

$$i_L \simeq 200 \, C_0 \tag{22}$$

and conditions under which diffusion control can be neglected will be given by

$$i \leqslant 20 \, C_0 \quad \text{(room temperature, unstirred solution).} \tag{23}$$

Pavela's data are plotted in Fig. 39 and show that diffusion control operates at methanol concentrations below about 0.5 molar in the temperature range 25–50°C in both acid and basic solutions. At higher concentrations limiting currents are much less than would be expected for purely diffusion control and indicate the onset of a different rate-limiting step. In the diffusion control region Pavela's data (at 25°C) can be summarized approximately as

$$i_L = 300 \ C_0$$

which is of the right order of magnitude and is in as close agreement with eqn. (22) as can reasonably be expected in view of the various approximations involved.

The influence of stirring was investigated by Gentile and co-workers[46], who, using a strongly alkaline electrolyte and a platinized platinum electrode, showed that even with methanol concentrations as low as 0.1 molar identical current/voltage curves are achieved in quiescent as in conventionally stirred solutions. Their results did not include limiting currents, though current densities as high as 400–500 mA/sq.cm (1 molar methanol, 60°C) were

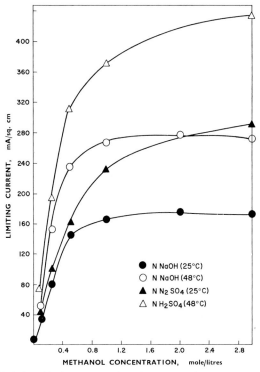

Fig. 39. Relationship between methanol concentration and limiting current.

*References pp. 153–155*

recorded. At such high current densities one might expect the effects of stirring to be clearly evident. That this was not the case may be due to the relatively high temperature at which the measurements were made; increased diffusion rates and hence increased limiting currents will result at higher temperatures.

Although the limitations of the methanol electrode due to mass-transfer processes cannot be precisely defined, it is evident that when the necessary steps are taken to maximize rates of diffusion, the maximum currents obtainable are much smaller then the calculated limiting current. Under these circumstances, it must be assumed that the rate-controlling process is associated with activation polarization.

When concentration polarization is absent, the process taking place at the surface of the electrode will be governed by the laws of ordinary chemical kinetics. This, as discussed in Chapter 3 leads to a statement of the Tafel equation

$$\eta = a + b \log i \tag{24}$$

where $a$ and $b$ are characteristic for each electrode process, and are readily obtained from the slope and intercept of a plot of potential against log $i$.

Pavela[1] reported linear Tafel plots for methanol on platinized platinum in both acid and basic electrolytes, and calculated $b$ as 0.08 in acid and 0.12 in base, though the reproducibility of his curves was poor. Buck and Griffith[47] found good agreement with the Tafel equation for methanol on platinized platinum in basic electrolyte and derived a value for $b$ at 25°C of 0.21–0.28 which was independent of pH for values from 10 to 14. In acid, the slope of the Tafel plot decreases at high current density in such a way as to suggest not the anticipated onset of concentration polarization but rather a limitation possibly due to adsorption processes.

The unreliable values for Tafel constants hitherto recorded may explain why no attempt has been made to use them as a basis for a mechanistic theory along the lines developed in connection with the hydrogen evolution reaction[48]. Inconsistencies arise because current/voltage curves for methanol (as well as for formaldehyde and formic acid) are independent neither of time nor of the history of the electrode. Buck and Griffith[47] recommended for platinum surfaces a pretreatment involving rapid hydrogen evolution from the surface for a few moments, but this treatment must be regarded as inadequate in view of, for example, Gilman's[22] or Giner's[23] more rigorous recommendations. Pavela[1] avoided the issue by preparing new electrodes (platinized-platinum) for each measurement, but since this preparation is not a process susceptible to close control[49], this fact may account for the inconsistencies in his results. Pavela took current/voltage measurements one to two minutes after each adjustment of current, whereas Buck and Griffith adopted the technique of voltammetry at linearly changing potential. The inadequacy of such arbitrary procedures will be realized by reference to the work of Giner[23] (Fig. 40), which shows that at constant

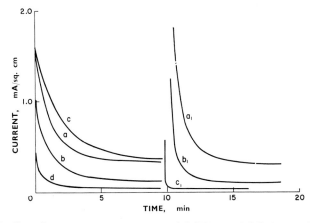

Fig. 40. Decline of current at constant potential (200mV, 95°C) for methanol in $2N$ $H_2SO_4$ on platinized Pt. Methanol concentration: (a) $10^{-3} M$, (b) $10^{-1} M$, (c) $6.10 \times 10^{-4} M$, (d) Nil. ($a_1$), ($b_1$), and ($c_1$) correspond to (a), (b), and (c) after interrupting the test and placing the electrode at 450 mV for 12 sec. (Potentials on standard hydrogen scale.)

potential the current produced from an acid solution of methanol at a platinum electrode decays rapidly over the first few minutes. A similar type of decay curve has been reported for formic acid[50]. In the authors' laboratory, this phenomenon has been found to be of fairly general occurrence, similar curves having been obtained for methanol, ethanol, isopropanol, formaldehyde and formic acid in both acid and basic electrolytes. Even after several hours at constant potential, a steady current is seldom attained. These results seem to be borne out in fuel cell practice, since it is a common observation that the output of methanol cells tends to decline. The picture is obscured somewhat since other factors may intrude, *e.g.* the conversion of base to carbonate or the adverse affect of the oxidant on the anode. However, factors such as these do not wholly account for the decline in performance, since Gentile and co-workers[46] have reported that the activity of a working methanol electrode in basic electrolyte can be restored simply by interrupting the current momentarily.

A complication that arises in the study of current/voltage curves is that of oscillations. As the voltage and current increase a point is reached where either the voltage (at constant current) or the current (at constant voltage) fluctuates. Oscillations in acid solutions of formic acid with rhodanized platinum were first reported by Müller and co-workers[51,52] and have since been observed for methanol[1,47,53] and formaldehyde[1,47] as well as for formic acid[1,37,47] in acid and neutral solutions with platinum surfaces. The phenomenon does not seem to occur as readily in alkaline solution though Hickling and Rodwell[33] have reported current–voltage fluctuations with formaldehyde in alkaline solution with gold and silver electrodes, and Vielstich[34] has reported oscillations with formaldehyde, acetaldehyde, isopropanol and formic acid, in alkaline solution. Pavela[1] offered two suggestions. The first involved the stirring effect of the liberated carbon dioxide gas; the second was that methanol oxidizes until depletion forces the potential in a more positive direction. Eventually an oxide layer is formed on the platinum surface and the electrochemical reaction stops. Reduction of the oxide is brought about chemically by methanol, the potential falls and the cycle repeats. The potential region in which the oscillations occur supports such a theory. Müller[51] observed oscillations in a rather lower potential region and assumed that the peak potential was due to the discharge of the formate ion, the minimum potential representing the discharge of the hydrogen resulting from the prior discharge of the formate ion. Periodicity in the anodic polarization of platinum in the presence of hydrogen has been discussed by Armstrong and Butler[54] in terms of the alternate oxidation of adsorbed hydrogen and of the hydrogen diffusing out from the bulk of the catalyst.

Periodic phenomena are well-known in the field of chemical kinetics[55]. Electrochemical periodicity is generally associated with a region of negative resistance, i.e., where the current decreases as the voltage increases. Methanol, formaldehyde and formic acid all exhibit such a region on a platinum electrode throughout the pH range 0–14. The potential limits of these regions vary with pH but are generally about 0.6–1.0 volt more positive than the reversible hydrogen electrode in the same solution[47]. The electrode system may be represented by the following electrical analogue, where $R$ represents external resistances (including the resistance of the cell), $C$ the double-layer capacity and $r$ the Faradaic resistance of the electrode. When $r$ becomes negative the system can oscillate, and will do so whether the energizing source is constant voltage or constant current. The characteristics of the oscillation will depend not only on the values of $R$, $C$, and $r$ but also on the impedances of associated instruments such as galvanometers and oscilloscopes. Oscillations are therefore as much a function of the measuring and control circuits as of the electrode itself and do not generally provide useful information.

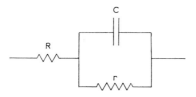

Fortunately for the fuel cell designer oscillations generally occur only at high overpotentials, that is to say under conditions unlikely to be realized in practice.

### (d) Catalysts and preparation of electrodes

For a simple electrochemical process such as the formation or discharge of a metallic ion, the function of the electrode is to provide a pathway for electrons to enter or leave the electrolyte. Any convenient, electronically conducting, chemically unreactive material can, in principle, be used. Other reactions, of which the formation and discharge of hydrogen ions is the most notable example, proceed at a negligible rate on all but a few specific surfaces. In such cases the electrode must not only provide or remove electrons as appropriate but must simultaneously catalyse the required electrochemical reaction.

Equation (16) shows that the current passing through an electrode is proportional to its area and to the rate constant for the reaction. Thus in order to assess different materials for catalytic activity it is necessary to compare them at equivalent surface areas. Measurement of true, as distinct from geometric surface areas, involves the use of specialized equipment[56]. For apparently smooth platinum surfaces the ratio of true to geometric surface area generally lies between 1 and 2, whilst electrolytic platinization may increase this ratio to several thousand. The reproducibility of surface area of platinized platinum even under the most carefully controlled conditions is no better than $\pm 15\%$[49]. Failure to appreciate this uncertainty may account for variations in rating of different catalysts by different workers. For economy the active material is frequently impregnated into a suitable support of high specific surface area, *e.g.* porous carbon or sintered Raney nickel.

The electrode must first adsorb and then activate the reacting species and so increase its susceptibility to oxidation (or reduction). Adsorption must be rapid if heavy currents are to be sustained. At the same time the chemisorption bond should preferably be weak since there is a loss of free energy on chemisorption and a consequent reduction in the theoretically available electrical energy[57]. Finally, the catalyst should preferentially adsorb the reactant rather than the product to avoid self-poisoning. The relationships between catalyst activity and factors such as the heat of adsorption, lattice parameters and *d*-bond vacancies in the metallic structure have attracted considerable attention over many years and a brief discussion of these relationships has been given in Chapter 3. In spite of this effort the selection of a catalyst for such a complex reaction as the electrochemical oxidation of methanol remains largely a matter for experiment. In acid electrolytes, corrosion effectively limits the choice to the metals of the platinum group. In alkaline solutions, a wider choice of material is, in principle, available.

One of the earliest studies of the anodic oxidation of methanol in alkaline solution on various catalytic surfaces was carried out by Tanaka (1929)[58] who showed that the reactivity on smooth surfaces decreased in the order Pd > Rh > Au > Pt.

Cohn[59] measured the catalytic activity of platinum, palladium, ruthenium, rhodium, iridium, osmium, gold and silver deposited on carbon powder for the oxidation of methanol and formic acid in acid solution. Platinum was rated by far the best, giving complete conversion of both fuels to carbon dioxide and water. An extensive survey was made by Gentile and co-workers[46], who studied a number of metal catalysts both in the form of smooth foil and after electroplating with a spongy surface coating. Tests were carried out in solutions of potassium hydroxide, potassium bicarbonate, sodium sulphate and sulphuric acid with methanol, formaldehyde and formic acid. Their results are summarized qualitatively in Table 8. Where differences in rating occur between rough and smooth surfaces the results for the smooth surfaces are likely to be the more reliable. This work also showed that the polarization of methanol on the best catalyst, platinum, was considerably greater in acid than in alkaline solution.

The DSK electrode (a dual-porosity Raney nickel electrode) is said by its inventor, Justi, to be a good catalyst for the anodic oxidation of methanol, as well as of formic acid and ethylene glycol, in alkaline solution[10]. However,

TABLE 8

RELATIVE EFFICIENCIES OF METAL CATALYSTS (GENTILE AND CO-WORKERS[46])

| Electrolyte | Catalyst surface | Methanol | Formaldehyde | Formic acid |
|---|---|---|---|---|
| $5M$ KOH | Smooth | Pt > Pd, Ir > Au > Rh | | |
| | Rough | Pd, Pt, Ir > Au > Rh | | |
| $1M$ Na$_2$SO$_4$ | Smooth | Ir > Ag, Pt, Pd > Au | Ir > Rh > Pt > Pd > Au | Pd > Ir > Pt, Rh > Au > Ag |
| | Rough | Au > Pt > Ir > Pd > Rh | Au > Ir, Rh > Pt > Pd | Pd, Ir > Pt, Au > Rh |
| $3.3M$ KHCO$_3$ | Smooth | Pt > Ir > Pd > Au > Ag > Rh | Ag > Rh, Pt, Ir > Au > Pd | Ag > Pt > Pd > Rh, Ir > Au |
| | Rough | Pt > Ir > Pd > Au > Rh | Au > Ir > Pt, Rh > Pd | Ir > Rh > Pt > Au |
| $M$ H$_2$SO$_4$ | Smooth | Pt, Ir > Pd | Pt, Ir > Pd > Au | Pt > Ir > Pd > Au, Ag |
| | Rough | Pt, Ir > Pd, Au > Rh | | Ir, Pt > Au > Pd > Rh |

Boies and Dravnieks[32] used porous Raney nickel merely as a high surface area carrier for noble metal catalysts electro-deposited on to the surface. Platinum appeared to be the most active material for this purpose. Krupp and co-workers[60] applied the Raney method to copper, cobalt, palladium, rhodium and platinum as well as nickel. Copper, cobalt and nickel were virtually inactive with methanol, whilst platinum, palladium and rhodium were said to be of about equal activity.

Undoubtedly the most reliable data available are those of Breiter[61] who used a linear voltage sweep method to obtain current/voltage curves. He gives the following order of activity for the anodic oxidation of methanol in acid solution: $Pt > Pd > Rh > Ir > Au$.

The widespread acceptance of platinum and palladium as catalysts for the methanol electrode supports Breiter's work. High activities reported by others for iridium[46] and rhodium[58,60] have found no general acceptance.

### (e) Intermediates in the anodic oxidation of methanol

It is generally observed that when methanol or formaldehyde is anodically oxidized in alkaline solution on a platinum electrode the principal product is formate and not carbonate[1,2,30]. Evidently formate is less readily oxidized than methanol under these circumstances. It is to be expected that the concentration of formate in the electrolyte will increase as the reaction proceeds until an equilibrium concentration is reached. The formation of such an intermediate of relatively low reactivity may give rise to a reduced current efficiency and will increase the activation polarization of the system. An understanding of the anodic oxidation of possible intermediates, notably formaldehyde and formic acid is therefore essential to the complete understanding of the anodic oxidation of methanol.

Hickling and Rodwell[33] determined the principal reaction products of the anodic oxidation of formaldehyde in acid, neutral and basic solutions on platinum, gold, lead and carbon. On bright platinum in acid solution the principal reaction product was formic acid (74–81 %) with smaller amounts of carbon dioxide (4–14 %) and carbon monoxide (1–2 %). In neutral solution (on bright platinum) the yield of oxygen was substantial (15–35 %). On platinized platinum the principal product was carbon dioxide (33–45 %) with some formic acid (27–33 %), though, in this case, only 66–75 % of the total current passed was accounted for. In alkaline solution the principal products were formic acid (65–93 %) and carbon dioxide (29–41 %). Hickling

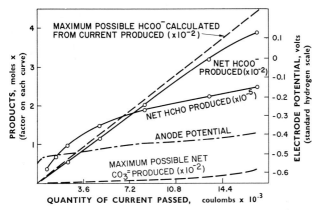

Fig. 41. Fuel cell products from 1.56 $M$ methanol in 4.5 $M$ sodium hydroxide at 24°C.

also found small amounts of hydrogen from formalhedyde in alkaline solution, thus confirming an earlier observation of Tanaka[58]. In these experiments the quantity of electricity passed was insufficient to cause any substantial change in the concentration of the formaldehyde in the electrolyte.

Pavela[1] determined the products formed during the anodic oxidation of methanol on platinum in acid and basic solution. In acid the principal product was carbon dioxide with some formic acid and a trace of formaldehyde.

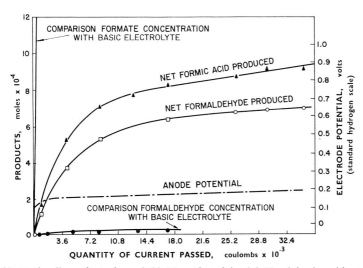

Fig. 42. Fuel cell products from 1.56 $M$ methanol in 4.6 $N$ sulphuric acid at 23°C.

With increasing methanol concentration the yields of formaldehyde and formic acid increased and that of carbon dioxide decreased. In base, the product was exclusively formate. When the reaction was allowed to take place at a current density greater than the limiting current density, that is to say, in the region where oxygen evolution might be expected, these ratios changed; in particular, the yields of formaldehyde and formic acid in acid increased, whilst that of carbon dioxide decreased. In base, substantial amounts of carbon dioxide were formed, together with traces of formaldehyde and there was a reduced formate yield.

The best data available are probably those of Schlatter[2], who measured the rate of formation of formate and formaldehyde from methanol on platinum. In basic solution the yield of formate was very nearly quantitative and there was a very small yield of formaldehyde (Fig. 41). In acid solution the main product was assumed to be carbon dioxide; only small amounts of formic acid and formaldehyde were detected (Fig. 42). These results suggest the following order of reactivities on platinum.

Acid solutions:          Formic acid > methanol $\rightleftharpoons$ formaldehyde
Basic solutions:          Formaldehyde > methanol $\gg$ formate

*(f) Mechanism of the anodic oxidation of methanol and related compounds*

Methanol, formaldehyde and formic acid can be anodically oxidized only in the presence of a suitable catalyst. Until recently, platinum was widely regarded as the best available catalyst and, for this reason, has been used as a basis for most mechanistic studies.

The electrochemical properties of a platinum surface immersed in an aqueous electrolyte have been discussed in Chapter 4. It will be recalled that hydrogen and oxygen atoms are deposited in characteristic potential regions and their presence may materially affect the catalytic properties of the metal. Thus at potentials more positive than about 0.9 volt (with respect to the reversible hydrogen potential in the same electrolyte) the oxide layer which is formed on platinum inhibits the catalytic activity for the anodic oxidation of many organic compounds as well as for hydrogen ionization[62]. As the potential rises further, oxidation of the organic compounds recommences though it seems likely that the mechanism will be different from that operative on the clean metal surface. Müller[63], as early as 1923, observed that the anodic oxidation of formic acid occurred in two separate potential regions and he correctly ascribed oxidation on the clean metal surface to the low potential region and oxidation on an oxide-covered surface to the high potential region. The high potential region is of no practical interest to the fuel cell technologist, and most studies have been concerned with the mechanism of oxidation at potentials below about 0.8 volt (with respect to the reversible hydrogen electrode in the same solution). The evidence suggests that the mechanism is not the same in acid as in basic solutions, and these systems will accordingly be discussed separately.

*Basic electrolytes*

Many of the earliest investigators were concerned with the oxidation of formic acid or formaldehyde rather than with methanol. Müller[63,64] periodically published various theories to explain the anodic oxidation of formaldehyde, being principally concerned with the mechanism of the formation of hydrogen. His final view was that the initial stage involved the discharge of the anion $CH_2(OH)O^-$ to yield the corresponding adsorbed radical; then either the adsorbed radical could decompose monomolecularly to formic acid plus an adsorbed hydrogen atom or, alternatively, two of the adsorbed radicals could undergo bimolecular decomposition to produce formic acid and free hydrogen. The low potential stage was considered to correspond to the discharge potential of the adsorbed radical, but on electrodes which gave little or no hydrogen it was supposed that the monomolecular decomposition of the adsorbed radical was catalysed by the electrode surface and that this process was fast enough to prevent the concentration of the radicals building up to a point where interaction would commence. Hickling and Rodwell[33] regarded these views as rather speculative. They carried out careful product analysis for the anodic oxidation of formaldehyde in basic (and acid) solution on a variety of metal surfaces. In their view the oxidation was a chemical process in which the primary oxidizing agent was hydrogen peroxide produced at the anode. Potential measurements showed that the reaction took place in the high potential region, that is on a surface at least partly covered by an oxide layer, and certainly at a potential at which the discharge of hydroxyl ions could be expected. On platinized platinum oxidation occurred in the low potential region where the reaction products were thought to arise chiefly via the eqn.:

$$HCHO + 2 OH^- \rightarrow H_2O + HCO_2H + 2 e. \qquad (25)$$

However, since hydroxyl ions are not discharged in this potential region, it is preferable to consider that the reaction takes place in the form given in reaction 7, Table 7.

Pavela[1] carried out an extensive survey of the anodic oxidation of methanol, formaldehyde and formic acid in both basic and acid electrolytes, determining the shapes of current/voltage curves, values of limiting currents and yields of intermediate products. He also observed a potential step characteristic for methanol during the course of voltammetric studies at constant current. According to Pavela, the hydroxylic hydrogen atom of methanol is the most readily removed, though it was not possible to decide whether this took place in the bulk solution or on the electrode surface. Recent measurements of the acidity constant for methanol[65] make it evident that only 2–3% of the methanol in a one-molar solution in normal alkali exists in the form of methoxy anions, $CH_3O^-$. That the rate process is not simply the discharge of this ion is evident from the fact that the process does not occur on many surfaces, *e.g.* gold. The most probable steps, according to Pavela, are

$$CH_3OH_{(soln)} \rightarrow CH_3OH_{(ads)} \rightarrow CH_3O \cdot + H^+ + e \qquad (26)$$

followed by

$$CH_3O \cdot \rightarrow HCHO + H^+ + e \qquad (27)$$

though the extent to which these processes take place in solution rather than on the electrode could not be ascertained.

The next step was considered to be the formation of the $H_2C(OH)O^-$ anion, in accordance with the following equations.

$$HCHO + H_2O \rightarrow H_2C(OH)_2 \qquad (28)$$

$$H_2C(OH)_2 + OH^- \rightarrow H_2C(OH)O^- + H_2O . \qquad (29)$$

Formaldehyde is almost entirely hydrated in aqueous solution and largely ionized at high pH. Solutions of formaldehyde were said by Pavela to give a region of low potential oxidation on gold and nickel as well as on platinum (a claim supported by Vielstich[34]), indicating that the next step in the reaction was simply the discharge of this anion. Finally, the resultant radical decomposed into formic acid and hydrogen ion, *i.e.*

$$H_2C(OH)O^- \rightarrow H_2C(OH)O \cdot + e \qquad (30)$$

$$H_2C(OH)O \cdot \rightarrow HCO_2H + H^+ + e . \qquad (31)$$

Of these several steps the rate of the first only (eqn. (26)) is liable to restriction by adsorption or diffusion processes. Pavela recognised that, except at low concentrations (less than 0.5 $M$) of methanol, diffusion processes were not rate-limiting, but he was unable to identify the slowest step in the proposed reaction sequence.

A further investigation of this field was made by Buck and Griffith[47], who obtained current/potential curves at linearly changing potential, and potential/time curves at constant current. Current/voltage curves at linearly changing potential are of complex form, but generally show a current peak which can be ascribed to oxidation of the organic substrate on an oxygen-free surface. At more positive potentials than that at which the maximum current occurs the current decreases because the reaction is less effectively catalysed by an oxide-covered surface. Delahay[66] has discussed the theory of voltammetry at linearly changing potential. For the particular case of a reversible process controlled by the rate of "semi-infinite linear diffusion"[66] the peak current is proportional to the concentration of the reacting species and to the square root of the voltage sweep rate. Though Buck and Griffith found peak currents to vary directly with fuel concentration (up to about 0.05 $M$) they were generally far smaller than required by theory and were not proportional to the square root of the sweep rate. Buck and Griffith concluded that peak currents were not diffusion limited.

Buck and Griffith also determined the applicability of the Tafel equation (in the form given in eqn. (16)) to the low current density region on the negative potential side of the current peak, and found that the product $Ak_b$ determined for an assumed electrochemical rate-limiting step such as, for example,

$$CH_3O^- + 2\, OH^- \rightarrow CH_2(OH)O^- + H_2O + 2\, e$$

was not constant. From this, it was concluded that a pre-electrochemical reaction occurs. This could be either an adsorption process or a reaction in the bulk solution producing the electroactive species.

Finally, Buck and Griffith determined transition times at constant current for methanol, formaldehyde and formic acid. In the case of either a reversible or an irreversible process controlled by the rate of semi-infinite linear diffusion, providing there are no other complicating kinetic features, eqn. (1) in Chapter 4 (the Sand equation)

$$\tau^{\frac{1}{2}} = \frac{\pi^{\frac{1}{2}} n F C_0 D^{\frac{1}{2}}}{2i}$$

where $\tau$ is the transition time in sec, $i$ is the current density in amp/sq.cm and the remaining symbols are as previously defined, will apply. However, when the electrochemical reaction is preceded by a chemical reaction such as

$$CH_3OH + OH^- \underset{k_{-1}}{\overset{k_1}{\rightleftharpoons}} CH_3O^- + H_2O \tag{32}$$

the Sand equation should be replaced by

$$i\tau^{\frac{1}{2}} = \frac{\pi^{\frac{1}{2}} nFC_0 D^{\frac{1}{2}}}{2} - \frac{\pi^{\frac{1}{2}} i}{2K(k_1 + k_{-1})^{\frac{1}{2}}} \tag{33}$$

where

$$K = \frac{C_{CH_3O^-}}{C_{CH_3OH}}.$$

The Sand equation was found to be inapplicable to methanol and formaldehyde in basic solution and, although the product $i\tau^{\frac{1}{2}}$ was constant for formate oxidation, the shapes of the chronopotentiograms were not entirely in accordance with theoretical requirements. Use of the more complex equation (33) yielded unacceptably low values for $k_1$. No firm conclusion could be drawn, though the indications were that adsorption processes were rate-limiting.

The final reaction scheme proposed by Buck and Griffith was basically similar to that of Pavela and can be represented as follows:

$$CH_3OH + OH^- \underset{k_{-1}}{\overset{k_1}{\rightleftharpoons}} CH_3O^- + H_2O \tag{32}$$

$$CH_3O^- \xrightarrow[slow]{} CH_2O^-_{(ads)} + H_{(ads)} \tag{34}$$

$$H_{(ads)} + OH^- \xrightarrow[fast]{} H_2O + e \tag{35}$$

$$CH_2O^-_{(ads)} \xrightarrow[slow]{} HCHO + e \tag{36}$$

$$HCHO + H_2O \xrightarrow[fast]{} CH_2(OH)_2 \tag{28}$$

$$CH_2(OH)_2 + OH^- \rightleftharpoons CH_2(OH)O^- + H_2O \tag{29}$$

$$CH_2(OH)O^- \xrightarrow[\text{moderate}]{} CH(OH)O^-_{(ads)} + H_{(ads)} \qquad (37)$$

$$H_{(ads)} + OH^- \xrightarrow[\text{fast}]{} H_2O + e \qquad (38)$$

$$CH_2(OH)O^-_{(ads)} + OH^- \xrightarrow[\text{slow}]{} HCO_2^- + H_2O + e . \qquad (39)$$

The above mechanism differs from that of Pavela principally in that $OH^-$ is not considered to participate in the rate-determining step which is here considered to be a slow dissociative chemisorption step (reaction (34)), preceded by a solution reaction which produces the electroactive species.

Shaw, Subcasky and Frick[67] also applied the constant current technique to methanol oxidation. Their results were in broad agreement with those of Buck and Griffith though their interpretation of the nature of the pre-electrochemical step was not the same.

Prigent and associates[68] studied the influence of methanol concentration on the current density at constant potential. The experimental relationship was expressed in the form

$$\frac{1}{i} = \frac{1}{K} + \frac{K'}{C_0} \qquad (40)$$

where $C_0$ is the concentration of methanol and $K$ and $K'$ are constants. An equation of this form follows from the assumption that the reaction involves adsorbed species and that the adsorption process is of the Langmuir type. It applies only at low surface coverages, *i.e.* in dilute solution; at high concentrations, when the surface is fully covered, the current should be constant, independent of concentration. The experimental data given in support are, however, not very convincing.

Plots of log $i$ against the reciprocal of the temperature given by Prigent *et al.*[68] yielded activation energy values varying from 10 to 11.3 kcal/mole. These values are rather high for diffusion-controlled processes, which generally have values of about 5 kcal/mole. Pavela[1] found rather lower, though variable activation energies in his experiments, in which, because he worked with unstirred solutions, diffusion control was to be expected. The general results indicate that, provided diffusion control is eliminated a pre-electrochemical step with an activation energy of around 10 kcal/mole becomes rate-limiting.

None of the reaction schemes advanced takes into account the fact that, as stressed by Prigent *et al.*[68], the current density at constant potential is a function of time. Acetone is known to inhibit the anodic oxidation of isopropanol[68], and acetaldehyde to inhibit the anodic oxidation of ethanol[69] but none of the known intermediates of the anodic oxidation of methanol has any such effect on the process. Some possible poisoning reactions are, however, discussed in the following section.

*Acid electrolytes*

The anodic oxidation of methanol in acid solution has been studied by Pavela[1], Buck and Griffith[47] and by Prigent *et al.*[68], none of whom obtained consistent results. The main practical difficulty is to achieve reproducible results.

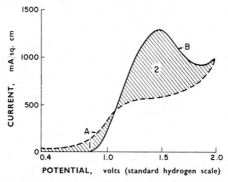

Fig. 43. Current/voltage curves. $dv/dt = 800$ $v$/sec in $N$ HClO$_4$ + $M$ CH$_3$OH (curve B) and in $N$ HClO$_4$ (curve A) starting from the open-circuit potential.

A fresh approach was adopted by Breiter and Gilman[18,19], who used linearly varying potentials to obtain information relating the rate of reaction to the degree of adsorption of substrate on the electrode surface. The amount of methanol adsorbed on platinum in acid solution was determined by two independent methods. When the potential of the test electrode was varied linearly in a positive direction, current/voltage curves with the characteristics shown in Fig. 43 (which shows typical results for a uni-normal perchloric acid solution with and without added methanol) were obtained. In the absence of methanol the current is due to the formation of surface oxide; in the presence of methanol a further contribution of current is derived from the oxidation of the fuel. The difference between shaded area 2 and shaded area 1 in Fig. 43 yields the charge required for the removal of the *adsorbed* methanol by anodic oxidation, if it is assumed that the process is so rapid that the number of methanol molecules reaching the surface by diffusion during the process is small. The second method for determining surface coverage was to compare the electric charges required to saturate the electrode with hydrogen atoms in the presence and in the absence of methanol. Using these techniques the adsorption isotherm was found to be of the Temkin form, *i.e.*

$$\log C_0 = K\theta \qquad (41)$$

where $\theta$ is the fraction of surface covered, and $C_0$ is the bulk concentration of the adsorbate. Breiter and Gilman were able to determine $\theta$ at any instant during the course of an anodic (positively changing) or cathodic (negatively changing) potential sweep. Their results are given in Figs. 44 and 45.

Figure 44 shows that during an anodic potential sweep the surface remains essentially saturated up to a potential of about 0.6 volt. Thereafter the surface coverage falls rapidly and concurrently with the formation of an

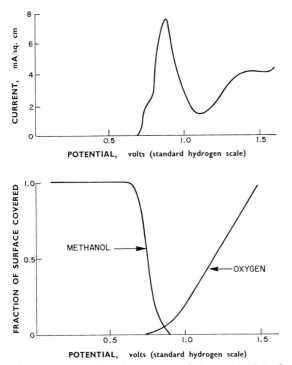

Fig. 44. Current/voltage curve and surface coverage (Pt) as a function of potential for a stirred solution of $N$ HClO$_4$ + $M$ CH$_3$OH at 30°C (potential increasing).

oxide layer. On the cathodic sweep the reduction of the oxide layer and the adsorption process both take place at more negative potentials than during the anodic sweep. The current/voltage curve on the anodic sweep shows a small pre-wave at the foot of the first wave (Fig. 44). For values of $\theta$ between approximately 0.3 and 0.9 the pre-wave curve obeys the equation

$$i = k_f \theta \exp\left(\frac{\alpha n_a F E}{RT}\right) \tag{42}$$

which is of the same form as eqn. (16) and is therefore a form of the Tafel equation. In the potential region where this equation applies, therefore, an electrochemical rate-controlling step was indicated. Analysis of the data gave $n_a$ the probable value of unity, indicating that the first electron discharge step is the slowest. The first main peak was ascribed to oxidation of methanol on a surface free from adsorbed methanol, because the current at equivalent potentials was higher on the cathodic sweep than on the anodic sweep,

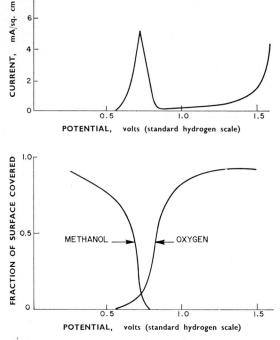

Fig. 45. Current/voltage curve and surface coverage (Pt) as a function of potential for a stirred solution of $N$ HClO₄ $+$ $M$ CH₃OH at 30°C (potential decreasing).

whereas the surface coverage was less. In other words, oxidation takes place fastest on the surface that is least covered by adsorbed methanol. The main current peak did not obey the kinetic equation applicable to diffusion control at linearly changing potential[66], and no mechanism was advanced. A second current peak was believed to take place on an oxide-covered surface as first suggested by Müller[63], but again, no specific mechanism was suggested.

These views have been criticized on the grounds that the adsorption measurements do not refer to steady state conditions[50]. Giner[23] examined this aspect and obtained results showing the variation of current with time (Fig. 40). His interpretation of current/voltage curves differs from that of Breiter and Gilman. Giner chose experimental conditions that would minimize diffusion processes during a linear voltage sweep. The resulting current/potential curve related solely to adsorbed material. Giner noted that a similar current/voltage curve was produced during an anodic sweep starting either with methanol or following the cathodic reduction of carbon dioxide, and he suggested that the anodic oxidation of methanol and the cathodic reduction of carbon dioxide give rise to the same product. At potentials more negative than the peak current potential, this product accumulates and "poisons" the electrode. Above the peak potential it is oxidized to carbon dioxide faster than it is formed, freeing the surface for continuous oxidation. Giner also observed that this adsorbed product was formed at open circuit from methanol (but at a slower rate) and he suggested that a possible poisoning reaction might be

$$CH_3OH + Pt \rightarrow Pt-CO + 4 H^+ + 4 e \qquad (43)$$

(where the chemisorbed product was assumed to be carbon monoxide) or that an alternative process gave rise to

$$Pt-C(O)OH .$$

Giner's views readily explain the observation of Breiter and Gilman that the main current peak is displaced towards more negative potentials on the cathodic sweep since the "reduced carbon dioxide" is not formed at higher potentials and is therefore not present at all until the later stages of the cathodic sweep are reached. The "pre-wave" of Breiter and Gilman is also interpreted as being due to the oxidation of "reduced carbon dioxide".

Giner observed that the anodic behaviour of formic acid was similar to that of methanol. Possible reactions suggested were that formic acid decomposes catalytically to carbon dioxide and hydrogen,

$$HCO_2H \rightarrow CO_2 + H_2 \tag{44}$$

and the carbon dioxide is then reduced

$$Pt + CO_2 + 2\,H^+ + 2\,e \rightarrow Pt\text{–}CO + H_2O \tag{45}$$

or alternatively formic acid decomposes directly, such as by

$$Pt + HCO_2H \rightarrow Pt\text{–}CO + H_2O \tag{46}$$

or

$$Pt + HCO_2H \rightarrow Pt-C{\overset{\displaystyle O}{\underset{\displaystyle OH}{\big\langle}}} + \tfrac{1}{2} H_2 . \tag{47}$$

Whilst it has not proved possible to identify "reduced carbon dioxide", the views of Giner are supported in a general way by Juliard and Shalit[70], Slott[37], Brummer and Makrides[50], and Kutschker and Vielstich[71].

Juliard and Shalit[70] conducted voltage sweeps with methanol and formic acid in the usual way but reversed the potential below 0.8 volt so that a surface oxide film was not formed. From the shapes of the current/voltage curves it was concluded that a "poison", formed at the lower potentials, was progressively eliminated at the higher potentials. The poisoning reaction was slower with formic acid than with methanol. Slott[37] confined his attention to formic acid only and studied the variation of the open circuit potential with electrode pretreatment. He also studied the variation of transition time at constant current with various electrode cleaning techniques and open circuit delays and concluded that formic acid decomposed on a clean platinum surface into hydrogen and an unidentified uncharged compound, possibly carbon monoxide.

Brummer and Makrides[50] also studied formic acid. They found that the current at constant potential decayed continuously, the rate of decay being greatest at the start and increasing at more positive potentials (Fig. 46). Current/potential curves, taken at increasing time intervals, yielded decreasing Tafel slopes ($b$, eqn. (24)) varying from 106 mV to 60 mV over the first three minutes and thereafter remaining constant. In agreement with the work of others, a limiting current was observed at potentials above 0.45 volt; this was not a diffusion-limited current. Surface coverage was measured as a function of both time and potential, both anodic and cathodic constant

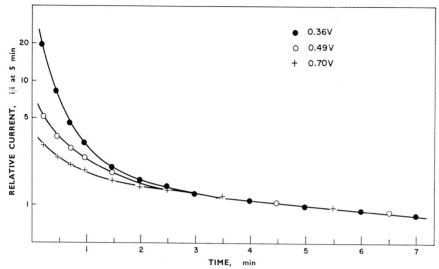

Fig. 46. Anodic oxidation of $M$ formic acid in $2M$ HClO$_4$ on platinum at constant potential. (Potentials on standard hydrogen scale.)

current charging techniques being used. The anodic method appears to be particularly unreliable since it depends on the measurement of a transition time, attributed to the anodic oxidation of the adsorbate, which has no clear end-point. In any case, the contention of Brummer and Makrides that the initial portion of the transition time does not include any contribution from surface oxidation of the electrode is indefensible since the potential arrest commences at above 1.0 volt. Nevertheless, the cathodic constant current method is well established and their general results may therefore be accepted. Surface coverages (measured after a waiting period of two minutes) varied with potential but the coverage decreased rather more rapidly at increasingly positive potentials than would be expected from the results of Breiter[72]. For example, coverage was about 75% of maximum at 0.4 volt and close to zero at 0.7 volt, whereas Breiter's results showed essentially complete coverages at all potentials up to 0.7 volt. The rate of adsorption at constant potential was tested by means of eqn. (48),

$$\frac{\mathrm{d}\theta}{\mathrm{d}t} = k(1-\theta) - k'\theta \tag{48}$$

which, at infinite time, gives rise to a Langmuir-type adsorption isotherm. Equation (48) was found to apply for values of $\theta$ between 0.3 and 0.6 at potentials between 0.35 and 0.45 volt. Derivation of the adsorption and desorption constants $k$ and $k^1$ (eqn. (48)) showed $k^1$ to be independent of the concentration of formic acid and of potential, a result taken to indicate that the main desorption process was not via oxidation. Because surface coverage (at constant potential) increases with time whereas the current declines, Brummer and Makrides concluded that oxidation takes place essentially on the clean surface, and that the adsorbed species detected by their experiments is not electrochemically active, but on the contrary, is a poison. Their main conclusions are similar to those of Giner and of Slott, *i.e.* that the reaction is poisoned, particularly at low potentials, by an uncharged unreactive species. The kinetics of carbon monoxide adsorption and anodic oxidation made it seem to them improbable that carbon monoxide plays an important role. A more probable reaction such as (49) was suggested:

$$2\ HCO_2H \rightarrow \underset{\underset{\displaystyle CO_2H}{|}}{CHO} + H_2O \tag{49}$$

*Conclusions*

The mechanism of the anodic oxidation of methanol and of formic acid in acid solution is not well understood. The earlier studies failed to take into account the time dependence of the process and do not therefore offer a complete picture of the process. There is little doubt that the reaction is self-poisoning and there is evidence to suggest that both methanol and formic acid oxidize faster on a surface that is free from adsorbed material. Whilst this observation seems to suggest, contrary to experience, that oxidation ought to take place on any electronically conducting surface it is in accordance with the theory of Martinyuk and Shlygin[35]. These authors observed the potential shift of a clean platinum surface in acid solution upon the addition of various organic compounds. In the case of ethanol, there was an instantaneous drop from about 0.6 volt to about 0.2 volt which was attributed to the donation of electrons from unadsorbed alcohol to the electrode. If the electrode was immediately removed and rinsed, cyclic voltammetry then showed no evidence of adsorbed material; however, if the electrode was left immersed for some minutes the potential drifted and subsequent cyclic voltammetry showed the presence of adsorbed material. From this and other observations, Martinyuk and Shlygin concluded that electron transfer is a necessary prerequisite of adsorption, and that electrochemical reaction can occur without preliminary adsorption.

## 2. THE HYDRAZINE FUEL CELL

The electrochemical activity of hydrazine is high and in many ways the material may be regarded as an ideal fuel. It is easily stored and transported as an aqueous solution though the pure material readily detonates. It has a high boiling point (about 115°C) and is electrochemically oxidized at potentials in the region of those at which hydrogen is oxidized. It is, however, mildly caustic, quite toxic and very expensive. Even with an increased demand and more efficient production it is difficult to visualize hydrazine as a commercially attractive fuel; it seems unlikely that it will ever be as cheap as ammonia which is itself economically borderline.

### (a) Complete fuel cells

In 1962 Gillibrand and Lomax[73] (The Chloride Electric Storage Company Ltd.) described a hydrazine–oxygen fuel battery (Fig. 47) comprising five oxygen and four hydrazine electrodes; the electrodes were double-sided and had apparent areas of about 150 sq.cm per side. When 7 $M$ potassium hydroxide containing 0.5 $M$ hydrazine was circulated to the hydrazine electrodes, a maximum power output of 50–60 watts at 20°C was obtained. This output corresponds to a current density of about 80 mA/sq.cm at a cell potential of nearly 0.6 volt. The use of air instead of oxygen reduced the power output by about 50%.

In May 1962 "Shell" Research Ltd. demonstrated a hydrazine–air fuel battery which provided power for its own auxiliary equipment and a display. Once started, by using an accumulator to drive the air blower and electrolyte pump, the battery was self-sustaining, driving its own air blower and circulating its own electrolyte–fuel mixture. A more detailed description of the battery is given in Chapter 11.

Another complete hydrazine–oxygen power unit has been described by Tomter and Antony[74] (Allis-Chalmers Manufacturing Company). This 36-volt 3-kilowatt battery was used to power a golf cart and ran at a free energy efficiency of 40%. The electrodes (465 sq.cm area) were 0.762 mm thick 80%-porous nickel sheets, the oxygen electrode being catalysed with silver and the hydrazine electrode with palladium. Stored oxygen was used and the premixed 3% hydrazine, 25% KOH solution was recirculated from a reservoir. These authors claim that air has been successfully used as oxidant (though operating figures are not given) but that, because of the high cost of

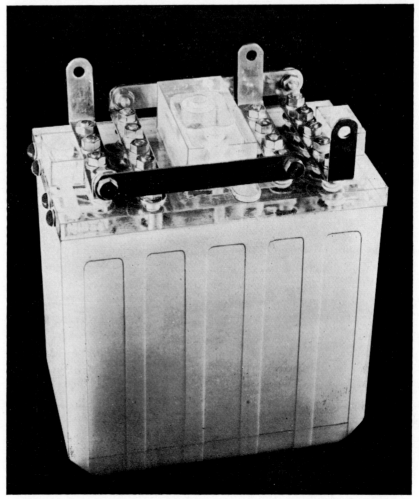

Fig. 47. Chloride Electrical Storage Co. Ltd. hydrazine–oxygen fuel cell.

hydrazine, the unit is not commercially attractive. Nevertheless, the system nicely demonstrates a use for a relatively small fuel cell power unit.

### (b) Open circuit potentials

Hydrazine is more easily oxidized in basic than in acid electrolyte and the processes involved are theoretically:

(1) at the hydrazine electrode

$$N_2H_4 + 4\,OH^- \rightleftharpoons N_2 + 4\,H_2O + 4\,e \qquad (50)$$

(2) at the oxygen electrode

$$O_2 + 2\,H_2O + 4\,e \rightleftharpoons 4\,OH^- . \qquad (51)$$

According to Latimer[27] the standard potentials for the processes are $-1.16$ volt and $0.40$ volt respectively. Thus the open circuit potential of a hydrazine–oxygen cell with all the components at unit activity should be $1.56$ volt and the hydrazine electrode potential should be $0.33$ volt more negative than that of the equilibrium:

$$H_2 + 2\,OH^- \rightleftharpoons 2\,H_2O + 2\,e . \qquad (52)$$

The open circuit potential of a hydrazine electrode is generally found to be about the same as that of a hydrogen electrode in the same medium and it seems that the equilibrium of eqn. (50) is not readily established. A possible reason for this discrepancy is that hydrazine breaks down chemically on the catalytic surface to hydrogen and nitrogen

$$N_2H_4 \rightarrow N_2 + 2\,H_2 \qquad (53)$$

and that the measured open circuit potential is due to adsorbed hydrogen. It has also been suggested that ammonia may be formed by the interaction of adsorbed hydrogen and hydrazine. Whatever may be the explanation there seems little doubt that the measured open circuit potential is a mixed potential.

### (c) Current/voltage curves

Pavela[75] noted that when platinized platinum was immersed in hydrazine solution vigorous gas evolution occurred which ceased within a short time. He attributed this phenomenon to the hydrogen formed catalytically preventing the further decomposition of hydrazine and considered that the anodic oxidation of hydrazine occurred in the two steps expressed by eqns. (53) and (52).

Gillibrand and Lomax[73] consider that reaction (50) is more likely. They base their view on the fact that the rate of decomposition of hydrazine, as determined by the evolution of gas from their electrodes under open circuit conditions, is too slow to give the current densities readily obtainable. This argument is invalid if their electrodes self-poison in the way Pavela suggests. Bard[76], using acid electrolytes, has recently observed the poisoning of platinum by hydrazine |and has also found that platinum which has been previously used as a cathode in the electrolyte is deactivated for the anodic oxidation of hydrazine. Bard's chronopotentiometric studies also indicate that variations in the ratio $i\tau^{\frac{1}{2}}/C$ may be due to the catalytic decomposition of hydrazine according to

$$3\,N_2H_5^+ + H^+ \rightarrow N_2 + 4\,NH_4^+ \ . \tag{54}$$

The production of ammonia, formed by the decomposition of hydrazine on platinum black surfaces, has also been observed by Tanatar[77] and by Gutbier and Neudlinger[78] and since ammonia is not readily electrochemically oxidized on platinum it is possible that it may also poison the surface.

Several mechanisms have been proposed for the anodic oxidation of hydrazine, the most detailed being that of Karp and Meites[79], but there remains uncertainty as to the real mechanism, and the variable state of the catalyst surfaces probably accounts for many of the anomalies. The current/voltage curves obtained by different workers may or may not be reproducible and in view of this uncertainty only the curves of Gillibrand and Lomax on an undisclosed catalyst are given here (Fig. 48). Even at current densities as high as 600 mA/sq.cm the hydrazine electrode potential departs only slightly from its open circuit potential but, unfortunately, about 0.3 volt is already lost at the open circuit potential and the voltage efficiency of a

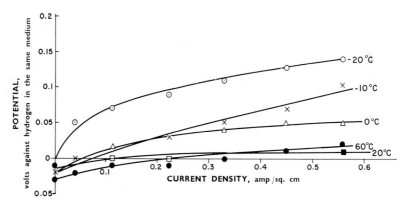

Fig. 48. The performance of a hydrazine electrode at various current densities and temperatures.

complete cell is correspondingly lowered. Whilst the hydrazine electrode undoubtedly has some voltage inefficiency, Gillibrand and Lomax[73] found that its Faradaic efficiency was 100%.

The present state of the hydrazine fuel cell may be summed up as follows:

(1) A catalyst is required to enable the hydrazine electrode to operate at lower potentials.

(2) Considerable improvement in the performance of air (oxygen) electrodes is needed to take advantage of the potentialities of the hydrazine electrode.

(3) The amount of hydrazine reaching the cathode must be minimized to prevent wastage of fuel by direct oxidation.

### 3. THE AMMONIA FUEL CELL

Ammonia is a relatively cheap, readily available material and, because of its fairly high hydrogen content, it has been considered as a fuel for use in fuel cells. In this respect it suffers major disadvantages in that it is gaseous (though easily liquefied), toxic (though its pungent odour gives adequate warning of its presence), and is not electrochemically oxidized at low overpotentials on known catalysts.

### (a) Complete fuel cells

Wynveen[80] (Allis-Chalmers Manufacturing Company) has described a complete ammonia–oxygen fuel cell with an alkaline electrolyte. The performance is illustrated in Fig. 49 which shows that outputs are somewhat lower than those obtainable from the methanol–air–sulphuric acid cells described in section 1(a) of this chapter and very much lower than those obtained with hydrazine as a fuel. Wynveen has shown that the current efficiency of these ammonia–oxygen cells is 100% for the reaction

$$2\,NH_3 + 6\,OH^- \rightarrow N_2 + 6\,H_2O + 6\,e$$

a result substantiated by Katan and Galiotto[81].

### (b) Open circuit potentials

The standard potential of the equilibrium

$$NH_3(g) + 3\,OH^-(aq) \rightleftharpoons \tfrac{1}{2} N_2(g) + 3\,H_2O(liq) + 3e \qquad (55)$$

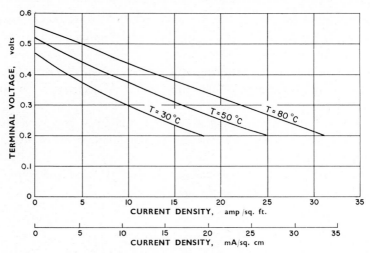

Fig. 49. Typical performance curves obtained for the ammonia–oxygen fuel cell at 30, 50, and 80°C. Oxygen at atmospheric pressure and a flow rate three times that needed to maintain reaction.

is −0.77 volt. A complete cell operating according to reaction (55) and (51) should have a potential of 1.17 volt with all components at unit activity. Potentials close to the theoretical for reaction (55) have not been reported, presumably owing to the low exchange current for the reaction.

4. CONCLUSIONS

Of the three fuels considered in this chapter, hydrazine is the most easily oxidized and, in consequence, hydrazine cells have by far the greatest power output.

However, hydrazine has the lowest theoretical energy content, *if it has to be stored as the hydrate*. The final column in Table 9 was calculated on the

TABLE 9

COMPARATIVE PERFORMANCES OF LIQUID FUELS

| Fuel | g/Faraday | cu.cm liquid/Faraday | watt h/g |
|------|-----------|----------------------|----------|
| Methanol | 5.33 | 6.7 | 5.9 |
| Hydrazine hydrate | 12.5 | 12.15 | 3.47 |
| Ammonia | 5.67 | 6.9 | 5.73 |

assumption that all the fuels are being used at 100% free energy efficiency with a perfect oxygen electrode. Whilst this state of affairs is unlikely to be realized in practice the fact that a greater weight of hydrazine hydrate than methanol or ammonia is required for a given energy output means that the potentialities of methanol and ammonia cells are greater than that of the hydrazine cell.

There seems to be little prospect of manufacturing costs being reduced sufficiently to allow hydrazine to be marketed at a price low enough to make even a highly efficient hydrazine fuel cell commercially attactive. On the other hand, the cheaper substances ammonia and methanol can be utilized only at low efficiencies in present-day fuel cells. In this respect the most urgent need is for improved electrocatalysts, the development of which would undoubtedly make the methanol fuel cell and, less probably the ammonia fuel cell practical propositions.

## REFERENCES

[1] T. O. Pavela, *Ann. Acad. Sci. Fennicae, AII*, **59** (1954) 7.
[2] M. J. Schlatter, in *Fuel Cells*, (ed. by G. J. Young), Vol. 2, Reinhold, New York, 1963, p. 190.
[3] J. E. Wynn, *Proc. Ann. Power Sources Conf.*, **14** (1960) 52.
[4] O. Bloch, M. Prigent and J. C. Balaceanu, *Extended Abstr. 120th Meeting Electrochem. Soc., Detroit, Oct. 1961, Battery Div.*, p. 159.
[5] S. Glasstone and A. Hickling, *Electrolytic Oxidation and Reduction*, Chapman and Hall, London, 1935, p. 329.
[6] M. E. Indig and R. N. Snyder, *J. Electrochem. Soc.*, **109** (1962) 1104.
[7] P. G. Grimes, B. Fidler and J. Adams, *Proc. Ann. Power Sources Conf.*, **15** (1961) 29.
[8] D. B. Boies and A. Dravnieks, *Preprints* 145th Natl. Meeting Am. Chem. Soc., New York, Sept. 1963, Vol. 7: Div. Fuel Chem., No. 4: Symp. Fuel Cell Systems*, p. 223.
[9] K. Kordesch and A. Marko, *Oesterr. Chemiker-Z.*, **52** (1951) 125.
[10] E. W. Justi and A. W. Winsel, *Brit. Patent 821,688* (1955).
[11] A. Hickling, *Trans. Faraday Soc.*, **41** (1945) 333.
[12] H. F. Hunger, *Proc. Ann. Power Sources Conf.*, **14** (1960) 55.
[13] J. N. Murray and P. G. Grimes, in *Fuel Cells*, (Chem. Eng. Progr. Tech. Manual), Am. Inst. Chem. Engrs., 1963, p. 57.
[14] K. R. Williams and D. P. Gregory, *J. Electrochem. Soc.*, **110** (1963) 209.
[15] J. F. Yeager, *Extended Abstr. 120th Meeting Electrochem. Soc., Detroit, Oct. 1961, Battery Div.*, p. 138.
[16] E. W. Justi, in *Fuel Cells*, (Chem. Eng. Progr. Tech. Manual), Am. Inst. Chem. Engrs., 1963, p. 79.

* Proceedings to be published by American Chemical Society as *Fuel Cell Systems* (Advan. Chem. Ser. No. 47).

17 B. L. TARMY, *Proc. Ann. Power Sources Conf.*, **16** (1962) 29.
18 M. W. BREITER AND S. GILMAN, *J. Electrochem. Soc.*, **109** (1962) 622.
19 S. GILMAN AND M. W. BREITER, *J. Electrochem. Soc.*, **109** (1962) 1099.
20 M. W. BREITER, *J. Electrochem. Soc.*, **110** (1963) 449.
21 S. GILMAN, *J. Phys. Chem.*, **67** (1963) 1898.
22 S. GILMAN, *J. Phys. Chem.*, **68** (1964) 70.
23 J. GINER, *Electrochim. Acta*, **9** (1964) 63.
24 D. E. ICENHOWER AND A. P. BOND, *Extended Abstr. 120th Meeting Electrochem. Soc. Detroit, Oct. 1961, Battery Div.*, p. 45.
25 J. F. WALKER, *Formaldehyde*, Reinhold, New York, 1944, p. 51.
26 M. WADANO, *Ber.*, **67B** (1934) 191.
27 W. M. LATIMER, *The Oxidation States of the Elements and their Potentials in Aqueous Solutions*, Prentice-Hall, New York, 2nd edn., 1952, p. 128.
28 L. C. GRUEN AND P. T. McTIGUE, *J. Chem. Soc.*, (1963) 5217.
29 E. MÜLLER AND K. SCHWABE, *Z. Elektrochem.*, **34** (1928) 170.
30 E. MÜLLER, *Z. Elektrochem.*, **27** (1921) 558.
31 E. MÜLLER, *Ber.*, **54B** (1921) 3214.
32 D. B. BOIES AND A. DRAVNIEKS, *Extended Abstr. 122nd Meeting Electrochem. Soc., Boston, Sept. 1962, Battery Div.*, p. 123.
33 A. HICKLING AND F. RODWELL, *J. Chem. Soc.*, (1943) 90.
34 W. VIELSTICH, *Extended Abstr. 120th Meeting Electrochem. Soc., Detroit, Oct. 1961, Battery Div.*, p. 149.
35 G. A. MARTINYUK AND A. I. SHLYGIN, *Zh. Fiz. Khim.*, **32** (1958) 164.
36 A. I. SHLYGIN AND G. A. BOGDANOVSKY, *Proc. 4th Conf. Electrochem., Moscow, 1956*, Acad. Sci. Moscow, 1959, p. 282.
37 R. SLOTT, *U.S. Govt. Rept. AD 401–932*, 1963.
38 K. SCHWABE, *Z. Elektrochem.*, **61** (1957) 744.
39 A. HICKLING, *Trans. Faraday Soc.*, **41** (1945) 333.
40 T. C. FRANKLIN AND S. L. COOKE, *J. Electrochem. Soc.*, **107** (1960) 556.
41 K. VESELY AND R. BRDICKA, *Collection Czech. Chem. Commun.*, **12** (1947) 313.
42 F. FISCHER AND O. PRZIZA, *Ber.*, **47** (1914) 256.
43 J. GINER, *Electrochim. Acta*, **8** (1963) 857.
44 L. L. BIRCUMSHAW AND A. C. RIDDIFORD, *Quart. Rev.*, **6** (1952) 157.
45 A. HICKLING, *Quart. Rev.*, **3** (1949) 95.
46 R. G. GENTILE, F. B. LEITZ, J. H. PORTER AND D. A. SAMA, *U.S. Govt. Rept. AD 272–352*, 1960.
47 R. P. BUCK AND L. R. GRIFFITH, *J. Electrochem. Soc.*, **109** (1962) 1005.
48 J. O'M. BOCKRIS, *Chem. Rev.*, **43** (1948) 528.
49 M. J. JONCICH AND N. HACKERMAN, *J. Electrochem. Soc.*, **111** (1964) 1286.
50 S. B. BRUMMER AND A. C. MAKRIDES, *J. Phys. Chem.*, **68** (1964) 1448.
51 E. MÜLLER AND G. HINDEMITH, *Z. Elektrochem.*, **33** (1927) 561.
52 E. MÜLLER AND S. TANAKA, *Z. Elektrochem.*, **34** (1928) 256.
53 T. O. PAVELA, *Suomen Kemistilehti*, **30B** (1957) 38.
54 G. ARMSTRONG AND J. A. V. BUTLER, *Discussions Faraday Soc.*, **1** (1947) 122.
55 E. T. HEDGES AND J. E. MYERS, *The Problem of Physico-Chemical Periodicity*, Edward Arnold, London, 1926.
56 R. J. BRODD AND N. HACKERMAN, *J. Electrochem. Soc.*, **104** (1957) 704.
57 L. G. AUSTIN, in *Fuel Cells*, (ed. by G. J. YOUNG), Vol. 1, Reinhold, New York, 1960, p. 34.
58 S. TANAKA, *Z. Elektrochem.*, **35** (1929) 38.
59 G. COHN, *Proc. Ann. Power Sources Conf.*, **15** (1961) 12.

60 H. KRUPP, R. MCJONES, H. RABENHORST, G. SANDSTEDE AND G. WALTER, *Extended Abstr. 120th Meeting Electrochem. Soc., Detroit, Oct. 1961, Battery Div.*, p. 47.
61 M. W. BREITER, *Electrochim. Acta*, **8** (1963) 973.
62 M. W. BREITER, *Electrochim. Acta*, **7** (1962) 601.
63 E. MÜLLER, *Z. Elektrochem.*, **29** (1923) 264.
64 E. MÜLLER AND S. TAKAGAMI, *Z. Elektrochem.*, **34** (1928) 704.
65 P. BALLINGER AND F. A. LONG, *J. Am. Chem. Soc.*, **82** (1960) 795.
66 P. DELAHAY, *New Instrumental Methods in Electrochemistry*, Interscience, New York, 1954.
67 M. SHAW, W. J. SUBCASKY AND G. FRICK, *Extended Abstr. 120th Meeting Electrochem. Soc., Detroit, Oct. 1961, Battery Div.*, p. 38.
68 M. PRIGENT, O. BLOCH AND J. BALACEANU, *Bull. Soc. Chim. France*, **(1962)** 368.
69 G. A. BOGDANOVSKII AND A. I. SHLYGIN, *Russ. J. Phys. Chem.*, **34** (1960) 26.
70 A. L. JULIARD AND H. SHALIT, *J. Electrochem. Soc.*, **110** (1963) 1002.
71 A. KUTSCHKER AND W. VIELSTICH, *Electrochim. Acta*, **8** (1963) 985.
72 M. W. BREITER, *Electrochim. Acta*, **8** (1963) 447.
73 M. I. GILLIBRAND AND G. R. LOMAX, in *Proc. 3rd Intern. Symp. on Batteries, Bournemouth, 1962*, (ed. by D. H. COLLINS), Pergamon, Oxford, 1963, p. 221.
74 S. S. TOMTER AND A. P. ANTONY, in *Fuel Cells*, (Chem. Eng. Progr. Tech. Manual), Am. Inst. Chem. Engrs., 1963, p. 22.
75 T. O. PAVELA, *Suomen Kemistilehti*, **30B** (1957) 240.
76 A. J. BARD, *Anal. Chem.*, **35** (1962) 1602.
77 S. TANATAR, *Z. Phys. Chem.*, **40** (1902) 475; *ibid.*, **41** (1902) 37.
78 A. GUTBIER AND K. NEUNDLINGER, *Z. Phys. Chem.*, **84** (1913) 203.
79 S. KARP AND L. MEITES, *J. Am. Chem. Soc.*, **84** (1962) 906.
80 R. A. WYNVEEN, Chap. 12 in *Fuel Cells*, (ed. by G. J. YOUNG), Vol. 2, Reinhold, New York, 1963.
81 T. KATAN AND R. J. GALIOTTO, *J. Electrochem. Soc.*, **110** (1963) 1022.

*Chapter 7*

# FUEL CELLS WITH MOLTEN CARBONATE ELECTROLYTES

## 1. INTRODUCTION

Chemical reactions proceed more rapidly at higher temperatures so that operation of a fuel cell at high temperatures should facilitate the electrochemical oxidation of fuels that react only slowly in low temperature cells. Cells with molten carbonate electrolytes have been operated at temperatures generally in excess of 500°C and it is the object of the present chapter to describe various aspects of the construction and operation of these cells.

Recent work on molten carbonate fuel cells stems from experiments described by Baur, Treadwell and Trumpler[1] in 1921 and from work carried out by the Russian scientist Davtyan[2] in 1946. The cell used by Baur *et al.* contained an electrolyte of mixed sodium and potassium carbonates and electrodes of iron and magnetite powders embedded in magnesia rods. Hydrogen was used as fuel and air as oxidant, the temperature of operation being 800–900°C. The design of the cell was not ideal and outputs of about 4 mA/sq.cm at 0.75 volt were obtained.

Davtyan described a fuel cell with a "solid" electrolyte consisting of 43% wt. calcined sodium carbonate, 27% wt. monazite sand, 20% wt. tungstic oxide and 10% wt. soda glass. Broers[3] thoroughly investigated this mixture in order to determine its true composition at operating temperatures of about 700°C. He concluded that Davtyan's "solid" electrolyte was not solid but consisted of a solid porous frame of high melting point rare earth oxides in which were held eutectic mixtures of molten carbonates, phosphates, tungstates and silicates which formed the electrolyte. When operated on hydrogen and carbon monoxide mixtures the electrolyte and electrodes underwent irreversible chemical changes which caused the cell resistance to increase. The principal requirement for long term operation of a fuel cell, the invariance of electrodes and electrolyte, was clearly not met by the Davtyan cell.

The cells of Baur and Davtyan were unnecessarily complicated and subsequent research was directed towards the development of simpler systems having invariant electrolytes and electrodes.

## 2. MOLTEN CARBONATE ELECTROLYTES

An ideal electrolyte for a fuel cell is an ionic oxide in which the oxide ions act as a means of transporting oxygen from the air electrode to the fuel electrode. For example, with hydrogen as fuel the electrode reactions would be

at the air electrode: $\qquad O_2 + 4\,e \rightleftharpoons 2\,O^{2-}$     (1)

at the fuel electrode: $\quad 2\,O^{2-} + 2\,H_2 \rightleftharpoons 2\,H_2O + 4\,e$ .   (2)

Simple ionic oxides, however, have high melting points ($> 1000°C$) and were therefore not used for early high temperature cells. In order to avoid very high operating temperatures, salts with oxygen-containing ions were used since these are ionically conducting at much lower temperatures.

Broers and Ketelaar[4] showed that carbonates are the salts best adapted for use as molten electrolytes in fuel cells. Other salts such as sulphates, nitrates and chlorides reacted with carbon dioxide produced from the anodic oxidation of a carbon-containing fuel, such as carbon monoxide, and became partially converted to carbonates. With fused carbonate electrolytes the carbon dioxide obtained from the anodic reaction can be withdrawn from the anodic products and fed into the air or oxygen stream at the cathode to maintain the carbonate electrolyte invariant. This idea was suggested by Greger[5] as early as 1939. Under these circumstances the overall electrode reactions with a fused carbonate electrolyte, oxygen or air as oxidant and carbon monoxide as fuel are

cathode: $O_2 + 2\,CO_2 + 4\,e \rightleftharpoons 2\,CO_3^{2-}$     (3)

anode: $\quad 2\,CO + 2\,CO_3^{2-} \rightleftharpoons 4\,CO_2 + 4\,e$ .   (4)

The transfer of oxygen from air to fuel electrodes thus proceeds as a transfer of carbonate ions.

The electrolytes used in practical cells have been mixtures of either lithium and sodium carbonates or lithium, sodium and potassium carbonates. The use of mixed carbonates enables operating temperatures in the range $400–800°C$ to be used. The binary mixture of about $45\%$ $Li_2CO_3$ and $55\%$ $Na_2CO_3$ has a melting point of $514°C$, as shown in the phase diagram[6]

(Fig. 50), whilst the ternary mixture of equal parts of $Li_2CO_3$–$Na_2CO_3$–$K_2CO_3$ melts at 390°C.

Janz and co-workers[7,8] have carried out mechanistic studies of carbonate ion discharge in molten carbonates. They studied the overpotential for oxygen evolution by discharge of carbonate ions in the ternary eutectic on platinum, silver and gold foil electrodes at temperatures up to 1000°C, measurements being made against a platinum reference electrode. Their observations on the

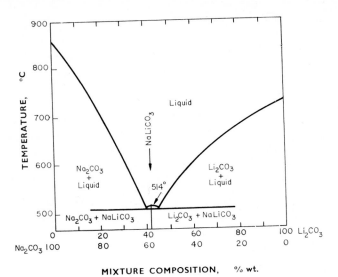

Fig. 50. Phase diagram of $Li_2CO_3$–$Na_2CO_3$ system.

dependence of overpotential on current density and temperature enabled them to advance possible mechanisms for oxygen evolution from molten carbonate electrolytes.

The overall reaction leading to oxygen evolution is

$$CO_3^{2-} \rightarrow CO_2 + \tfrac{1}{2} O_2 + 2e, \tag{5}$$

carbonate ions being considered to be in equilibrium with oxide ions in the following manner,

$$CO_3^{2-} \rightleftharpoons CO_2 + O^{2-}. \tag{6}$$

In view of this equilibrium Janz cites two possible anodic mechanisms for oxygen evolution:

(1) The formation of an "oxide" on the electrode surface M,

$$O^{2-} + M \rightarrow MO + 2e \qquad (7)$$

followed by reaction between the "oxide" and oxide ions:

$$MO + O^{2-} \rightarrow M + O_2 + 2e . \qquad (8)$$

(2) The formation of a surface "oxide" as before followed by reaction of one surface "oxide" species with another:

$$MO + MO \rightarrow 2M + O_2 . \qquad (9)$$

By comparison of measured Tafel slopes with those predicted for mechanisms (1) and (2) Janz concluded that at 600–700°C mechanism (1) was the more likely on platinum and gold, whilst on silver the issue was complicated by metal dissolution.

This work is important when considering the reaction mechanism in a molten carbonate fuel cell where carbonate ion discharge occurs at the fuel electrode. The precise species with which the fuel reacts is uncertain. Chambers and Tantram[9] consider the molten carbonate fuel cell to be an oxygen–carbon dioxide concentration cell in which the fuel acts as a means of preserving a low partial pressure of oxygen at the fuel electrode. The idea of considering the fuel cell as an oxygen–carbon dioxide concentration cell has been criticized by Gorin and Recht[10] and by Liebhafsky and Cairns[11], who point out that a fuel cell is normally operating irreversibly, when conditions at the electrode surface may be such that the fuel is not in equilibrium with oxygen. Trachtenberg[12], as will be discussed later, considers the fuel to react with a surface "oxide".

Janz and co-workers[13,14] have also made precise measurement of many physical properties of molten carbonate electrolytes. They measured surface tension, density, viscosity and electrical conductance of lithium, sodium and potassium carbonates and some mixtures over a wide range of temperature. An explanation for the limited variation of equivalent conductance among the simple alkali metal carbonates is that a paired ion species such as $(M^+ CO_3^{2-})^-$ is involved in electrical conductance in these salts. The mechanism of conductance is thought to involve the transfer of $M^+$ from one paired ion species to another in a similar manner to the Grotthuss chain mechanism for proton transport in aqueous solution.

### 3. ELECTRODES USED IN MOLTEN CARBONATE CELLS

Electrodes used in molten carbonate cells are usually fabricated from the material to be used as the catalyst. They must possess the properties of chemical stability towards the electrolyte, fuel and air, physical stability at the operating temperature, high catalytic activity and good mass transfer properties. Electrodes used in molten carbonate cells can, in general, be made with satisfactory mass transfer properties with respect to reactant and product gases whilst the required catalytic activity is aided by the high operating temperature. The problem of chemical stability is severe owing to the highly corrosive nature of the electrolyte at the operating temperature.

Metals have been used as electrode materials in numerous forms, principally powders, sintered structures, thin films and gauzes. The actual materials used must be selected carefully since the operation of many practical cells has been terminated by corrosion of the electrodes. Many workers have, for instance, used nickel as anode material but Broers[15] has recently pointed out that nickel electrodes will themselves oxidize if polarized by more than 200–300 millivolts. Degobert and Bloch[16] have sought to establish a realistic choice of materials useful as electrodes in molten carbonate cells. Current density/potential curves were obtained for electrodes of simple geometry in a ternary eutectic mixture of lithium, sodium and potassium carbonates. Curves taken under an atmosphere of carbon dioxide permitted the materials studied to be classified in order of decreasing nobility, or oxidation potential, as follows:

$$10\% \text{ Ir–Pt alloy} > 10\% \text{ Rh–Pt alloy} > Pt > Pd > Au > Ag > Cu$$
$$> C > Co > Ni > 18/8 \text{ stainless steel} > Fe.$$

Similar current/potential curves were taken either with hydrogen or with oxygen bubbling over the electrodes and with an atmosphere of carbon dioxide over the melt. Orders of reactivity of the metals could then be obtained at different potentials both for the oxidation of hydrogen and for the reduction of oxygen. This type of study is of fundamental importance in selection of an electrode catalyst since it defines the working potential range over which an electrode can be used for a given reaction before oxidation of the metal itself begins.

In low temperature fuel cells a waterproofing material is often applied to the electrodes to prevent flooding. Such treatment is not applicable to cells with fused carbonate electrolytes and two other methods have been devised to prevent electrode flooding. In the first method the electrolyte is held within a porous magnesia diaphragm or is mixed with magnesia powder to form a stiff paste. The pore size of the matrix or the particle size of the magnesia powder is chosen so that the melt is retained by surface tension forces and does not penetrate to any great extent into the electrodes. The second method is an adaptation of the Bacon method[17] where the free electrolyte is held between electrodes having a two-pore structure, consisting of a coarse-pore layer on the gas side of the electrode and a fine-pore layer on the electrolyte side. The two-pore structure enables the gas/electrode/electrolyte interface to be stabilized at the junction of the fine and coarse pore layers.

Before the discussion of electrodes for use in molten carbonate fuel cells is concluded it is necessary to consider briefly the reference electrodes that have been used in such cells. Janz and Saegusa[18] studied the platinum–oxygen–carbon dioxide system as a reference electrode in molten carbonate electrolytes and found it to be reasonably stable and reproducible to within $\pm 5$ millivolts. It also shows a high degree of reversibility when tested by micro-polarization techniques. The gold–oxygen–carbon dioxide system has been similarly studied by Janz and Saegusa who found that this combination also formed an excellent reference system.

The problem of using a reference electrode in practical cells is as much one of cell geometry as one of choosing an appropriate system. In cells with free electrolyte and gas-diffusion electrodes the problem is simpler than for cells having a magnesia diaphragm since a third electrode can be inserted into the electrolyte. Douglas[19] has used the silver (or gold)–oxygen–carbon dioxide system in such a cell and found it to be satisfactory within $\pm 20$ millivolts. In cells of the magnesia matrix-type Trachtenberg[12] has used a reference system consisting of an isolated portion of one of the working electrodes from which no current was drawn. Thus a direct measurement of electrode polarization was obtained between the polarized and unpolarized portion of the electrode with the same electrode material. This arrangement has been found sufficiently accurate for most practical purposes.

## 4. THERMODYNAMICS

The reversible e.m.f. of a cell, $V^\circ$, when the reactants are in their standard states of unit activity or fugacity was shown in Chapter 2 to be given by the expression

$$V^\circ = \frac{-\Delta G^\circ}{nF} . \tag{10}$$

In order to apply this equation to high temperature fuel cells it is necessary to know $V°$ and, therefore, $\Delta G°$ at the temperature of operation. In molten carbonate cells we have seen that, in order to maintain the electrolyte invariant, it is necessary to supply carbon dioxide to the cathode. When hydrogen is used as fuel the overall electrode reactions are

$$\text{cathode: } O_2 + 2\,CO_2 + 4\,e \rightleftharpoons 2\,CO_3^{2-} \tag{3}$$

$$\text{anode: } 2\,H_2 + 2\,CO_3^{2-} \rightleftharpoons 2\,H_2O + 2\,CO_2 + 4\,e. \tag{11}$$

Since the partial pressures of carbon dioxide may be different at anode and cathode, the overall cell reaction should be written

$$O_2 + 2\,CO_2 + 2\,H_2 \rightarrow 2\,H_2O + 2\,CO_2 \tag{12}$$

$$p_{O_2} \quad {}_cp_{CO_2} \quad p_{H_2} \quad p_{H_2O} \quad {}_ap_{CO_2}$$

where ${}_cp_{CO_2}$ is the partial pressure of carbon dioxide at the cathode, ${}_ap_{CO_2}$ that at the anode, $p_{H_2}$, $p_{O_2}$ and $p_{H_2O}$ are the partial pressures of hydrogen, oxygen and water vapour respectively.

Hence the e.m.f. of the cell is

$$V = V° - \frac{RT}{4F} \ln \frac{p_{H_2O}^2}{p_{H_2}^2\, p_{O_2}} - \frac{RT}{2F} \ln \frac{{}_ap_{CO_2}}{{}_cp_{CO_2}}. \tag{13}$$

Carbon dioxide must be considered as both reactant and product in a molten carbonate cell since its partial pressures at the anode and cathode contribute to the observed e.m.f. of the cell.

### 5. KINETICS OF MOLTEN CARBONATE CELLS

As has been shown in Chapter 2, the voltage efficiency of a fuel cell for a given rate of reaction is dependent on the polarization of the electrodes from their theoretical potentials. Total electrode polarization may be made up of concentration, ohmic or activation polarization effects. Fundamental equations for determining the magnitude of these three polarization effects have been given in Chapter 3 and in general they relate to any type of fuel cell. It is only necessary, therefore, at this point to add comments which relate specifically to high temperature cells with molten carbonate electrolytes.

## (a) Concentration polarization

*Mass transfer of gases*

If the diffusion coefficient of the gas is $D_e$, the gas pressure at the reaction interface is $p_e$, the pressure of the free gas is $p_0$, and the electrode thickness is $d$, then the current per unit area, $i$, is given by

$$i = \frac{nFD_e}{d}(p_0 - p_e).\tag{14}$$

Gas concentration polarization is given by

$$\eta_c = \frac{RT}{nF}\ln\frac{p_0}{p_e}.\tag{15}$$

Concentration polarization will arise if the partial pressure of the reactant gas at the electrode is lowered owing to back diffusion of reaction products. In the extreme case where $p_e = 0$, a limiting current $i_L$ will be observed where

$$i_L = \frac{nFD_e}{d}p_0.\tag{16}$$

Such limiting currents have been observed in molten carbonate cells in which complete oxidation has been achieved using lean fuel mixtures[3].

*Mass transfer in the electrolyte*

Broers[3] has considered in detail mass transfer phenomena in molten carbonate electrolytes and the reader is refered to the original text for a detailed discussion. He finds that, if no carbon dioxide is added to the cathodic air stream the carbonate becomes partially converted to oxide and a limiting current $i_L$ arises. At any lower current $i$ the concentration polarization $\eta_c$ in the steady state is given by

$$\eta_c = \frac{RT}{nF}\ln\left(\frac{i_L}{i_L - i}\right).\tag{17}$$

It has been found[10] that when no carbon dioxide is added to the cathodic air the concentration polarization is substantial. In practice it is always found necessary to add carbon dioxide to the air stream to minimize concentration polarization and Broers and Ketelaar[4] have shown the effect of varying the ratio of carbon dioxide to oxygen on the current and voltage of a fuel cell (Fig. 51). Some concentration polarization may also occur even when the cathodic carbon dioxide is sufficient to maintain the electrolyte invariant since there will be a concentration gradient of $O^{2-}$ ions between the electrode surface and the bulk electrolyte.

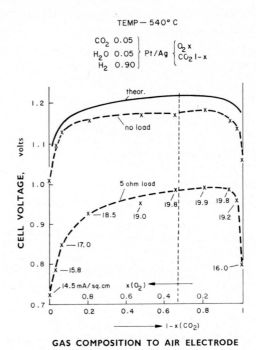

GAS COMPOSITION TO AIR ELECTRODE

Fig. 51. Influence of cathodic CO₂ on the terminal voltage and current density of a fuel cell with molten carbonate electrolyte.

*(b) Ohmic polarization*

Polarization from purely resistive effects within a molten carbonate cell have been discussed in Chapter 3 where it was shown that there is an effective increase in the specific resistance of the electrolyte due to the porosity and tortuosity of the supporting matrix. In addition there is an effective increase in cell resistance due to discontinuous contacts of the electrode with the electrolyte. This increase in resistance is dependent on the area of electrode/ electrolyte contact and the distribution of the contact area over the surface. Internal resistance has in general been found to be the major limit to cell power output in cells with molten carbonate electrolytes. The means of minimizing ohmic polarization are to decrease the thickness of the electrolyte and to increase the porosity of a magnesia diaphragm if one is used. Increasing the porosity of the diaphragm will increase its fragility, however, and some compromise will be necessary. As will be seen later the development of the paste electrolyte system has helped not only to minimize leakage of gas across the electrolyte but also to lower effective electrolyte resistance. Methods of increasing the area of contact between electrode and electrolyte have not been investigated in detail but the vacuum evaporation technique[20,21] and paints of dispersed metals[21] offer possible solutions.

### (c) Activation polarization

As the temperature at which a chemical reaction takes place is increased, the rate of the reaction also increases. In fuel cells with molten carbonate electrolytes, operating in the region of about 550–700°C, no activation polarization is found even at high current densities when hydrogen and carbon monoxide or mixtures of these are used as fuels on a variety of anodes of large surface area. Similarly, silver cathodes of large surface area fed with oxygen or air and carbon dioxide are found to be virtually free of activation polarization[12].

Hart and Powell[22] studied the oxygen–carbon dioxide–silver system using an electrode structure which was much better defined than most electrodes used in practical cells. They used as cathode a number of strands of silver wire tightly packed into the end of an alumina tube, giving approximate uniformity of pore size. This electrode structure was used to simulate that of a gas diffusion electrode. The electrode was placed in a molten eutectic mixture of lithium, sodium and potassium carbonates at 625°C. High current densities (> 300 mA/sq.cm) were drawn from the electrode (the electrode area being taken as being equal to the cross-section of the bundle of wires). A Tafel relationship was found between overpotential and current density at current densities greater than 100 mA/sq.cm both when the electrode system was flooded with electrolyte and when the reactant gases were bubbling through the electrode into the electrolyte. Hart and Powell concluded that the process was activation-controlled at current densities greater than 100 mA/sq.cm, with some additional contribution from concentration polarization due to slow diffusion of reactants to the reaction sites when the electrode was flooded. The observation of activation control for the oxygen–carbon dioxide–silver reaction in this electrode system of fairly low true surface area emphasizes the need for electrodes of high surface area in practical cells to minimize activation polarization effects. At temperatures below 600°C the oxidation of hydrocarbons such as methane and propane, fed directly to the cell, is accompanied by some activation polarization. However, the lower hydrocarbons also deposit carbon by thermal cracking at these temperatures. Both of these problems may be overcome by steam reforming the hydrocarbon as discussed in Chapter 9.

### 6. PRACTICAL CELLS

In previous sections of this chapter some of the more general aspects of molten carbonate fuel cells and factors which affect their performance have been discussed. We shall now consider some practical developments that have been made with molten carbonate cells, which will be considered in the following three categories dependent on the form of cell construction used.

(1) Matrix cells, in which the electrolyte is held within a porous sintered magnesia diaphragm.

(2) Free-electrolyte cells, in which the electrolyte is held freely between the electrodes.

(3) Paste-electrolyte cells, in which the electrolyte is formed into a stiff paste with magnesia powder.

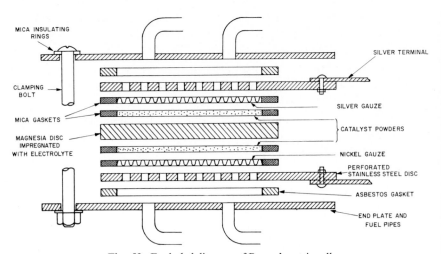

Fig. 52. Exploded diagram of Broers' matrix cell.

An attempt will be made to present typical power outputs and the problems encountered with each form of construction will be discussed.

### (a) Matrix cells

The matrix construction has been most widely used in the fabrication of molten carbonate cells. One of the principal contributors to matrix cell development has been Broers of the Central Technical Institute, The Hague, Netherlands. In much of his earlier work[3] he repeated the work of Davtyan[2] and realized the need for simpler and invariant electrolyte and electrode systems. In subsequent cells Broers used as electrolyte a binary system of lithium and potassium carbonates or a ternary system of lithium, sodium and potassium carbonates contained in a magnesia diaphragm having a porosity of 40–50%. The construction of Broers' cell, which is typical of others described in this section, is shown in Fig. 52. Some results which Broers obtained using carbon monoxide as fuel are given in Fig. 53; limiting currents are exhibited at low fuel concentration. The dotted curve shows the effect of adding steam to the feedstock, when a somewhat higher output is obtained owing to formation of hydrogen by a shift reaction.

Broers and Ketelaar[4] found that platinum and nickel were suitable as hydrogen electrodes. For carbon monoxide at 700°C they gave a series of

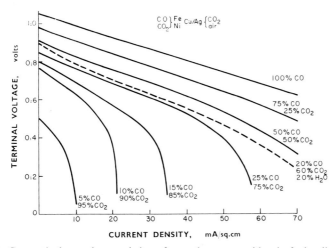

Fig. 53. Current/voltage characteristics of a carbon monoxide–air fuel cell at 720°C.

metals in order of decreasing activity:

$$Pt > \text{platinized Fe or Ni} > Fe > Ni > Co > Cu > Cr > Mn .$$

They pointed out, however, that this order of reactivity might be altered by differences in particle size of the metals. When methane was used directly as fuel none of these metals was sufficiently active to produce high outputs and steam injection was necessary. Under these circumstances nickel was a satisfactory catalyst. Broers found that silver was an excellent catalyst for the air electrode and constructed cells with silver powder cathodes and nickel powder anodes which have been operated continuously for periods up to six months on hydrogen, carbon monoxide and methane–steam mixtures. Typical outputs for cells at 500–700°C using a hydrogen–steam fuel in 1 : 1 molar ratio and air and carbon dioxide as oxidant are 50 mA/sq.cm at 0.7–0.8 volt and 100 mA/sq.cm at 0.4–0.6 volt. Cells up to twelve centimetres in diameter have been operated in this way.

After many years research with matrix cells Broers has pointed out the disadvantages of this system. A major weakness is that matrix cells cannot be made completely gas- or electrolyte-tight which would set serious problems when large scale applications are considered. Broers' cells possessed negligible activation and concentration polarization and were limited in output only by internal resistance. Loss of electrolyte from the cell increased the internal resistance and Broers found that for a typical cell of 10 sq.cm electrode area the internal resistance increased from 0.3 ohm to 1.5 ohms over a period of six months.

A second problem is likely to arise when matrix cells are scaled up to larger sizes. Increasing the diameter of the magnesia diaphragms whilst keeping them as thin as possible to minimize internal resistance may lead to increased fragility of the discs. This problem is being tackled by Truitt[23] whose work is considered later.

Chambers and Tantram[9,24] at Sondes Place Research Institute, Dorking, England undertook the development of general purpose fuel cells to operate on conventional gaseous fuels and this work is now being continued by Energy Conversion Ltd., England. Both matrix cells and free-electrolyte cells were studied but, on the whole, the matrix cells proved the more stable. As has been mentioned earlier Chambers and Tantram considered the fused carbonate fuel cell to function merely as an oxygen and carbon dioxide concentration cell in which the fuel functions as a means of preserving a low partial pressure of oxygen at the fuel electrode. The implication of such a consideration is that the same catalyst should function at both electrodes since the fuel electrode process is the reverse of the air–carbon dioxide electrode process. These workers therefore used an electrode material consisting of silver–zinc oxide for both fuel and air electrodes. A 50 % porosity magnesia diaphragm with maximum pore size of 25 microns was used as electrolyte support for a binary eutectic mixture of lithium and sodium carbonates. The electrodes were quite stable and life tests of up to 1000 hours of intermittent operation were carried out on cells of twelve centimetres diameter. Life tests were terminated by the corrosion of cell bodies or gaskets. Hydrogen, carbon monoxide and methanol vapour were used as fuels and each gave about the same output which was dependent largely upon cell internal resistance for current densities up to 140 mA/sq.cm. Internal resistances varied from about 4–12 ohm/sq.cm which made comparison of cells difficult, and no attempt appears to have been made to analyse the polarization curves after elimination of the ohmic component. Hydrocarbons were also used as fuels. With propane, carbon deposition occurred by thermal cracking and this problem is discussed in greater detail in Chapter 9. When kerosine vapour and methane were used as fuels kerosine performed almost as well as hydrogen but cells fed with methane exhibited activation polarization at temperatures below 600°C. No problem of carbon deposition was found with kerosine, although the duration of the test was not stated. Typical current/voltage curves for hydrogen, carbon monoxide and kerosine are given in Fig. 54; the difference of performance of hydrogen, which is included as a reference fuel, is due to different internal resistances of the test cells.

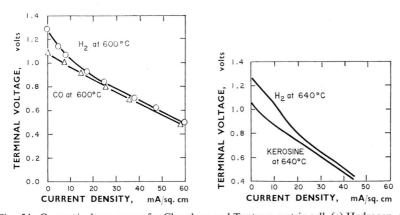

Fig. 54. Current/voltage curves for Chambers and Tantram matrix cell. (a) Hydrogen–air and carbon monoxide–air cells at 600°C. (b) Hydrogen–air and kerosine–air cells at 640°C.

Chambers and Tantram arranged their flow rates such that current densities of 50 mA/sq.cm corresponded to about 10–20% conversion of fuel to oxidation products. Both they and Broers have pointed out the necessity for stating the degree of conversion of the fuel in recording cell output since, if the percentage conversion is very low, curves of terminal voltage against current density would give an optimistic picture of cell output. In a battery of cells having fuel gas fed in series the downstream cells would receive a mixture which was lean in fuel and would therefore have somewhat lower outputs.

Gorin and Recht[25] were also concerned with the development of fused carbonate cells. Their cell was similar to that of Broers and used nickel or iron anodes and silver or lithiated nickel oxide cathodes. They, like other workers, used a magnesia disc to contain the electrolyte. The disc had a porosity of 28% and a thickness of 0.2 cm. Measured cell resistances were of the order of 5–10 ohm/sq.cm. The cells of Gorin and Recht were similar in output to those of Broers, being limited largely by internal resistance. They found that tests often had to be terminated through cracking of the magnesia discs, the consequent mixing of fuel and oxidant gases lowering the terminal voltage.

A more recent investigation of molten carbonate cells with magnesia diaphragms has been undertaken by Trachtenberg and co-workers[12,26–29] of Texas Instruments Incorporated. These workers are making a detailed study of cell polarization and also carrying out development of fuel cell batteries. The test cells had an area of 16 sq.cm and used as electrolyte a binary eutectic mixture of lithium and sodium carbonates contained in a magnesia matrix. Cathodes were of pure silver and anode materials were described as being either of silver or base metal substrates containing a variety of inexpensive catalysts which were unspecified. Open circuit potentials as high as 1.4 volt have been recorded with pure hydrogen as fuel, and power outputs of about 60 mW/sq.cm at 0.7 volt have been achieved with no evidence of a limiting current. When the fuel stream contained added carbon dioxide to simulate the gas composition of a reformed hydrocarbon, the open circuit potential was about 1.06 volt with a power output of about 40 mW/sq.cm at 0.7 volt terminal voltage. Figure 55 illustrates the results which Trachtenberg has obtained from a typical cell. $V_T$ shows the terminal voltage of the cell and $E_A$ and $E_C$ the single electrode polarization curves taken against a reference electrode. The values $R_A$ and $R_C$ represent the ohmic resistance of the electrodes as measured by a current interruption method and the curves

$E_A - IR_A$ and $E_C + IR_C$ are the current/voltage curves with the ohmic components of the electrode resistance removed. The remaining polarization in these curves is attributed to concentration polarization due to back diffusion of reaction products.

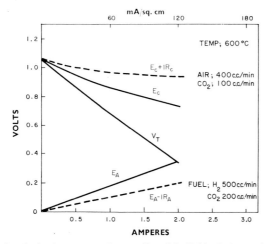

Fig. 55. Typical polarization curves for a cell and individual electrodes operating on a hydrogen–carbon dioxide fuel and air–carbon dioxide oxidant.

Trachtenberg has used a fast response current interruption technique to analyse the various components of electrode polarization. As indicated in Chapter 3, ohmic, activation and concentration polarization at electrodes may be studied by following the potential decay as a function of time after interruption of the steady current. Voltage/time curves were recorded from $10^{-6}$ second up to 1 second after a single current interruption. Typical voltage/time curves are shown in Fig. 56 for pure hydrogen as fuel and for a hydrogen–carbon dioxide mixture. The pre-interruption current densities using the two fuel feeds are represented by points on the ordinate. The rapid drop in potential in less than a microsecond is attributed to the removal of the ohmic component of the polarization. The horizontal line in the $10^{-5}$–$10^{-4}$ second region indicates that no measurable activation polarization exists at the electrode. Polarization at times greater than $10^{-4}$ second are attributed to concentration polarization effects due to back diffusion of products which affects the relative amounts of potential-determining species at the electrode. Similar studies were made on silver cathodes fed with oxygen–carbon dioxide mixtures. Results were similar but cathodes showed some-

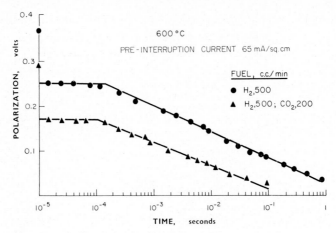

Fig. 56. Anode polarization/time curves after current interruption.

what higher ohmic polarization and less concentration polarization than anodes. The higher ohmic polarization at cathodes is attributed to the presence of silver oxide on the electrode whilst a lower concentration polarization results since there is no back diffusion of products.

On the basis of these observations Trachtenberg considers that the following electrode reactions are operative. At the anode, since carbonate ions are always in equilibrium with oxide ions as expressed by eqn. (6), the electron transfer reaction is considered to be

$$O^{2-} + M \rightleftharpoons MO + 2\,e \tag{7}$$

where M is the active metal catalyst. Fuel is consumed in the chemical reduction of the surface metal "oxide":

$$MO + H_2 \rightleftharpoons M + H_2O . \tag{18}$$

At the cathode the first reaction is the adsorption of oxygen to form a surface oxide:

$$O_2 + 2\,M \rightleftharpoons 2\,MO . \tag{19}$$

The electron transfer step is

$$2\,MO + 4\,e \rightleftharpoons 2\,M + 2\,O^{2-} . \tag{20}$$

Finally

$$2\,CO_2 + 2\,O^{2-} \rightleftharpoons 2\,CO_3^{2-} . \tag{21}$$

In addition to using hydrogen and hydrogen–carbon dioxide mixtures, Trachtenberg *et al.* have operated cells using reformed propane as fuel and obtained an output of about 90 mA/sq.cm at 0.35 volt which was only slightly less than the output obtained with hydrogen as fuel. Kerosine fed directly to the cell as a liquid gave an output of 30 mA/sq.cm at 0.5 volt whilst gasoline gave an output similar to that of hydrogen. These cells have also operated on a range of hydrocarbons from methane to heptane and on ammonia and various alcohols. The results indicate that molten carbonate fuel cells are capable of accepting a wide variety of fuels although direct comparison of fuel reactivity is only possible when results are taken on the same cell or on cells with similar resistances and electrode structures. Promising results have also been obtained with regard to stability towards thermal cycling. A number of cells have remained unaffected when continuously cycled between 25°C and 600°C.

Truitt[23] has described some of the engineering aspects of Texas Instruments Incorporated fuel cells used with hydrocarbon fuels. Life tests of over 2000 hours duration have been carried out on test cells, and on the basis of such tests a 100-watt fuel cell battery has been built to operate continuously on the partial oxidation products of the jet fuel JP-4. The fuel stream consists of hydrogen (30), carbon monoxide (23), nitrogen (38), methane(3), ethylene (1) and carbon dioxide (5), where figures in parentheses represent volumes per cent. Bearing in mind the materials problems encountered by other workers the outcome of the work will be of some importance in assessing the future of matrix cells.

Sandler[30] of Westinghouse Electric Corporation has recently reported operation of a magnesia matrix fuel cell using a nickel anode and silver cathode, both electrodes being in the form of powders embedded in a mesh. The cell design was similar to that of Broers and the operating temperature was 580°C. Outputs of 120 mA/sq.cm at 0.5 volt were recorded for reformed methane at 28 % conversion. Cell resistance was about 2 ohms/sq. cm but the operating life was extremely poor, being limited to about one week. Loss of electrolyte from the disc accounted for the termination of tests.

Kronenberg[31] of Union Carbide Corporation has used a porous magnesia tube impregnated with a ternary eutectic mixture of lithium, sodium and potassium carbonates as an alternative to the disc method. This design was used for laboratory testing since it appeared to have fewer gasketing problems. Silver electrodes were applied to the inner and outer faces of the ceramic tube as slurry powders and were baked at 500°C. A silver–

oxygen–carbon dioxide reference electrode was included in the cell. A Kordesch–Marko current interrupter technique[32] was used to study the polarization characteristics of the tubular matrix cell which was found to possess a high internal resistance which limited its operating voltage. Typical outputs were 80 mA/sq.cm at 0.5 volt with hydrogen as fuel and 50–60 mA/sq.cm with methanol vapour as fuel. Tubular cells were operated intermittently for about ten weeks during which time they were subjected to over fifty heating and cooling cycles. Cell failure was caused by loss of electrolyte and development of cracks in the matrix.

Sufficient has now been said about matrix cells to provide a general picture of their power outputs and of their inherent advantages and disadvantages. In the best cells, power outputs of about 60 mW/sq.cm at 0.6–0.7 volt terminal voltage have been obtained which were largely controlled by the internal resistance factors. Practical cells have exhibited internal resistances which were dependent on the thickness, porosity and tortuosity of the magnesia diaphragms used to support the electrolyte and improvements in output will be largely dependent on the production of thinner, stronger and more porous diaphragms. Life tests of up to 2000 hours have been recorded and have been terminated by corrosion of gaskets, loss of electrolyte from the magnesia diaphragms or development of fine cracks in the diaphragms. Cracking of the magnesia discs causes partial mixing of fuel and oxidant gases with consequent lowering of terminal voltage. The absence of activation polarization in these cells has shown, however, that catalysis problems are not severe.

### (b) Free electrolyte cells

Compared with matrix cells, relatively little work has been carried out with free-electrolyte cells. Chambers and Tantram[9] have described cells of this type in which the two-pore electrode structure developed by Bacon[17] was used to establish the gas/electrode/electrolyte interface. The electrodes were made of silver–zinc oxide which was also used in their matrix cells. Taking the surface tension of the electrolyte to be 225 dynes/cm at 550°C they calculated the required pore sizes to be 160–270 microns for the coarse-pore layer and 76–140 microns for the fine-pore layer. These pore sizes allowed a working gas pressure in the range 50–160 cm of water. The outputs obtained from these cells were similar to those obtained from their matrix cells but the mechanical strength of their electrodes was insufficient for extended life tests although the electrodes were quite stable chemically over short periods. A molten carbonate cell of the free-electrolyte type was described in 1959 by Douglas[19] of the General Electric Company. It was designed primarily to study electrode design and materials problems and no attempt was made to obtain large power outputs and long life. A ternary eutectic electrolyte mixture of lithium, sodium and potassium carbonates was contained in a gold crucible and electrodes were fabricated from sintered powders of nickel, silver and gold having porosities of 30–50% and a range of pore sizes from 1 to 50 microns. For a reference electrode, Douglas used an oxygen–carbon dioxide electrode on a gold or silver catalyst, operated at its open circuit potential. Since the cell was not designed to produce high outputs, the main contribution of this work was in pointing out the limitations of metals used in electrode construction in the highly corrosive environment. Douglas found that, although nickel and silver were catalytically suitable materials for anode and cathode respectively, appreciable corrosion of silver occurred. After a test of 100 hours duration about a gram of silver had been transferred to the anode causing a short circuit to be set up. Douglas concluded that with close spacing of electrodes the best outputs which he had obtained (about 40 mA/sq.cm at 0.5 volt) could be substantially improved upon and that corrosion of the electrodes was most likely to limit the usefulness of cells with gas diffusion electrodes.

In spite of their lower internal resistances research on free-electrolyte cells has been much less extensive than on matrix cells. Their main disadvantage is the highly corrosive nature of the free electrolyte which presents formidable materials problems.

### (c) Paste-electrolyte cells

Cells with paste-electrolyte systems are of comparatively recent development compared to other types of construction and they represent a compromise between the magnesia diaphragm cells and free-electrolyte cells. The electrolyte is immobilized by being formed into a stiff paste with magnesia powder by special techniques, but it has a specific conductivity approaching that of the free electrolyte. Moreover, it is claimed that electrolyte systems prepared in this way are gas tight in that they do not permit mixing of gases through the electrolyte—a major weakness of the matrix type.

Broers has recently turned his attention from the magnesia diaphragm cells and is now developing cells with paste electrolytes. Magnesia particles

of submicron size are mixed with an approximately equal weight of the carbonate electrolyte. Above the melting point of the electrolyte the mixture
forms a stiff white paste and can be moulded by appropriate methods into
any desired shape. The specific conductivity of the paste is between 50 and
70% of that of the pure liquid phase. Broers and Schenke[33] have described
three types of cell construction with a paste electrolyte. Firstly, they consider
the use of "canal" cells in which a solid block of the paste electrolyte is
drilled out and fuel and air admitted through metal tubes. A second model
which they describe is a tube cell, the general mode of construction of which
is shown in Fig. 57; thirdly, the conventional flat disc type of cell has been

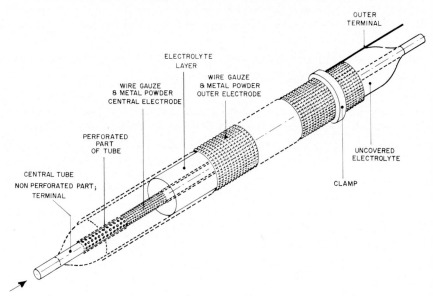

Fig. 57. Broers' tube cell construction.

developed. So far Broers and Schenke have concentrated on the production
of stable, gas-tight electrolytes. Silver powder embedded in silver gauze has
been used as the air–carbon dioxide electrode and nickel or iron powders as
fuel electrodes.

The production of gas-tight cells has enabled Broers to carry out some
quantitative observations on fuel consumption which had previously been
impossible with the magnesia disc cells. The interdependence of fuel consumption and current has been established for short duration experiments
with hydrogen, carbon monoxide and methanol vapour as fuels at 700°C.

Figure 58 shows the initial performance of a typical disc cell operating at 700°C on a lean fuel mixture of hydrogen, 20% vol., carbon monoxide, 10% vol., and carbon dioxide, 70% vol., on a sintered Inconel sieve fuel electrode with air 85% vol. and carbon dioxide, 15% vol. as oxidant on a silver powder electrode[15]. The power output of this cell was high in the early stages but when the cell was held at a constant terminal voltage of 700 milli-volts the current density declined to about one-sixth of its highest value over a test period of 400 hours. Broers[15] has investigated the influence of anode polarization on the cell performance over long periods. He found that with a cell operated at low current density ( ~ 10–15 mA/sq.cm) neither the terminal

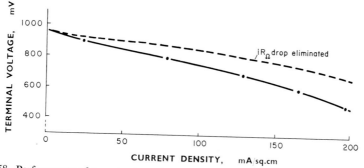

Fig. 58. Performance of a paste–electrolyte disc cell at 700°C. Fuel: $H_2$, 20% vol.; CO, 10% vol.; $CO_2$, 70% vol.; on Inconel sieve. Oxidant: air, 85% vol.; $CO_2$, 15% vol.; on silver powder.

voltage nor the internal resistance changed significantly over a period of 36 days. The current density was then increased to 50 mA/sq.cm when a marked fall in performance occurred with a corresponding increase in cell resistance. When the cell was dismantled the nickel anode was found to be seriously corroded. Further tests with nickel anodes have shown that if cell polarization is not allowed to exceed 200–300 millivolts long operating peri-ods are possible. It is apparent therefore that the choice of metal to act as anode in a cell with molten carbonate electrolyte must be made with care so that anodic polarization under operating conditions does not exceed the potential at which the metal itself is oxidized.

The paste-electrolyte system is also being investigated by workers at the Institute of Gas Technology (I.G.T.) in Chicago[21,34], where the cells of the disc type are being studied with the object of producing cells to consume methane or natural gas. The main areas of study are in paste electrolyte development, electrode evaluation, natural gas reforming, battery design and scale-up and economic evaluation.

The paste-electrolyte is prepared by essentially the same method as that described by Broers and Schenke[33]. Binary and ternary eutectics of lithium and sodium carbonates and lithium, sodium and potassium carbonates are used; typical paste mixtures are 50% by weight of the eutectic with 50% of magnesia powder. The magnesia powder is preferably of submicron grade since the resultant electrolyte structure then possesses a greater capacity for melt retention. A number of different electrode structures have been studied, particularly hydrogen-permeable foils, thin films, sintered powders and sintered fibres. The use of hydrogen-permeable foils gives rise to mass transfer problems completely different from those that are usually encountered at a fuel electrode since the products cannot diffuse back but must be rejected through the electrolyte. With anodes of this type, cell outputs become limited by the rate at which products diffuse away through the electrolyte. These anodes, however, were found to be stable over seven months operation at 25 mA/sq.cm when used in conjunction with thin silver-film cathodes. Hydrogen-permeable foil anodes are likely to be rejected largely on the grounds of their high cost.

Considerable success has been achieved when thin silver films are used as cathodes. These are applied either by vacuum deposition or by the use of silver paint which is applied in the form of a fine dispersion of silver in an organic binder. The vacuum deposition method has also been used for low temperature cells[20] and is especially useful if expensive materials are needed since layers of only a few microns thickness are easily deposited. Silver cathodes have been operated for 4000 hours but some silver dissolution, as discussed by Douglas[19] and more recently by Janz and co-workers[35], was observed. The fact that this dissolution was of minor proportions was attributed to the electrode being continuously cathodically polarized and not flooded to any great extent. Attempts to produce similar thin-film anode structures was not entirely successful owing to electrode flooding. Anode life was restricted to about 30 hours, with vacuum-deposited palladium giving the best results. Sintered nickel powders have also been used as anodes when corrosion difficulties similar to those described by Broers were encountered when electrodes were operated at potentials of much more than 200 millivolt from their open circuit potential. To avoid serious nickel corrosion, operation of nickel anodes was restricted to conditions of low polarization and, therefore, low current densities.

Baker and co-workers[21] at I.G.T. have succeeded in developing the fabrication of the paste-electrolyte system to produce thin plates six inches square, and a ten-cell battery of this size has been developed to operate on natural gas. The apparatus is shown schematically in Fig. 59. A portion of the natural gas is passed through an activated carbon purifier to remove sulphur compounds and, after addition of steam, is passed through a nickel reforming catalyst and thence to the anode chambers of the cell. Another portion of the

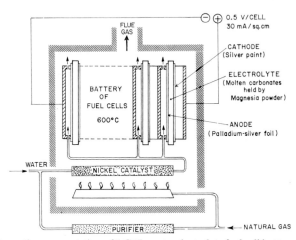

Fig. 59. Schematic representation of I.G.T. paste–electrolyte fuel cell battery operating on natural gas.

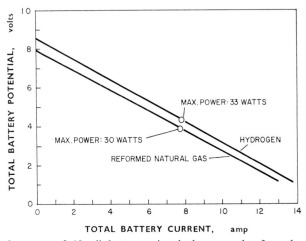

Fig. 60. Performance of 10-cell battery using hydrogen and reformed natural gas.

natural gas stream is burned directly in a burner beneath the reformer and fuel cell battery. The hot combustion gases containing excess air, carbon dioxide and water vapour rise past the reformer, sustaining the endothermic reforming reaction and then enter the cathode chambers of the battery supplying the oxygen and carbon dioxide needed to carry out the cathode reaction. To conserve fuel and carbon dioxide the spent anode gases are recycled to the burner. The battery output when reformed natural gas and hydrogen are used as fuels is shown in Fig. 60. Each cell operated at a terminal voltage of 0.5 volt and produced a current density of 30 mA/sq.cm. The electrodes consisted of a silver paint cathode and a hydrogen-permeable palladium–silver foil anode. The complete system efficiency was low, as might be expected for a small battery, but the feasibility of operating a molten carbonate fuel cell battery has been demonstrated.

## 7. PROSPECTS FOR MOLTEN CARBONATE FUEL CELLS

The three types of molten carbonate cell described in the previous sections were capable of producing high initial outputs limited largely by cell resistance. By minimizing cell internal resistance, molten carbonate cells should therefore possess high voltage efficiencies. However, all types have limitations when subjected to extended life tests and even the most stable cells have not yet operated for much longer than six months. Failure of matrix cells has usually been due to loss of electrolyte, corrosion of gaskets or cracking of the ceramic diaphragm. With free-electrolyte cells the highly corrosive nature of the free melt and insufficient mechanical strength of the electrodes were the main causes of the termination of tests. The development of the paste-electrolyte technique is likely to prove a means of solving the problems encountered with ceramic diaphragms and, in addition, should lower cell resistances to values approaching those of free-electrolyte cells.

One of the main advantages claimed for high temperature cells is that the temperature of operation minimizes problems of catalysis, and the general absence of activation polarization in these cells bears out this claim. The choice of electrode material is, however, not as wide as was once envisaged since corrosion of electrode materials in the molten carbonate electrolyte has been found by a number of workers to be a limiting factor. Work such as that described by Degobert and Bloch[16] will prove valuable in deciding on suitable electrode materials to operate at high current densities at which electrode polarization might be substantial.

The main advances to be expected in the near future in the field of molten carbonate cells may be expected from work now in progress with paste-electrolyte cells where the fundamental work of Broers in Holland and the development being carried out by workers at the Institute of Gas Technology at Chicago should together reveal the extent to which this system can be adapted to the production of large power units. The development of multi-cell batteries with sintered magnesia diaphragms by Texas Instruments Incorporated will also be of major interest in view of the materials difficulties which many workers have encountered using this construction.

Economic assessments of power generation with fused carbonate cells have been carried out by Hart, Powell and DeWhalley[36] and by von Frieders-dorff[37]. They concluded that, provided that cell lives of years rather than months can be achieved, there is a need for a two-fold to eight-fold improvement in power densities from molten carbonate cells to bring them within the economic framework of domestic or large scale power generation.

The future prospects for molten carbonate fuel cells must therefore be considered in the light of these assessments and on the assumption that the laboratory systems so far developed can be scaled up into large power units. Furthermore, the future of molten carbonate cells may also be affected by the rate of development of solid oxide fuel cells with stabilized zirconia electrolytes, which are discussed in the next chapter. These cells appear to possess advantages over molten carbonate cells in that, whilst they operate at higher temperatures, they contain no corrosive liquid electrolyte and have no carbon dioxide recycle problem.

## REFERENCES

1  E. BAUR, W. D. TREADWELL AND G. TRUMPLER, Z. Elektrochem., 27 (1921) 199.
2  O. K. DAVTYAN, Bull. Acad. Sci. U.R.S.S., Classe Sci. Tech., (1946) 107, 125.
3  G. H. J. BROERS, High Temperature Galvanic Fuel Cells, Ph. D. Thesis, Univ. Amsterdam, The Netherlands, 1958.
4  G. H. J. BROERS AND J. A. A. KETELAAR, Chap. 6 in Fuel Cells, (ed. by G. J. YOUNG), Vol. 1, Reinhold, New York, 1960, p. 78.
5  H. H. GREGER, U.S. Patent 2,175,523 (1939).
6  E. M. LEVIN, H. F. McMURDIE AND F. P. HALL, Phase Diagrams for Ceramists, Am. Ceram. Soc., 1956, p. 194.
7  G. J. JANZ, F. COLOM AND F. SAEGUSA, J. Electrochem. Soc., 107 (1960) 581.
8  G. J. JANZ AND F. SAEGUSA, J. Electrochem. Soc., 108 (1961) 663.
9  H. H. CHAMBERS AND A. D. S. TANTRAM, Chap. 7 in Fuel Cells, (ed. by G. J. YOUNG), Vol. 1, Reinhold, New York, 1960, p. 94.
10  E. GORIN AND H. L. RECHT, Chap. 5 in Fuel Cells, (ed. by W. MITCHELL), Academic Press, New York, 1963.

[11] H. A. LIEBHAFSKY AND E. J. CAIRNS, *General Electric Tech. Rept. 63-RL-3480 C*, 1963.

[12] I. TRACHTENBERG, *Preprints\* 145th Natl. Meeting Am. Chem. Soc., New York, Sept. 1963, Vol. 7: Div. Fuel Chem., No. 4: Symp. Fuel Cell Systems*, p. 196.

[13] G. J. JANZ AND M. R. LORENZ, *J. Electrochem. Soc.*, **108** (1961) 1052.

[14] G. J. JANZ AND F. SAEGUSA, *J. Electrochem. Soc.*, **110** (1963) 452.

[15] G. H. J. BROERS, in *Fuel Cells*, (Chem. Eng. Progr. Tech. Manual), Am. Inst. Chem. Engrs., 1963, p. 90.

[16] P. DEGOBERT AND O. BLOCH, *Bull. Soc. Chim. France*, (1962) 1887.

[17] F. T. BACON, Chap. 5 in *Fuel Cells*, (ed. by G. J. YOUNG), Vol. 1, Reinhold, New York, 1960, p. 51.

[18] G. J. JANZ AND F. SAEGUSA, *R. P. I. Tech. Rept. No. 13*, 1961, (Project No. 441.35), U.S. Office Naval Res. Contract No. Nonr 591–(10).

[19] D. L. DOUGLAS, Chap. 9 in *Fuel Cells*, (ed. by G. J. YOUNG), Vol. 1, Reinhold, New York, 1960, p. 129.

[20] K. R. WILLIAMS AND D. P. GREGORY, *Brit. Patent 874,283*.

[21] B. S. BAKER, L. C. MARIANOWSKI, J. MEEK AND H. R. LINDEN, *Preprints\* 145th Natl. Meeting Am. Chem. Soc., New York, Sept. 1963, Vol. 7: Div. Fuel Chem. No. 4: Symp. Fuel Cell Systems*, p. 209.

[22] A. B. HART AND J. H. POWELL, *Proc. 3rd Intern. Symp. on Batteries, Bournemouth, 1962*, (ed. by D. H. COLLINS), Pergamon, Oxford, 1963, p. 265.

[23] J. K. TRUITT, in *Fuel Cells*, (Chem. Eng. Progr. Tech. Manual), Am. Inst. Chem. Engrs., 1963, p. 1.

[24] H. H. CHAMBERS AND A. D. S. TANTRAM, *Proc. 2nd Intern. Symp. on Batteries, Bournemouth, 1960*, Interdepartmental Committee on Batteries, paper 20.

[25] E. GORIN AND H. L. RECHT, Chap. 8 in *Fuel Cells*, (ed. by G. J. YOUNG), Vol. 1, Reinhold, New York, 1960, p. 109.

[26] I. TRACHTENBERG, *Extended Abstr. 122nd Meeting Electrochem. Soc., Boston, Sept. 1962, Battery Div.*, p. 39.

[27] C. G. PEATTIE, B. H. BARBEE, K. W. KREISELMAIER, S. G. PARKER, I. TRACHTENBERG AND A. WHITE, *Proc. Pacific Energy Conversion Conf., San Francisco, 1962, Direct Conversion*, Am. Inst. Elec. Engrs. p. 17–1.

[28] C. G. PEATTIE, I. TRACHTENBERG, B. H. BARBEE, K. W. KREISELMAIER, S. G. PARKER AND A. WHITE, in *Power Systems for Space Flight*, (ed. by M. A. ZIPKIN AND R. N. EDWARDS), *Progr. Astron. Aeron.*, Vol. 11, Academic Press, New York, 1963, p. 269.

[29] I. TRACHTENBERG, *J. Electrochem. Soc.*, **111** (1964) 110.

[30] Y. L. SANDLER, *J. Electrochem. Soc.*, **109** (1962) 1115.

[31] M. L. KRONENBERG, *J. Electrochem. Soc.*, **109** (1962) 753.

[32] K. KORDESCH AND A. MARKO, *J. Electrochem. Soc.*, **107** (1960) 480.

[33] G. H. J. BROERS AND M. SCHENKE, Chap. 2 in *Fuel Cells*, (ed. by G. J. YOUNG), Vol. 2, Reinhold, New York, 1963, p. 6.

[34] E. B. SCHULTZ, K. S. VORRES, L. G. MARIANOWSKI AND H. R. LINDEN, Chap. 3 in *Fuel Cells*, (ed. by G. J. YOUNG), Vol. 2, Reinhold, New York, 1963, p. 24

[35] G. J. JANZ, A CONTE AND E. NEUENSCHWANDER, *Corrosion*, **19** (1963) 292 t.

[36] A. B. HART, J. H. POWELL AND C. H. DEWHALLEY, *Proc. 3rd Intern. Symp. on Batteries, Bournemouth, 1962*, (ed. by D. H. COLLINS), Pergamon, Oxford, 1963, p. 277.

[37] C. G. VON FRIEDERSDORFF, Chap. 5 in *Fuel Cells*, (ed. by G. J. YOUNG), Vol. 2, Reinhold, New York, 1963, p. 50.

---

\* Proceedings to be published by American Chemical Society as *Fuel Cell Systems* (Advan. Chem. Series No. 47).

# Chapter 8

# SOLID OXIDE ELECTROLYTES

It is clear from Chapter 7 that many difficulties are encountered in the operation of high temperature fuel cells with fused carbonate electrolytes; two inherent disadvantages of this system are the highly corrosive nature of the molten salts and the necessity of feeding carbon dioxide with the oxidant gas to regenerate the carbonate ions required to keep the electrolyte invariant. For many years it has been realized that a simpler fuel cell would result from the use of a solid oxide electrolyte. An ideal solid oxide electrolyte has none of the disadvantages of a molten carbonate electrolyte and should yield a stable system capable of continuous long term operation with no fall-off in cell output. This chapter describes work carried out by various investigators on this latter type of fuel cell, mainly with hydrogen as the fuel, hydrocarbon fuels being considered in Chapter 9.

## 1. HISTORICAL BACKGROUND

The history of solid oxide electrolytes can be considered to begin at the end of the 19th century when Nernst[1], in 1899, produced his "glower". The metal filaments used before the introduction of tungsten in the electric lamp industry were poor light sources, a large proportion of the electrical energy being wasted as heat. Nernst realized that this was due to free electrons in the metal radiating too strongly in the infra-red and proposed that ionic conductors be substituted for the metal filaments; as ionic conductors contained practically no free electrons they should be more efficient light sources.

Nernst's discovery that the very high electrical resistance of pure solid oxides could be greatly reduced by addition of certain other oxides was an important step in the development of his glower. The mixed oxides exhibited the characteristic rapid increase in conductivity with rise in temperature associated with ionic conductors. The most promising of these mixtures consisted mainly of zirconia ($ZrO_2$) with small amounts of added yttria

$(Y_2O_3)$ or ceria $(CeO_2)$; the mixture that Nernst finally used, often called "the Nernst mass", contained $85\%$ wt. $ZrO_2$ and $15\%$ wt. $Y_2O_3$.

The Nernst glower could be operated for long periods on either alternating current or direct current even though, in the latter case, electrolysis was bound to occur. According to Nernst[1] the explanation of the satisfactory operation on d.c. was possibly that any loss of oxygen, liberated at the anode, was balanced by an equal amount of oxygen diffusing into the glower at the cathode; he confirmed experimentally that oxygen was needed, albeit in very small amounts, for d.c. operation of the glower. His views are illustrated in Fig. 61; oxygen entering the glower at the cathode migrates as oxide ions, under the influence of an electric field, to the anode, where it is liberated. The reactions occurring at the anode and cathode respectively are

$$2 O^{2-} \rightarrow O_2 + 4 e \tag{1a}$$

$$O_2 + 4 e \rightarrow 2 O^{2-} . \tag{1b}$$

It is now known that if oxygen at the anode reacts with, for example, carbon, the oxygen pressure is reduced to a very low value corresponding to the equilibrium

$$C + \tfrac{1}{2} O_2 \rightleftharpoons CO \tag{2}$$

and the state of affairs existing in a high temperature solid oxide fuel cell is realized where, at equilibrium, the open circuit voltage $(V)$ is equal to the e.m.f. of an oxygen concentration cell operating between 1 atmosphere oxy-

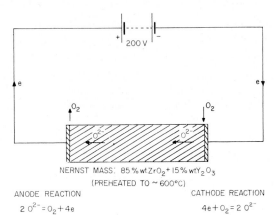

NERNST MASS: $85\%$ wt $ZrO_2 + 15\%$ wt $Y_2O_3$
(PREHEATED TO ~ 600°C)

ANODE REACTION                    CATHODE REACTION

$2 O^{2-} = O_2 + 4e$                    $4e + O_2 = 2 O^{2-}$

Fig. 61. Schematic diagram of a Nernst glower.

gen pressure at the cathode and a very small equilibrium pressure at the anode.

As mentioned in Chapter 7 many investigators confined their attempts to employ highly conductive electrolytes to the field of fused carbonate systems in various forms. The resultant early cells were characterized by their inability to operate for long periods without severe drop in output, attributed to instability of the electrolyte–electrode systems. By 1937 Baur and Preis[2] had discarded molten salts in their search for an invariant electrolyte and directed their activities towards solid oxide systems.

The Preis cell (Fig. 62) consisted of a ceramic crucible, which acted as the solid electrolyte, filled with a fuel such as coke, immersed in an iron

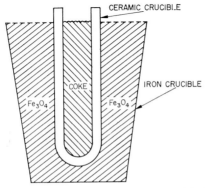

Fig. 62. Preis solid oxide cell using $Fe_3O_4$ as source of oxide ions and coke as fuel.

crucible containing magnetite as the oxidant. At temperatures around 1000°C Baur and Preis obtained open circuit voltages between 1.1 and 1.2 volt, although factors such as the use of relatively unreactive carbon as fuel and the excessive thickness of the electrolyte with its accompanying high internal resistance made the cell impracticable. They varied the composition of the ceramic crucible, paying particular attention to the resistance of the solid electrolyte as a function of temperature and current flow.

The most important solid oxide electrolytes studied by Baur and Preis were $[ZrO_2]$, $[(ZrO_2)_{0.9}(MgO)_{0.1}]$ and $[(ZrO_2)_{0.85}(Y_2O_3)_{0.15}]$. At the present time, extensive investigations of invariant solid oxide systems are being carried out in the United States, Russia and Europe.

## 2. PROPERTIES OF OXIDE ELECTROLYTES

The ideal properties of a solid oxide electrolyte can be stated as follows.

(1) It should be chemically stable under oxidizing and reducing conditions.

(2) It should be physically stable, *i.e.* it should show no tendency towards shrinking, cracking or loss of mechanical strength.

(3) It should be impermeable to gases at elevated temperatures (1000°C).

(4) It should enable rapid migration of oxide ions through it with an oxide transference number of unity (*i.e.* no electronic or cationic contribution).

The most practical solid oxide electrolytes investigated so far have been those based on zirconia ($ZrO_2$). Pure zirconia is chemically stable even under severe oxidizing and reducing conditions; its great weakness, however, is its tendency to fracture on thermal cycling.

According to Ruff and his collaborators[3] zirconia crystallizes at room temperature in the monoclinic form which transforms at about 1150°C into a tetragonal form. This transformation is accompanied by a considerable volume contraction, amounting to about 9%. On cooling, the reverse transformation occurs at a lower temperature, 900°C, giving a typical hysteresis effect which hinders the use of zirconia in the ceramics industry. Since both modifications differ only slightly from a cubic form, addition of other oxides which have a cubic structure and form solid solutions with zirconia, forces the zirconia to assume a cubic structure after firing, with only small stresses in the initial monoclinic zirconia lattice. The zirconia is then said to be "stabilized", having assumed a fluorite type lattice[4]; this results in the elimination of the hysteresis effect to give greater physical stability. Stabilized zirconia can be formed into relatively non-porous discs or tubes suitable for incorporating into fuel cells. The various methods used are discussed at a later stage in this chapter. The oxide electrolyte should be impermeable to gases at the high cell operating temperature since any diffusion of gaseous fuels into the oxygen compartment, and the reverse process, lead to reduced open circuit potentials and hence to lower overall outputs.

The type of conductivity is of great importance when considering oxide systems for use as a fuel cell electrolyte. It is essential that the transference number of the oxide ion be close to unity so that only oxygen ions and not cations are transferred through the oxide. Any cation conductivity would result in permanent changes in composition and severe damage to the contacts at the electrode/electrolyte interfaces when drawing current from the cell. As will be discussed in section 2(b), the electronic conductivity should also be small since this leads to a lower cell voltage.

*(a) Ionic conductivity in oxide electrolytes*

Pure zirconia is a typical insulator with a specific resistance of the order of $10^{14}$ ohm cm at room temperature, decreasing to about $10^7$ ohm cm at 1000°C. In addition to the stabilizing effect, discussed previously, produced by the addition of small amounts of oxides such as calcia and yttria (which are themselves poor conductors even at high temperatures), solid solutions are formed which exhibit remarkably high electrical conductivities at temperatures above about 800°C or 900°C.

Wagner[5] proposed in 1943 that solid solutions with an imperfect fluorite lattice of the type $[(ZrO_2)_{1-x}(CaO)_x]$ or $[(ZrO_2)_{1-x}(Y_2O_3)_x]$ contain vacant oxygen lattice sites, one vacancy occurring for each $Ca^{2+}$ or two $Y^{3+}$ ions that are randomly substituted for $Zr^{4+}$ ions in the crystal lattice. Density measurements of these oxides by X-ray and pycnometric methods carried out by Hund[6] support this model. In the fluorite structure (Fig. 63) the

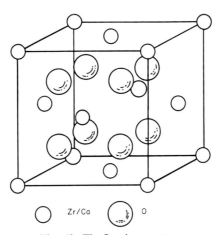

$\bigcirc$   Zr/Ca    $\bigcirc$   O

Fig. 63. The fluorite structure.

negative ions are in simple cubic packing with half the interstices filled by metal ions. The unit cell has metal ions arranged in face-centred cubic packing, the centre space corresponding to the unfilled interstice in the simple cubic negative ion lattice.

Owing to the very stable tetravalent state of zirconium, replacement of the zirconium ions by ions of a metal of lower valency results in a proportionate number of oxide ion lattice sites being vacant. Under the influence of increased temperature, oxide ions can migrate via these vacant sites, leading to high electrical conductivity[6,7], the conductivity increasing in direct proportion to the concentration of oxide ion vacancies at low vacancy concentration. With calcia-stabilized zirconia, the decrease in conductivity at concentrations higher than about 15 mole % calcia is attributed to increased ordering of the vacancies[8], which cannot then take part in the conduction process. Kiukkola and Wagner[7] have shown that at temperatures at which solid oxide fuel cells have been operated, the conductivity is almost purely ionic in character. The migration of oxide ions through a solid oxide electrolyte can be considered as a diffusion process. Using radioactive tracer techniques for studying oxide ion diffusion in the system $[Zr_{0.85} Ca_{0.15} O_{1.85}]$ over the temperature range 700–1100°C, Kingery and co-workers[9] calculated the electrical conductivity of the oxide ion resulting from the ionic mobility $S_{O^{2-}}$ determined from the diffusion coefficient by means of the Nernst–Einstein relation for oxide ions

$$S_{O^{2-}} = \frac{D \, n_i z^2 e^2}{kT}, \tag{3}$$

where $D$ is the diffusion coefficient of $O^{2-}$, $n_i$ is the number of ions per unit volume, $z$ is the valency of an ion, $e$ is the electronic charge, $k$ is the Boltzmann constant, and $T$ is the absolute temperature.

The results obtained, when compared with the results of direct measurements of conductivity, indicated that the entire electrical conductivity could be attributed to the mobility of the oxide ion.

In a solid oxide fuel cell, the diffusion rates of the oxide ions, and hence the ionic conductivity of the electrolyte, should be as high as possible in order to obtain practical current densities. High diffusion rates are favoured by decrease in the thickness of the electrolyte and increase in temperature and concentration gradient. The highest concentration gradient that can be realized will be limited by the concentration of oxygen at the cathode surface and an oxygen concentration of zero at the anode. With the present oxide systems based on zirconia, an operating temperature of about 1000°C and electrolyte thickness of less than 0.625 mm are required to produce practical current densities of greater than 100 mA/sq.cm.

The variation of ionic conductivity with composition, investigated by measuring the a.c. resistance of the electrolyte, is discussed in section 2(c).

*(b) Electronic conductivity in oxide electrolytes*

Conductivity measurements made by many investigators[7,9-12] on calcia-stabilized zirconia all show that the transference number of the oxygen ion in such a system is almost unity; the very small difference can be attributed to electronic conduction by a mechanism involving the formation of excess electrons $\ominus$ and, less probably, by the formation of positive holes $\oplus$.

The concentrations of oxide ion vacancies are fixed by the composition of the oxide system and are independent of the oxygen pressure. Hence the ionic contribution to electrical conductivity will not be pressure-dependent although change in oxygen pressure may affect the electronic contribution.

This dependency of electronic conductivity on oxygen pressure can be shown as follows.

(1) The migration of an oxide ion $(O^{2-})$ from a normal lattice site, liberating oxygen and two electrons and leaving an oxygen ion vacancy $\square$

$$O^{2-} \rightleftharpoons \square + \tfrac{1}{2} O_2(g) + 2\ominus \tag{4}$$

where $\ominus$ is the excess electron available for conduction.

(2) The filling of a normally vacant site to form an oxide ion and two electron holes

$$\tfrac{1}{2} O_2(g) + \square \rightleftharpoons O^{2-} + 2\oplus \tag{5}$$

where $\oplus$ is the electron hole, available for conduction.

The concentrations of the excess electrons or electron holes will depend on oxygen pressure. If the electronic contribution, and hence the concentrations of excess electrons and electron holes, is small we can assume that association or interaction effects will be negligible and the above relations can be represented by mass action equations, *e.g.*

$$K = \frac{[\ominus]^2 [p_{O_2}]^{\frac{1}{2}} [\square]}{[O^{2-}]} \tag{6}$$

where $p_{O_2}$ is the partial pressure of oxygen.

Since $[O^{2-}]$ and $[\square]$ are fixed by the composition of the oxide, then the electron concentration $[\ominus]$ is given by

$$[\ominus] = K_1 [p_{O_2}]^{-\frac{1}{4}} \tag{7}$$

and similarly the concentration of electron holes $[\oplus]$ is given by

$$[\oplus] = K_2[p_{O_2}]^{+\frac{1}{4}}. \tag{8}$$

Even if the concentration of electrons and electron holes is small their mobilities are high and they make a substantial contribution to the conductivity $S$

$$S_{total} = S_{ionic} + F\mu_-\,[\ominus] + F\mu_+\,[\oplus] \tag{9}$$

where $F$ is Faraday's constant and $\mu$ mobilities (sq.cm/sec volt).
$S_{total}$ is then related to the oxygen pressure by

$$S_{total} = S_{ionic} + K_1'[p_{O_2}]^{-\frac{1}{4}} + K_2'[p_{O_2}]^{\frac{1}{4}}. \tag{10}$$

Thus if there is any appreciable electronic contribution, the total conductivity should be pressure-dependent. Kiukkola and Wagner[7] observed such a dependence with certain oxide systems, for example, $ThO_2$–$La_2O_3$ and $ThO_2$–$CaO$, indicating some electronic contribution. Work carried out at temperatures of 1400–1600°C by Kingery and co-workers[9] showed that for [$Zr_{0.85}Ca_{0.15}O_{1.85}$] the total conductivity was independent of oxygen pressure over the range $1$–$10^{-10}$ atmosphere, indicating that the conduction in this case is largely ionic (Fig. 64).

Hund[6], Kiukkola and Wagner[7] studied the variation of conductivity with oxygen pressure at lower temperatures. Their results also showed that there is no appreciable electronic conductivity in the $ZrO_2$–$CaO$ system, the transference number for oxide ions ($t_{O^{2-}}$) approaching unity. Since their methods measured the sum of ionic and electronic components, and the conductivity

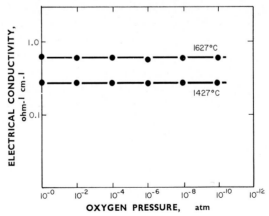

Fig. 64. Electrical conductivity of [$Zr_{0.85}\,Ca_{0.15}\,O_{1.85}$] at different oxygen pressures.

was predominantly ionic, it is possible that a small electronic component would not have been observed. Because of the small value of the transference number of the electron ($t_e$) it is preferable to use direct electrochemical methods for its determination.

To do this we must first consider the ideal process which occurs in an oxygen concentration cell having an oxide electrolyte with the oxide ion transference number equal to unity (Fig. 65).

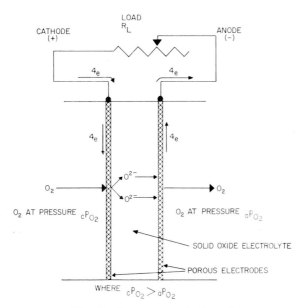

Fig. 65. Oxygen concentration cell.

When the external circuit is closed, oxygen molecules at the higher pressure enter the electrolyte as oxide ions by each picking up four electrons at the cathode. The reverse process can be considered to occur at the anode, oxide ions from the electrolyte losing electrons at the anode and producing oxygen molecules. Each oxygen molecule produces two oxide ions which migrate through the electrolyte and four electrons move simultaneously through the external circuit.

The net result is a transfer of one molecule of oxygen from cathode to anode.

If electronic conduction is present, however, some oxygen transfer will occur even at open circuit and the measured open circuit voltage will be lower than the maximum value calculated from free energy data or that measured in a cell in which $t_e = 0$.

The continuous transfer of oxygen at open circuit from the high pressure to the low pressure compartment can be attributed to a concentration gradient of oxide vacancies and excess electrons set up within the electrolyte and maintained by the pressure differential of oxygen at the electrodes. This transport of oxide ions and electrons through the electrolyte is considered as an internal current flowing through the cell (Fig. 66).

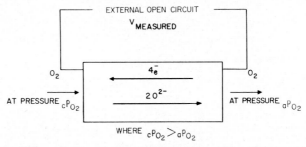

Fig. 66. Internal flow of oxygen ions and electrons in a solid oxide electrolyte for which $t_{O^{2-}} < 1$.

An oxide of total resistance $R$ acts both as the electrolyte with an oxide ion resistance of $R_{O^{2-}}$ and as the external load of electrical resistance $R_e$. This is shown in the equivalent circuit (Fig. 67) for which the following relationships apply:

$$t_e + t_{O^{2-}} = 1$$

$$\frac{R}{t_e} = R_e$$

$$\frac{R}{t_{O^{2-}}} = R_{O^{2-}}.$$

From Fig. (67) it can be seen that the measured cell e.m.f. is related to the theoretical e.m.f. by

$$V_{\text{measured}} = V_{\text{theoretical}} - IR_{O^{2-}}$$

and

$$I = \frac{V_{\text{theoretical}}}{R_{O^{2-}} + R_e}.$$

whence

$$V_{\text{measured}} = V_{\text{theoretical}}\left(1 - \frac{R_{O^{2-}}}{R_{O^{2-}} + R_e}\right).$$

By substituting for $R_e$ and $R_{O^{2-}}$ it follows that

$$V_{\text{measured}} = V_{\text{theoretical}}(1 - t_e). \tag{11}$$

From this equation Weissbart and Ruka[10] determined the average electronic transference number for $[Zr_{0.85} Ca_{0.15} O_{1.85}]$ by measuring the open circuit potentials near 1000°C of the oxygen concentration cell designated by

$$O_2/Pt//Zr_{0.85} Ca_{0.15} O_{1.85}//Pt/O_2$$
at pressure ${}_cp_{O_2}$                 at pressure ${}_ap_{O_2}$

where ${}_ap_{O_2}$ and ${}_cp_{O_2}$ are the pressure of oxygen at the anode and cathode respectively.

The e.m.f. of this system was measured at two different oxygen pressures in the anode compartment; the oxygen pressure in the cathode compartment was maintained at 1 atmosphere. By comparing the measured potentials with the theoretical potential defined by the Nernst equation

$$V_{\text{theoretical}} = \frac{RT}{4F} \ln \frac{{}_ap_{O_2}}{{}_cp_{O_2}} \tag{12}$$

they were able to show $t_e$ had the values 0.002 and 0.006 when ${}_ap_{O_2}$ equalled $2 \times 10^{-1}$ and $10^{-17}$ atmosphere respectively.

A second method used by Weissbart and Ruka[10] to determine $t_e$ was to

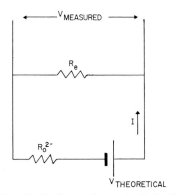

Fig. 67. Equivalent internal cell circuit.

measure the rate of transfer of oxygen ions through the electrolyte at open circuit for two sets of constant oxygen pressures at anode and cathode.

Since $t_e \ll t_{O^{2-}}$ and therefore $V_{\text{theoretical}} \simeq V_{\text{measured}}$ it is possible to write

$$t_e \simeq 4F \left[ \frac{dn_{O_2}}{dt} \right] \frac{R}{V_{\text{measured}}} \tag{13}$$

where $F$ is the Faraday number, $R$ is the resistance of the electrolyte in ohms ($\simeq R_{\text{cell}}$) and $dn_{O_2}/dt$ is the number of moles of oxygen transferred per second and is a constant at constant open circuit potential $V_{\text{measured}}$.

The results obtained were not as accurate as those from the first method but indicate that $t_e$, for [$Zr_{0.85} Ca_{0.15} O_{1.85}$], is 0.02 at temperatures near 1000°C. Additional evidence as to the smallness of $t_e$ has been based on the stability of the same electrolyte system to long periods of electrolysis at high temperatures. Weissbart and Ruka[10] electrolysed a pellet of the stabilized zirconia for 1875 hour at 21 mA/sq.cm near 1100°C and observed little change in resistance or damage to electrode contacts. Pal'quev et al.[11,12] have recently used the cell e.m.f. method to study several solid oxide electrolytes. They also found there was no significant electronic contribution in the [$Zr_{0.85} Ca_{0.15} O_{1.85}$] electrolyte system, but oxide mixtures containing ceria ($CeO_2$) or thoria ($ThO_2$) showed appreciable electronic conductivity.

### (c) Variation of resistivity with oxide composition

Until quite recently little information was available regarding the resistivity of zirconia–metal oxide systems. Various investigators[9,13,14] had determined resistivities of zirconia–calcia solid solutions (mainly the system [$(ZrO_2)_{0.85}$ $(CaO)_{0.15}$]) at high temperatures. Noddack et al.[15] had obtained results for a series of zirconia–yttria solutions.

More recently, Dixon and co-workers[16] have investigated zirconia– calcia and zirconia–yttria systems in the range of compositions with the lowest resistivities; they also examined solid solutions of zirconia with $Nd_2O_3$, $Yb_2O_3$ and $Sc_2O_3$. Determination of resistivity was carried out by using a four probe technique. Four platinum leads, spaced at definite intervals along the sample, formed the pressure contacts, the outer pair of leads being used to supply current while the centre pair served as reference electrode. Comparison of the voltage drop across the sample with the voltage drop across a known resistor measured by an oscilloscope enabled resistivities to be calculated. With a.c. current, resistivity was found to be reasonably independent of frequency over the range 1–1000 c/s. Samples were prepared by convention-al pressing and sintering methods. The results obtained by Dixon and others can be summarized as follows.

*Zirconia–calcia solutions*

Resistivities of these solutions at 1000°C, plotted against mole % CaO are shown in Fig. 68. The minimum resistivity occurs at about 12–13 mole % CaO which is about the lower limit of CaO concentration for the cubic phase

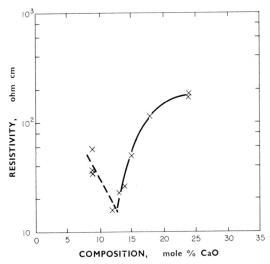

Fig. 68. Resistivities of zirconia–calcia solutions at 1000°C.

stabilization of zirconia. Other workers[14,17] also find a resistivity minimum near this composition. Figure 69 shows the temperature dependency of the resistivity of various zirconia–calcia solutions. Solid solutions with 18 and 24 mole % calcia exhibit deviations from an exponential relationship and this deviation is attributed by Dixon to some disordering of the cubic solid solutions at the lower temperatures.

Carter and Roth[18] of the General Electric Research Laboratories have published a recent paper on ionic conductivity and vacancy ordering in calcia-stabilized zirconia in which they showed that the resistivity of a single oxide crystal increased with time if the crystal were maintained below a specific temperature that depended on the composition. All solid solutions with compositions between 10 and 20 mole % calcia showed this dependence of conductivity with time. Carter and Roth found that for 13 mole % CaO in $ZrO_2$ the transition temperature was 1150°C; for 19 mole % CaO, the transition temperature was about 1280°C. Above these transition temperatures the conductivity was independent of time, below them the resistivities increased linearly with $(time)^{\frac{1}{2}}$. Annealing at temperatures above the transition temperature would restore the conductivity to its original value.

Conductivity measurements on polycrystalline specimens also showed a time-dependency although the rate of ageing was slower than for a single crystal.

Results obtained from neutron diffraction analysis of aged specimens indicated the presence of more than one phase in specimens containing more than 16 mole % CaO. Carter and Roth considered that ordered zones, with

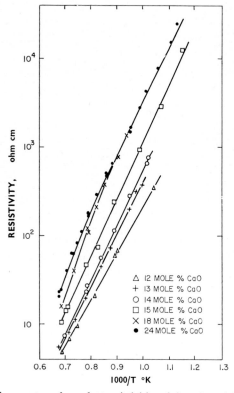

Fig. 69. Temperature-dependent resistivities of zirconia–calcia solutions.

a structure intermediate between calcia-stabilized zirconia and calcium zirconate, partially control the electrical conductivity of the stabilized zirconia. Alteration of the zonal structure, either by increasing the CaO content or by annealing, thus appears to control the conductivity.

In recent measurements by Johansen and Cleary[19] of the a.c. electrical conductivities of the mixed oxide system $CaO-ZrO_2$ and the analogous system $CaO-HfO_2$ in the temperature range 800–1000°C, both systems exhibited conductivity maxima at about 12 mole % calcia.

*Zirconia–yttria solutions*

Figure 70 shows the variation of resistivity with composition of zirconia–yttria solutions at 1000°C. The minimum resistance occurs at about 8–9 mole % yttria, which, as in the calcia system, coincides with the lower limit for stabilization of the cubic zirconia phase. In the temperature range 800–1000°C, zirconia stabilized with this amount of yttria has a conductivity of up to five times that of zirconia stabilized with 12 mole % of calcia. The use of yttria-stabilized zirconia as a fuel cell electrolyte would therefore result

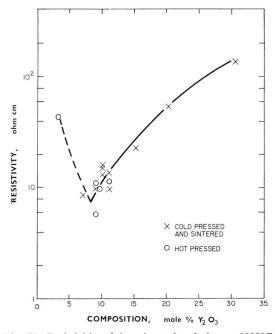

Fig. 70. Resistivities of zirconia–yttria solutions at 1000°C.

in much higher current densities than previously obtained with calcia. In Fig. 71 the temperature resistivity characteristics for several zirconia–yttria samples are presented. At yttria contents of less than 9 mole % deviations from the simple exponential relationship occur at temperatures below 800°C and these are also attributed to some disordering of the cubic solid solutions.

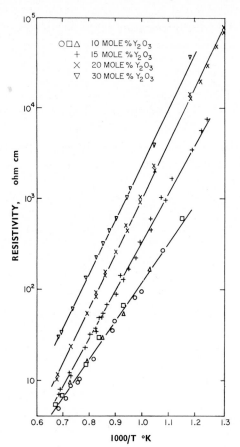

Fig. 71. Temperature-dependent resistivities of cold-pressed, sintered zirconia–yttria solutions.

*Zirconia stabilized with other oxides*

Dixon and co-workers have carried out resistivity measurements on other mixed oxide systems. Figure 72 shows the results obtained from mixtures of $ZrO_2$ with 15 mole % of $Sc_2O_3$ and $Yb_2O_3$ with the results from 15 mole

% $Y_2O_3$ in $ZrO_2$ included for comparison. The existence of tetragonal as well as a cubic phase in the system is said to account for the marked deviations from exponential behaviour. Measurements were also made on mixtures of $ZrO_2$ with 10 mole % of $Nd_2O_3$, $Sc_2O_3$ and $Yb_2O_3$. For a given molar concentration the resistivities are in the order $Nd > Y \geqslant Yb > Sc$

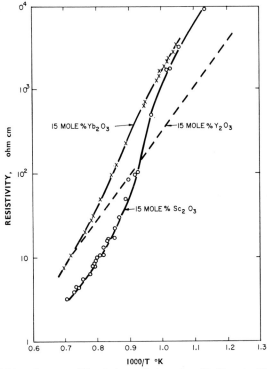

Fig. 72. Resistivities of some solid solutions of zirconia with 15 mole % of other oxides.

when determined at the higher temperatures at which only cubic and tetragonal phases are likely to exist.

Within the range of mixed oxide systems considered in this chapter two important features affecting the resistivity of the zirconia system are revealed.

(1) Solid solutions of zirconia with other oxides have their lowest resistivities when the amount of added oxide is just sufficient to stabilize the zirconia in the cubic form.

(2) The smaller the atomic radius of the metal ion of the added oxide, the lower the resistivity of the stabilized solid solution.

References pp. 212–213

Although, from the work of Carter and Roth[18] the conductivity and structure of these stabilized solutions are more complex than previously assumed, solid oxide fuel cells have been operated continuously for upwards of 1000 hours without an appreciable drop in output.

### 3. THERMODYNAMICS OF A SOLID OXIDE CELL

The oxide ceramic fuel cell can be considered as an oxygen concentration cell, shown schematically in Fig. 65 and represented by

$$+ \ O_2 \ {}^{cathode}_{cp_{O_2}} \Big/ Pt//oxide \ electrolyte//Pt. \Big/ O_2 \ {}^{anode}_{ap_{O_2}} \ - \qquad \text{(Cell A)}$$

for which the reactions are

$$\text{cathodic reaction:} \ O_2 + 4\,e \rightleftharpoons 2\,O^{2-} \qquad (14)$$

$$\text{anodic reaction:} \quad 2\,O^{2-} \rightleftharpoons O_2 + 4\,e \qquad (15)$$

$$\text{cell reaction:} \quad O_2 \ \text{at pressure} \ {}_c p_{O_2} \to O_2 \ \text{at pressure} \ {}_a p_{O_2} \qquad (16)$$

where $_c p_{O_2} > {}_a p_{O_2}$.

The maximum electrical energy, $4FV$, for the spontaneous transfer of one mole of oxygen from the cathode compartment at pressure $_c p_{O_2}$ to the anode compartment at pressure $_a p_{O_2}$ is given by

$$4FV = -\Delta G_1 = T\Delta S_1 = RT \ \ln \frac{{}_c p_{O_2}}{{}_a p_{O_2}} \qquad (17)$$

where $\Delta G_1$ is the free energy change and $\Delta S_1$ the entropy change for the isothermal expansion of oxygen for the process defined by eqn. (16) at temperature $T(°K)$. Since this process is endothermic the heat adsorbed at $T$ is $T\Delta S_1$.

If a fuel such as carbon monoxide is fed into the anode compartment, the cell may now be represented by

$$O_2 \ \text{at pressure} \ {}_c p_{O_2}/Pt//oxide \ electrolyte//Pt/CO-CO_2 \qquad \text{(Cell B)}$$

where $CO-CO_2$, the equilibrium gas mixture, is equivalent to the low oxygen pressure $_a p_{O_2}$ in the previous case.

Since the overall cell reaction is

$$2\,CO + O_2 \to 2\,CO_2 \qquad (18)$$

(which represents the transfer of one mole of oxygen from the cathode at pressure $_cp_{O_2}$ to the anode at pressure $_ap_{O_2}$) the partial pressures of carbon monoxide and carbon dioxide are related to an oxygen pressure under equilibrium conditions by the relation

$$\frac{p_{CO_2}}{p_{CO}} = k\,[p_{O_2}]^{\frac{1}{4}} \tag{19}$$

where $k$ is the equilibrium constant for the reaction and $p$ is in atmospheres.

The reaction represented by eqn. (18) can be considered to occur in two stages.

(1) The transfer of one mole of oxygen from cathode to anode compartment as given by eqn. (16), the heat absorbed in this process at $T°K$ being given by $q_1 = T\Delta S_1$.

(2) The chemical reaction of oxygen at the anode with the fuel, the heat evolved being given by $q_2 = \Delta H_2$, where $\Delta H_2$ (the heat of reaction) is negative for this exothermic process.

The net heat evolved or absorbed in the complete process is given by

$$q_{(net)} = T\Delta S_2 = q_2 + q_1 = \Delta H_2 - \Delta G_1$$

where $\Delta S_2$ is the entropy change for the complete process.

If the partial pressures of oxygen are the same for the oxygen concentration cell A and for the fuel cell B then $\Delta G_1 = \Delta G_2$ and

$$T\Delta S_2 = \Delta H_2 - \Delta G_2 . \tag{20}$$

If it is assumed that there is no electronic conductivity in the oxide electrolyte, the maximum electrical energy from the cell reaction is given by

$$-4FV = \Delta G_2 = \Delta H_2 - T\Delta S_2 . \tag{21}$$

The e.m.f. of the fuel cell can also be expressed by

$$V = V_0 + \frac{RT}{4F} \ln \frac{[_ap_{CO}]^2 [_cp_{O_2}]}{[_ap_{CO_2}]^2}$$

$$= V_0 + \frac{RT}{4F} \ln {_cp_{O_2}} + \frac{RT}{2F} \ln \frac{_ap_{CO}}{_ap_{CO_2}} \tag{22}$$

where $V_0$ is the standard cell potential for the system, $_cp_{O_2}$ is the partial pressure of oxygen in the cathode compartment, $_ap_{CO}$ is the partial pressure of carbon monoxide in the anode compartment, and $_ap_{CO_2}$ is the partial pressure of carbon dioxide in the anode compartment.

Weissbart and Ruka[20] have studied the system

$$O_2/Pt//(ZrO_2)_{0.85}\ (CaO)_{0.15}//Pt/H_2/H_2O$$

in which the theoretical e.m.f. is given by the standard relation

$$V = V_0 + \frac{RT}{4F} \ln [_c p_{O_2}] + \frac{RT}{2F} \ln \frac{[_a p_{H_2}]}{[_a p_{H_2O}]} \ . \tag{23}$$

They have calculated theoretical values of $V$ from this relation over a wide range of $H_2/(H_2 + H_2O)$ ratios, shown by the curve in Fig. 73. Experimentally

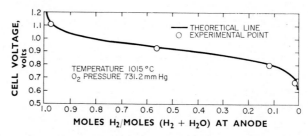

Fig. 73. Comparison of measured voltage with theoretical e.m.f. of the cell, $O_2/Pt//$ $(ZrO_2)_{0.85}(CaO)_{0.15}//Pt/H_2, H_2O$.

determined points, based on the measured e.m.f.'s and the analytically determined $H_2/(H_2 + H_2O)$ mole ratios agreed to within about 5 millivolts with the theoretical values. The maximum open circuit potentials obtained at the high temperature of operation $(900–1000°C)$ for the mole ratio $H_2/(H_2 + H_2O)$ $\sim 1$ were of the order of 1.2 volts. Most investigators have quoted values approaching this figure when using hydrogen but open circuit voltages of slightly less than 1 volt are obtained with hydrocarbon fuels.

The electrode reactions of a high temperature fuel cell with solid oxide electrolyte are much simpler than those of low temperature cells. The simple thermodynamic treatment of the open circuit potentials given in the previous sections was based on the concept of oxygen concentration cells. However, the anode reactions can occur in one of two ways[21], either (i) $O^{2-}$ forming $\frac{1}{2}O_2$ at the electrode surface and the latter then reacting with the fuel or, the more probable reaction (ii) $O^{2-}$ reacting directly with the fuel at the electrode/electrolyte interface. As Liebhafsky and Cairns have pointed out[22], under useful operating conditions a fuel cell is working irreversibly and the equilibrium, fuel $+ n\,O_2 \rightleftharpoons$ oxidized fuel, is not established.

They, therefore, consider that under such conditions the anode reaction should be written

$$\text{fuel} + n\, O^{2-} \rightarrow \text{oxidized fuel} + 2\, ne. \tag{24}$$

With either mechanism, if a high current density is required, the oxidation of the fuel must take place on the electrode surface since the effective oxygen pressure at the anode/electrolyte interface is so low that any reaction involving transport of oxygen from the surface would severely limit the current.

No significant catalysis problems should be encountered at the fuel electrode since the operating temperatures are so high. Similarly, the catalysis of the cathode reaction is easy, the reaction

$$\tfrac{1}{2} O_2 + 2\, e \rightleftharpoons O^{2-} \tag{25}$$

being quite straightforward with no intermediate peroxide formation.

### 4. PRACTICAL FUEL CELLS WITH SOLID OXIDE ELECTROLYTES

As discussed in Chapter 3, when current is drawn from a fuel cell the voltage will be lower than the open circuit potential owing to three main polarization effects, the magnitudes of which depend on the current density. These effects are (i) *activation polarization*, which is dependent on the rate-determining chemical or electrochemical reaction occurring at the electrodes; (ii) *concentration polarization*, which involves mass transfer of reactants and products to and away from the electrodes; (iii) *ohmic polarization* which is dependent mainly on the electrical resistivity of the electrolyte and, to a lesser extent, on the contact resistances of the electrodes. While activation polarization is often encountered with cells operating at low temperatures the increased temperature eliminates it to a very great extent in fuel cells with solid oxide electrolytes. Concentration polarization is a function of the supply of fuel and oxidant and is usually negligible in a high temperature cell. Current–voltage data of many investigators have shown that the output of a high temperature solid oxide fuel cell is essentially limited by the resistance of the electrolyte. The relationship between current and voltage is substantially linear so that the equation

$$V_{\text{measured}} = V_{\text{open circuit}} - IR \tag{26}$$

applies; in order to obtain higher current densities the thickness of the electrolyte must be decreased.

*(a) Methods of producing thin oxide films*

The early efforts to produce practical solid oxide fuel cells were hindered by the use of excessively thick electrolytes. This resulted in poor current voltage characteristics under load owing to the relatively high resistance across the electrolyte. Various methods have been evolved for the production of thin films of electrolyte to obtain significantly high current densities without resorting to excessively high cell operating temperatures. The main problem is to produce a thin oxide film which is impermeable to fuel and oxidant gases at these temperatures.

Thin oxide wafers have been prepared by conventional slip-casting, pressing and sintering at high temperatures, sometimes followed by grinding and polishing to a predetermined thickness. Weissbart and Ruka[20] have used discs about 0.15 cm thick; investigators at Westinghouse Research Laboratories, Pittsburg, Pennsylvania[23] have used slip-cast tubes with a wall thickness of 0.04 cm. Unfortunately, although relatively non-porous, these forms of electrolyte are very fragile.

Electron beam vaporization can be used to produce ultra-thin (about 0.001 mm) coatings of stabilized zirconia on porous sintered-metal electrodes. The technique involves impingement of a high energy electron beam onto the oxide target which vaporizes and condenses on the cool metal specimen. There is evidence[24] that these films are porous and not sufficiently adherent to the metal substrate.

A method has been devised by the Armour Research Foundation, Chicago, Illinois[25], for producing ceramic coatings. This involves spraying an aqueous solution of zirconium or other salts, which are easily decomposed by heat, onto the heated metal substrate. These coatings, although very adherent, are porous to gases.

Armour Research Foundation have also produced thin fuel cell electrolyte wafers of from 0.10 to 0.25 mm thickness by a flame-spraying technique. Calcia-stabilized zirconia powder is entrained in the flame of an oxy–hydrogen torch and the semimolten oxide particles are impinged on a metal substrate. If the substrate is first coated with a soluble salt the oxide wafer can be removed by dissolving the salt with water. The wafers can be made more dense by impregnation with a zirconium salt, such as zirconium acetate, followed by firing[26]. Whether this results in useful fuel cells has not been disclosed.

*(b)  Methods of attachment of electrodes*

For the successful practical operation of any fuel cell, electrode contact resistances as well as electrolyte resistance must be kept as small as possible. The electrode material for high temperature oxide fuel cells must be porous to the fuel and oxidant gases used and must also be chemically and physically stable under the operating conditions existing within the cell.

Methods of forming electrodes on the electrolyte are similar to those used in fused carbonate systems (Chapter 7). Materials such as silverized zinc oxide can be applied by flame-spraying to give a highly conducting electrode with a large surface area. Some metals, including silver, can be evaporated from a tungsten or molybdenum heater under high vacuum and allowed to condense onto the oxide specimen. Higher melting metals, such as platinum or palladium, can be applied more easily by the electron beam technique mentioned in the previous section.

Coatings of many electrode materials, silver, gold, platinum, etc., can be applied to the electrolyte as a dispersion in an organic binder that is easily decomposed on heating to leave a porous highly conducting metal film. Carbon has also been investigated as an electrode material; in the new General Electric fuel cell the natural gas used as fuel breaks down into carbon and hydrogen, the carbon building up inside the cell to form the fuel electrode[27].

*(c)  Cell assemblies*

At the present time there are two main types of cell assemblies under investigation by research workers; they will be discussed in greater detail at the end of this chapter. Broadly speaking, these cell assemblies comprise an oxide ceramic formed into either thin flat discs or thin-walled tubing, with porous metal electrodes applied by one of the conventional techniques. Scaling up from experimental laboratory cells to practical multicell units raises the same problems as for any fuel cell battery, namely, those of gas distribution and current pick-up through the cells. Gas flow in either series or parallel can be used, the former being preferred for the economic ultilization of the fuel. (Recycling of incompletely spent fuel exhaust gases can be employed for further economy.) Similarly, for electrical connection of individual cell units, series or parallel systems can be used, dependent on whether the production of high voltage or high current is envisaged.

Constructional materials for high temperature fuel cells are naturally limited, high grade stainless steel, Vycor and refractory oxides, such as alumina, being most commonly used.

### (d) Examples of practical fuel cells

Weissbart and Ruka[20] have constructed a high temperature solid oxide fuel cell, shown diagrammatically in Fig. 74. The flat bottom portion of a tube made from the mixed oxide $[(ZrO_2)_{0.85} (CaO)_{0.15}]$ acted as the electrolyte,

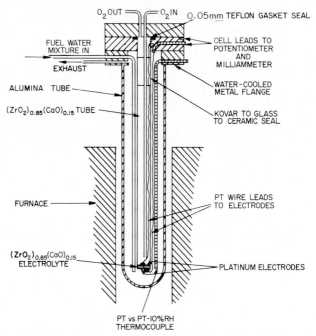

Fig. 74. Schematic diagram of galvanic cell with solid oxide electrolyte.

each face of which carried a porous platinum electrode of less than 0.025 mm in thickness. The cell element itself had an effective area of 2.5 sq.cm and a thickness of 0.15 cm.

Oxygen at atmospheric pressure was fed down through the ceramic tube and allowed to flow slowly past the cathode. Various fuel mixtures were passed through the anode compartment. Owing to the design of the cell an

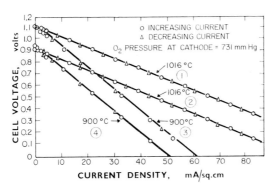

Fig. 75. Current–voltage behaviour of the cell, $O_2/Pt//(ZrO_2)_{0.85}(CaO)_{0.15}//Pt/H_2$, $H_2O$ at two temperatures and two $H_2/(H_2 + H_2O)$ ratios. $H_2/(H_2 + H_2O) = 0.97$ for curves 1 and 3; $H_2/(H_2 + H_2O) = 0.54$ for curves 2 and 4.

appreciable amount of the fuel mixture flowing through the anode compartment did not come in contact with the fuel electrode, and therefore, high rates of fuel flow were required to reduce any concentration polarization effects. The fuel gases were passed through water bubblers prior to entering the cell feed line; after reacting in the cell the exhaust gases from the anode compartment were analysed for both unchanged fuel and oxidation products to enable calculation of the ratio of fuel/products to be made. Figure 75 shows the current/voltage curves for this cell with hydrogen as fuel, at two temperatures and two $H_2/(H_2 + H_2O)$ ratios and constant oxygen pressure.

The straight-line relationship between current and voltage shows that the output of the cell was limited by ohmic polarization only, since any activation

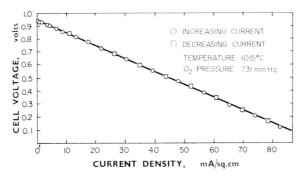

Fig. 76. Current–voltage behaviour of the cell, $O_2/Pt//(ZrO_2)_{0.85}(CaO)_{0.15}//Pt/CH_4,H_2O$. Composition of inlet fuel gas: $CH_4$, 3.8% vol.; $H_2O$, 2.1% vol.; $N_2$, 94.1% vol.

*References pp. 212–213*

or concentration effect would have resulted in some departure from linearity. Weissbart and Ruka found that although the cell resistance stayed almost constant during measurements of individual output curves, larger variations in resistance occurred over longer periods of time and were independent of the current drawn from the cell. Open circuit potentials were reproducible; the effect of lowering the $H_2/(H_2 + H_2O)$ ratio was to reduce these potentials to values consistent with those calculated from eqn. (23). Using dilute natural gas mixtures (*e.g.* 3.8 % vol. $CH_4$; 2.1 % vol. $H_2O$; 94.1 % vol. $N_2$) at such a flow rate that only 20 % of the methane reacted, Weissbart and Ruka obtained the results shown graphically in Fig. 76. The open circuit potentials obtained were those to be expected if hydrogen and carbon monoxide were the principal reactants at the anode, being produced from the water shift reaction:

$$CH_4 + H_2O \rightarrow CO + 3 H_2 . \qquad (27)$$

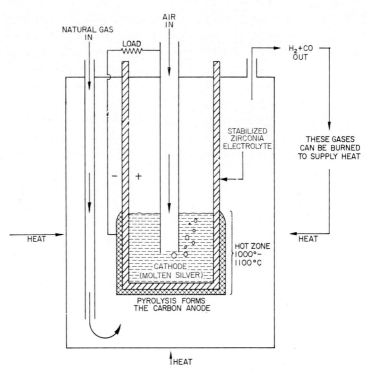

Fig. 77. General Electric high temperature fuel cell.

Although no carbon deposition was reported when such dilute mixtures were used, at lower flow rates and higher $CH_4/H_2O$ ratios carbon formation sometimes occurred.

This type of cell has been operated continuously at a current density of 10mA/sq.cm for two months at 1000–1200°C with 30 : 1 hydrogen–water mixtures as fuel.

Carter and co-workers[27] of General Electric Research Laboratory, Schenectady, New York, have developed a fuel cell operating at about 1100°C, in which natural gas breaks down in the anode compartment to carbon and hydrogen. The carbon builds up on the tubular zirconia electrolyte to provide the anode. Air or oxygen is bubbled through a pool of molten silver which forms the cathode of the cell, a schematic drawing of which is given in Fig. 77.

The cell may be heated initially by burning methane; the exhaust gases from the cell, which contain carbon monoxide and hydrogen, can be used to supply heat for a self-sustaining system.

Several of these cells have been stacked together in the form of a fuel battery but no details of output have been revealed. For laboratory versions of cells maintained at 1100°C in a furnace the following data have been given: with methane and oxygen, current densities of up to 150 amp/sq.ft. at 0.7 volt are generated. This type of cell on life test at lower current densities has been operated for up to 3000 hours with no deterioration of the electrolyte.

The Westinghouse Research Laboratories are carrying out intensive investigations of zirconia-type solid oxide cells, including studies of the physical shape of the electrolyte, methods of application of electrodes and methods of sealing[23,28]. Two electrolytes $[(ZrO_2)_{0.85} (CaO)_{0.15}]$ and $[(ZrO_2)_{0.9}(Y_2O_3)_{0.1}]$ have been tested, fabricated into either flat discs or segmented tubes. Both single and multi-cell packs have been tested over long operating periods, usually with hydrogen as fuel. Typical outputs obtained with flat disc calcia- and yttria-stabilized zirconia electrolytes are shown in Fig. 78. One single stage flat disc fuel cell is reported to have given 75 mA/sq. cm for over 1000 hours. Electrode materials tested have included both evaporated and painted films of porous platinum. Evaporated nickel films have been tried as fuel electrodes.

With sufficiently porous electrodes no activation or concentration polarization effects were observed over the temperature range 810–1094°C. Resistance changes, however, did occur when cells were operated for a long time and were partly attributed to the loss of platinum from the electrodes.

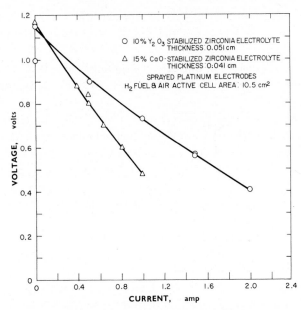

Fig. 78. Current/voltage curves of calcia and yttria stabilized zirconia electrolytes.

This loss, caused by the slow formation of volatile oxides of platinum after long exposure to air or oxygen at these temperatures, can be effectively reduced by the use of certain alloys of platinum[29].

Segmented tubes of tapered and "bell-and-spigot" design have been fabricated and tested in series connection. Construction of a multi-cell-unit with bell-and-spigot components fabricated from $(ZrO_2)_{0.9}$ $(Y_2O_3)_{0.1}$ is shown in Fig. 79. The electrodes consisted of porous coatings of platinum (0.04 mm) applied to the inside and outside surfaces of the segments. Individual segments were joined together to form tubular batteries by a metal brazing technique. This involved further coatings, by electrodeposition, of platinum (0.08 mm) and gold (0.18 mm) onto the seal areas after which an 18% nickel, 82% gold brazing alloy shim was placed between the jointing faces. Heating to 1125°C for about 20 min in a hydrogen atmosphere resulted in a highly conducting, gas-tight seal. Joining the outer electrode of one segment to the inner electrode of the next segment by this method was used to connect a number of cells in a tubular battery in series[30].

Fuel was fed through an alumina tube placed along the axis of each battery so that fresh fuel gas was introduced just under the top cap of the battery.

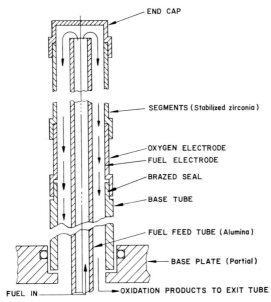

Fig. 79. Stacked tube fuel cell assembly.

Fuel gas and oxidation products flowed downward in the annular space between the alumina feed tube and the fuel electrodes. Oxygen or air, as oxidant, was allowed to flow around the exterior of the battery.

The output from a three-element tube stack in which the maximum power of 2.1 watts at 1.4 volts was attained is shown in Fig. 80. Power/current density optimization studies for the fabrication of cell segments indicated a critical diameter of 1.05 cm and length of electrode portion of the cell of 0.6 cm. Operating temperatures of these cells are between 950°C and 1100°C.

It has recently been reported that Westinghouse Research Laboratories have produced a 20-element stabilized-zirconia fuel cell giving an output of 10 watts at 10 volts using hydrogen fuel and air. A multicell pack capable of generating 100 watts is also reported as being under construction[31].

From the reported results of many investigators it is apparent that the high temperature solid oxide system is not yet ready for the extensive engineering development that is required for the construction of a stable fuel cell battery. Much research is still required into the efficient utilization of fuel, preparation of electrodes stable at temperatures greater than 1000°C and further investigation into invariant oxide systems.

*References pp. 212–213*

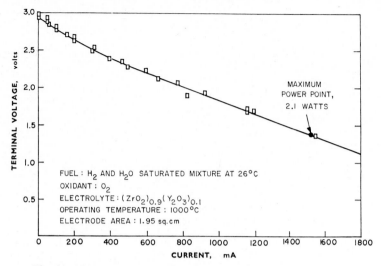

Fig. 80. Measured performance of three-cell bell-and-spigot battery.

## REFERENCES

1 W. NERNST, Z. Elektrochem., 6 (1899) 41.
2 E. BAUR AND H. PREIS, Z. Elektrochem., 43 (1937) 727.
3 O. RUFF AND F. EBERT, Z. Anorg. Chem., 180 (1929) 19.
4 E. RYSHKEWITCH, Oxide Ceramics, Academic Press, New York, 1960, p. 353.
5 C. WAGNER, Naturwissenschaften, 31 (1943) 265.
6 F. HUND, Z. Phys. Chem., 199 (1952) 142.
7 K. KIUKKOLA AND C. WAGNER, J. Electrochem. Soc., 104 (1957) 379.
8 Z. S. VOLCHENKOVA AND S. F. PAL'QUEV, Trans. Inst. Electrochem. (English Transl.),
   1 (1961) 97.
9 W. D. KINGERY, J. PAPPIS, M. E. DOTY AND D. C. HILL, J. Am. Ceram. Soc., 42 (1959)
   393.
10 J. WEISSBART AND R. RUKA, Extended Abstr. 120th Meeting Electrochem. Soc., Detroit,
   Oct. 1961, Battery Div., p. 112.
11 S. F. PAL'QUEV AND A. D. NEUIMIN, Trans. Inst. Electrochem. (English Transl.), 1 (1961)
   90.
12 S. F. PAL'QUEV, S. V. KARPACHEV, A. D. NEUIMIN AND Z. S. VOLCHENKOVA, Doklady
   Akad. Nauk. S.S.S.R., 134 (1960) 1138.
13 F. HUND, Z. Elektrochem., 55 (1951) 363.
14 F. TROMBE AND M. FOEX, Compt. Rend., 236 (1953) 1783.
15 W. NODDACK, H. WALCH AND W. DOBNER, Z. Phys. Chem., 211 (1959) 180.
16 J. M. DIXON, L. D. LAGRANGE, U. MERTEN, C. F. MILLER AND J. T. PORTER, J. Electrochem. Soc., 110 (1963) 276.
17 F. ODELL AND F. H. BROWN JR., J. Am. Ceram. Soc., 35 (1952) 107.
18 R. E. CARTER AND W. L. ROTH, General Electric Tech. Rept. 63-RL-3479M, 1963.
19 H. A. JOHANSEN AND J. G. CLEARY, J. Electrochem. Soc., 111 (1964) 100.

20  J. Weissbart and R. Ruka, *J. Electrochem. Soc.*, **109** (1962) 723.
21  J. Weissbart and R. Ruka, Chap. 4 in *Fuel Cells*, (ed. by G. J. Young), Vol. 2, Reinhold, New York, 1963, p. 45.
22  H. A. Liebhafsky and E. J. Cairns, *General Electric Tech. Rept. 63-RL-3480C*, 1963.
23  D. H. Archer, *Westinghouse Res. Lab., 2nd Quart. Tech. Progr. Rept. A. D. 283434*, 1962.
24  E. B. Schultz, K. S. Vorres, L. G. Marianowski and H. R. Linden, Chap. 3 in *Fuel Cells*, (ed. by G. J. Young), Vol. 2, Reinhold, New York, 1963, p. 34.
25  J. W. Bradstreet and J. S. Griffith, *The Frontier*, **17** (1954) 24.
26  J. L. Blitan, H. L. Rechter and Y. Harada, *Ceram. Bull.*, **42** (1963) 6.
27  R. E. Carter, W. E. Rocco, H. S. Spacil and W. E. Tragert, General Electric Res. Lab. Press Release, December 26th, 1962.
28  D. H. Archer, *Westinghouse Res. Lab., 3rd Quart. Tech. Progr. Rept. A.D. 291882*, 1962.
29  A. S. Darling, Gold–platinum alloys, *Platinum Metals Rev.*, **6** (1962) 106; *ibid.*, **8** (1964) 134.
30  D. H. Archer, E. F. Sverdrup, W. A. English and W. G. Carlson, *Wright-Patterson Rept. No. ASD-TDR-63-448*, 1963.
31  D. H. Archer, R. L. Zahradnik, E. F. Sverdrup, W. A. English, L. Elikan and J. J. Alles, *Proc. Ann. Power Sources Conf.*, **18** (1964) 36.

*Chapter 9*

# HYDROCARBON FUELS

In order to compete with conventional power sources a practical fuel cell system must be able to utilize readily available, inexpensive fuels. Although, in many laboratories, experimental cells have been operated successfully on hydrogen and hydrazine, they are not commercially attractive because of the high cost of their fuel. As pointed out in earlier chapters, it should be possible to obtain very high efficiencies from an electrochemical fuel cell, and therefore the development of systems operating on low cost hydrocarbon fuels would be of great economic importance. In the United States vast quantities of methane, in the form of natural gas, are available as a potential fuel; higher homologues, such as propane produced as a by-product of the petroleum refining industry, could also be utilized.

Whilst no actual commercial fuel cell using a hydrocarbon fuel has yet been developed, many laboratories are investigating various fuel cell systems which may be capable of effectively utilizing simple saturated and unsaturated hydrocarbons.

## 1. HISTORICAL BACKGROUND

Practical evidence of the activity of a carbonaceous fuel was reported in 1937 by Baur and co-workers[1,2] when they obtained small but significant outputs at temperatures above 1000°C from the first real solid oxide cell, with coke as fuel. A crucible of yttria-stabilized zirconia was used as the solid oxide electrolyte. Following the work of Davtyan[3], various investigators have utilized hydrocarbons as fuel for cells with molten carbonate electrolyte; Chambers and Tantram[4] and Broers and Schenke[5] have reported electrochemical oxidation of methane and kerosine. Using a fuel cell containing an alkaline electrolyte, Justi and co-workers[6] obtained small currents with diesel oil as the fuel. Other workers, including Schlatter[7,8] have reported electrochemical reactivity with alcohols and some hydrocarbons. Heath and Worsham[9], of the Esso Research and Engineering Company, have obtained significant outputs from ethane in a cell using aqueous potassium hydroxide as electrolyte at 200°C and 28 atmospheres pressure.

Binder and co-workers of the Battelle Institute, Frankfurt[10] have operated a solid oxide fuel cell using carbon monoxide, propane and hexane as fuels. Weissbart and Ruka[11] obtained reasonable current densities from a solid oxide cell using lean methane–steam mixtures. Niedrach[12] has recently reported on the performance of hydrocarbons in ion exchange membrane fuel cells. Although much less than with hydrogen, some electrical current could be produced from fuels such as ethylene and propane.

General Electric Research Laboratory of Schenectady, New York[13] has developed a solid oxide cell operating at atmospheric pressure and at a temperature of 1100°C. Natural gas is used as the fuel; the carbon produced by thermal cracking deposits on the electrolyte to form a consumable anode. In 1963 the same laboratory announced the discovery of their acid electrolyte cell[14] which can utilize a broad range of hydrocarbon fuels at normal pressures and in the temperature range 120–200°C.

## 2. ELECTROCHEMICAL OXIDATION OF HYDROCARBONS AT HIGH TEMPERATURES

In order to achieve reactivity of hydrocarbon fuels most investigators are obliged to operate their fuel cells at high temperatures. Molten carbonate cells, for example, are run at temperatures of 500°C to 650°C; solid oxide cells operate at temperatures in excess of 1000°C, these elevated temperatures being required to give acceptable oxide-ion conductivity. Unfortunately, thermal cracking readily occurs at these temperatures, more complex hydrocarbons degrading to lower members and finally to carbon. Hydrogen released by the cracking process is utilized as fuel but the carbon produced may be deposited in the fuel lines and anode compartment of the cell. Examples of hydrocarbons used in high temperature fuel cells include methane, propane, hexane, kerosine, petroleum spirit and light diesel fuel oil.

For maximum efficiency the reaction of a hydrocarbon in the fuel cell should be complete, the only products being carbon dioxide and water. If blocking of the electrode by carbon deposition is to be avoided, the hydrocarbon must be electrochemically oxidized, rather than undergo thermal cracking to give carbon and hydrogen, of which only the hydrogen is subsequently oxidized. Simple fuels, such as hydrogen, are considered to be directly electrochemically oxidized at the electrode in high temperature cells, as shown in

$$2 \text{ H (at electrode)} + O^{2-} \text{ (from anion)} \rightarrow H_2O + 2 \, e \text{ (at electrode)} . \qquad (1)$$

Carbon monoxide, although of inferior performance to hydrogen, gives some indication of reacting directly at the anode, the overall reaction being

$$CO + O^{2-} \text{(from anion)} \rightarrow CO_2 + 2 \, e . \qquad (2)$$

In the presence of steam, however, use of a suitable reforming catalyst in the cell allows the water gas shift reaction to occur

$$H_2O + CO \rightleftharpoons H_2 + CO_2 . \qquad (3)$$

The favourable effect, observed by Ketelaar and Broers[15,16], of steam reforming on the kinetics of the anode reaction when carbon monoxide is used as fuel indicates that it may be more practical to utilize the carbon monoxide indirectly, by means of the water gas shift reaction. The anode would then function as a hydrogen electrode.

Carbon monoxide also undergoes the Boudouard equilibrium reaction

$$2 \text{ CO} \rightleftharpoons CO_2 + C \qquad (4)$$

but deposition of carbon may be prevented by operation at elevated temperatures and by ensuring that small amounts of carbon dioxide are present in the fuel gas stream.

It is unlikely that hydrocarbons are utilized directly at the fuel electrode of a high temperature fuel cell; oxidation probably occurs by an indirect mechanism. According to Gorin and Recht[17] a sequence of reactions may be visualized in which thermal cracking is followed by steam reforming, the active constituent of the fuel being the hydrogen produced in these reactions.

For example, for ethane:

$$C_2H_6 \rightleftharpoons C_2H_4 + H_2 \qquad \text{(thermal cracking)} \qquad (5)$$

$$C_2H_4 + 2 \, H_2O \rightleftharpoons 2 \text{ CO} + 4 \, H_2 \qquad \text{(steam reforming)} \qquad (6)$$

$$CO + H_2O \rightleftharpoons CO_2 + H_2 \qquad \text{(water gas shift)} \qquad (7)$$

followed by electrochemical oxidation of the hydrogen

$$H_2 + O^{2-} \rightarrow H_2O + 2 \, e . \qquad (8)$$

The overall results of the above sequence is the same as would be obtained by direct utilization of ethane at the fuel electrode:

$$C_2H_6 + 7\,O^{2-} \rightarrow 2\,CO_2 + 3\,H_2O + 14\,e\,. \tag{9}$$

### (a) Steam reforming

Attempts to oxidize hydrocarbon fuels electrochemically directly at the high temperature of operation of molten carbonate and solid oxide fuel cells result in low outputs and rapid fall-off in cell performance owing to thermal cracking of the fuel. The hydrogen liberated by the cracking process is consumed normally by the cell but the carbon produced tends to build up on the fuel electrode and in the gas feed pipes.

Milder conditions, however, usually result in increased activation polarization and incomplete oxidation of the fuel. Some investigators[9,14] have studied electrochemical oxidation of hydrocarbon fuels at lower temperatures using very reactive catalysts. Cases with aqueous alkali and acid electrolyte will be considered later in this chapter.

With most hydrocarbons, the addition of steam and temperatures of the order of 750°C are required to utilize the fuel effectively. A reforming catalyst, usually nickel, is necessary; this can be in the form of a sintered nickel powder anode or nickel gauze incorporated in the cell, or as a special prereactor containing either nickel gauze or a conventional nickel-based reforming catalyst.

The reaction of methane (or any hydrocarbon) with steam in a high temperature fuel cell can be interpreted in terms of an indirect mechanism involving steam reforming of the fuel, followed by a water gas shift reaction, e.g. for methane:

$$CH_4 + H_2O \rightleftharpoons CO + H_2 \tag{10}$$

$$CO + H_2O \rightleftharpoons CO_2 + H_2\,. \tag{11}$$

This reforming of the hydrocarbon yields a hydrogen-rich gas suitable for electrochemical oxidation in the fuel cell. Continued removal of the hydrogen by electrochemical reaction in the cell ensures that the equilibria lie well to the right.

If insufficient steam is present two further equilibria resulting in carbon formation may be approached, namely,

$$2\,CO \rightleftharpoons CO_2 + C \tag{12}$$

$$CH_4 \rightleftharpoons 2 H_2 + C .$$ (13)

The minimum steam/hydrogen ratio necessary to prevent carbon formation can be calculated from the thermodynamics of the system.

Chambers and Tantram[18], of Sondes Place Research Institute, have shown that, for propane as fuel, steam/propane ratios of about 5 : 1 are necessary to avoid carbon deposition. However, as shown by Peattie and co-workers of Texas Instruments Incorporated[19], and by Chambers and Tantram, some fuels such as kerosine can be utilized directly with no steam reforming; very little carbon is deposited, although for long term operation some steam reforming would be expedient. An alternative method of effecting steam reforming of a hydrocarbon fuel is by recycling the exhaust gases back through the anode compartment of the cell[20]. Steam produced from the electrochemical oxidation of the fuel serves to participate in the reforming reaction, preventing carbon deposition.

Chambers and Tantram[18] have considered the problem of carbon deposition from propane in some detail. They point out that the two main problems arising from carbon deposition are blocking of the fuel pipes and loss of free energy caused by this irreversible side reaction. Since hydrocarbons become increasingly unstable at higher temperatures it is necessary to consider conditions which affect carbon deposition. These are

(1) the temperature of operation;
(2) the material of the catalyst and the fuel pipes;
(3) the composition of the fuel gas stream.

Chambers and Tantram in the course of evaluating catalysts for use in molten carbonate fuel cells have considered the effect of temperature on carbon deposition from propane on various catalysts. Their results show that carbon deposition is considerably less on silver and zinc oxide than on iron and nickel at temperatures above 550°C. It appears, however, that there is always likely to be some carbon deposition when a pure hydrocarbon is fed to a fuel electrode whatever catalyst is used, and this deposition will eventually block the fuel pipes during prolonged operation.

It has been found that the best means of preventing carbon deposition is to change the composition of the fuel gas stream and this is best accomplished by carrying out a steam reforming reaction on the hydrocarbon. For example, with propane as fuel, the steam reforming reaction at 600°C would be

$$C_3H_8 + 3 H_2O \rightarrow 3 CO + 7 H_2 ; \quad \Delta H = +127{,}060 \text{ cal}$$ (14)

followed by the cell reaction

$$3 CO + 7 H_2 + 5 O_2 \rightarrow 3 CO_2 + 7 H_2O; \quad \Delta H = -615,650 \text{ cal} . \qquad (15)$$

There are two possible methods of utilizing mixtures of hydrocarbon and steam. The mixture may be fed directly to the electrode and the reaction allowed to take place on the electrode itself. This method was tried by Chambers and Tantram, who obtained low operating voltages which they attributed to the high partial pressure of the unchanged steam. They found that a better method was to use a prereactor to carry out the steam reforming reaction and then to feed a mixture consisting largely of hydrogen and carbon monoxide to the cell.

The essential requirements of reforming treatment are that the free energy losses in the hydrocarbon–steam reaction should be small and that there should be sufficient waste heat from the cell to provide for the endothermic nature of the reforming reaction. When propane and steam are used in a cell the heat required for the reforming reaction (eqn. (14)) is about 20% of that available from the cell reaction (eqn. (15)), so that there is sufficient waste heat available as long as the cell operates below 80% thermal efficiency. From thermodynamical considerations this is about the maximum efficiency possible, since the maximum electrical energy obtainable is equal to the free energy change, $\Delta G$, where

$$\Delta G = \Delta H - T\Delta S . \qquad (16)$$

The entropy change, $T\Delta S$, appears as unavoidable waste heat and at 600°C has the value 136,000 cal for eqn. (15). For the utilization of hydrocarbon fuels by this indirect method the fuel electrode requires a catalyst which is active for the oxidation of hydrogen and carbon monoxide.

### (b) Thermodynamics of the carbon–hydrogen–oxygen system

The use of fuels containing carbon and hydrogen (C–H fuels) or carbon, hydrogen and oxygen (C–H–O fuels) has stimulated investigations into the thermodynamics of reactions which may take place in the fuel compartment of a high temperature cell. An important consideration, especially in cells operating for long periods, is whether or not it is thermodynamically possible for carbon to deposit from the fuel gas during any stage of its oxidation. For practical cells it is desirable that carbon deposition should be suppressed completely since even at a very low rate continued build-up of carbon on the fuel electrode surface would adversely affect cell performance.

From their recent work on carbon deposition boundaries in the C–H–O system Cairns and Tevebaugh[20] were able to calculate the conditions under which carbon deposition at equilibrium can be eliminated for any C–H or C–H–O fuel system.

Their computations provided a basis for the determination of the gas phase compositions and maximum theoretical e.m.f. values for fuel cells operating in the region where carbon deposition does not occur.

*Carbon deposition boundaries*

In order to determine the carbon deposition boundaries, the concentrations of all species in the gas phase in equilibrium with solid carbon must be known. The total number of stable species possible in the C–H–O system is very large, but fortunately it is necessary to consider only six major species, present in amounts several orders of magnitude higher than those of any other species. Cairns and Tevebaugh justify this approach since errors resulting from the procedure amount to only about 1 part in $10^5$ for each of the major species. The determination of these species was made by consideration of the various equilibrium constants of formation and the equilibrum constants for reaction among the species. With methane as fuel the major species found were

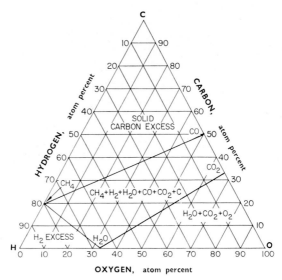

Fig. 81. Regions of the C–H–O diagram.

$CH_4$, $H_2$, $H_2O$, CO, $CO_2$ and C, and the chemical equations which defined the system were

$$CH_4 \rightleftharpoons C + 2\,H_2 \tag{17}$$

$$C + H_2O \rightleftharpoons CO + H_2 \tag{18}$$

$$CO + H_2O \rightleftharpoons CO_2 + H_2 \,. \tag{19}$$

By presenting thermodynamic data for the ternary C–H–O system as a set of triangular co-ordinates, Cairns and Tevebaugh were able completely to delineate the region of carbon deposition. The triangular diagram also shows the region of C–H–O composition in which free oxygen, free hydrogen and solid carbon are important as major species at equilibrium, as shown in Fig. 81. In the central region the gaeous species, CO, $CO_2$, $H_2$, $CH_4$ and $H_2O$ are present in varying amounts and solid carbon may also be present, depending on C–H–O ratios and on temperature.

The carbon deposition boundary for 500°K, representing the C–H–O atomic ratios of the gas phase in equilibrium with carbon is shown in Fig. 82; above this boundary line solid carbon is present at equilibrium, below this

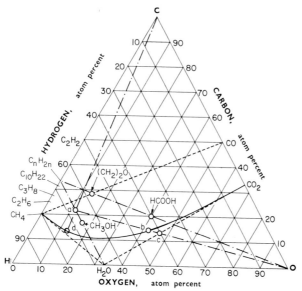

Fig. 82. Carbon deposition from and oxidation of a C–H–O fuel at 500°K. (Composition points for other fuels are also indicated.)

line carbon is absent. This boundary is useful for the prediction of fuel compositions that will not deposit carbon on achieving thermodynamic equilibrium.

Consider the oxidation process for a mixture of overall composition $a$ (Fig. 82) prepared by mixing $C_nH_{2n}$ and $H_2O$. On approaching thermodynamic equilibrium the mixture will deposit carbon, causing the compositions of the gas phase to move along line $aC$ towards $d$, which represents the compositions of the gas phase at equilibrium. The amount of carbon deposited can be calculated by the lever rule. On oxidation of mixture $a$ the overall composition of the mixture will move along line $aO$ towards point $b$. The equilibrium composition of the gas phase follows line $db$ during the oxidation process. At point $b$ all solid carbon which was originally deposited will have been consumed leaving only the gas phase of composition $b$. On further oxidation the composition of the gas phase will continue along line $aO$, until point $c$ is reached when the system is completely oxidized and contains essentially $CO_2$ and $H_2O$.

It is only along the path $bc$ that the fuel cell will operate without carbon deposition at equilibrium. The calculation of the gas phase composition along line $bc$ was made by an extension of the graphical method of Mayland and Hays[21].

By a similar line of reasoning the oxidation of any C–H or C–H–O compound or mixture of compounds is represented by a line joining the O-vertex with the point on the C–H–O diagram representing the overall composition of the system. A line joining $C_nH_{2n}$ to the O-vertex represents the oxidation of compounds of general formula $(CH_2)_nO_x$ as well as that of $C_nH_{2n}$. For example, ethylene oxide and formic acid are indicated in Fig. 82. The line joining the C-vertex through the C–H–O composition point of interest intersects the carbon deposition boundary at a point representing the composition of the gas phase at equilibrium.

Cairns and Tevebaugh have calculated deposition boundaries for the C–H–O system at 1 atmosphere pressure over the temperature range 298–1500°K. Earlier work[22] has shown that at temperatures above 1100°K the major gas phase species are $H_2$ and CO. At temperatures below 1100°K other species become increasingly important and the composition of the gas phase may no longer be determined by simple graphical calculations. However, the ratios of the contents of various gas phase species such as $CO/CO_2$ and $H_2/CH_4$ may be calculated from the appropriate intercepts on the H–C and C–O axes. In practice, carbon deposition can be prevented by two main methods, both involving steam reforming of the hydrocarbon; in one method the exhaust gases from the cell, containing steam as oxidation product are recycled; in the other method steam is fed in with the fuel. These alternative methods of preventing carbon deposition when methane is used as fuel have been studied thermodynamically by Cairns and Tevebaugh[20].

*Case I.* Recycling of oxidation products from a methane fuel cell at 500°K and 1 atmosphere absolute pressure.

A first requirement is to establish those conditions under which carbon deposition cannot be present at equilibrium. Data selected by Cairns and Tevebaugh as pertinent to this problem are shown in Fig. 83. Free carbon will be present above the carbon deposition boundary, whereas below this boundary all the carbon will be in a combined state as $CH_4$, CO or $CO_2$ and in the gas phase. $CH_4$ is represented by a point on the H–C axis; a line drawn from $CH_4$ to the O-vertex is the path of the overall composition of the system during oxidation. The composition of the equilibrium gas phase follows a path along the carbon deposition boundary until point $a$ is reached. On further oxidation carbon is no longer present at equilibrium as the gas phase composition follows the path $aO$ to $b$. Point $b$, on the line joining $CO_2$ and $H_2O$ represents complete oxidation of the fuel mixture.

It is only under the conditions defined by the line $ab$ that the fuel cell will operate free of carbon at equilibrium.

According to Cairns and Tevebaugh, point $a$ determines the number of moles of oxidation products ($1\ CO_2 + 2\ H_2O$) to be recycled with 1 mole of the methane fuel in order to avoid carbon deposition. This amount can be calculated from eqn. (20), which is obtained from the overall C–H–O ratio at point $a$ representing $CH_4 + x(CO_2 + 2\ H_2O)$; the atomic fraction of hydrogen, $f_H$, in the gas mixture is given by $f_H = (4 + 4x)/(9x + 5)$ whence

$$x = \frac{4 - 5f_H}{9f_H - 4}.\tag{20}$$

From Fig. 83 it can be seen that $f_H$, in this case, is equal to 0.5 and hence $x = 3$. Therefore recycling three moles of the oxidation product mixture ($1\ CO_2 + 2\ H_2O$) for each mole of methane passing into the anode compartment will (at equilibrium, 500°K and 1 atmosphere pressure) allow complete oxidation of methane without carbon deposition.

Calculation of the gas phase composition along the fuel cell operating line $ab$ was performed by an extension of the graphical method of Mayland and Hays[21]. It was then possible to calculate the relative partial pressures of

$H_2$, $CH_4$, $CO_2$ and CO. Insertion of their values in the mass action equation

$$K = \frac{[H_2] \, [CO_2]}{[CO] \, [H_2O]} \qquad (21)$$

enabled the relative partial pressure of $H_2O$ to be determined. Since the total pressure of all gaseous reactants is 1 atmosphere the true partial pressure of each species could be calculated.

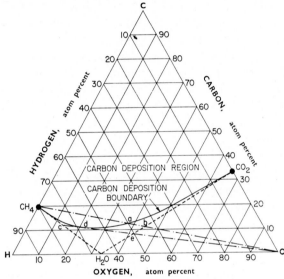

Fig. 83. Graphical determination of $CH_4$ fuel mixture compositions which will not deposit carbon at equilibrium, 500°K, 1 atm.

Point *a* in Fig. 83 was defined as the composition representing 0% oxidation of the fuel and point *b* as defining 100% oxidation. Gas phase compositions calculated over the total range of oxidation by a graphical method[20] were used to determine open circuit cell potentials, by substitution in the Nernst equation.

*Results for Case I.* Figure 84 shows the results of the graphical method outlined above when applied to the prevention of carbon deposition by recycling three moles of oxidation products per mole of methane as fuel.

It will be seen that the e.m.f. of the cell remains nearly constant throughout almost the full oxidation range, varying from 1.036 volt at 0% oxidation to 1.006 volt at 99% oxidation, although there is a rapid fall-off as 100% oxidation is approached. The partial pressure of hydrogen at equilibrium in the methane fuel mixture is sufficiently high for the performance of the fuel cell on the fuel mixture to be almost equal to the performance on hydrogen alone, if chemical equilibrium can be maintained. On the other hand, the partial pressure of carbon monoxide is sufficiently low at equilibrium for the poisoning effect, on, for example, platinum electrodes, to be very small.

*Case II. Prevention of carbon deposition by adding water to the fuel.*

The conditions under which free carbon cannot be present at equilibrium were determined in a similar manner to Case I.

All mixtures of $CH_4$ and $H_2O$ are defined by the line joining points $CH_4$ and $H_2O$ in Fig. 83. Line $cde$O, drawn from the O-vertex tangential to the carbon deposition boundary for 500°K intersects the $CH_4$–$H_2O$ line at point $c$. Point $c$ represents the methane–water mixture which can be oxidized completely (to point $e$) without carbon deposition at equilibrium. The water–methane mole ratio was calculated from the C–H–O ratio at point $c$, representing $CH_4 + xH_2O$, for which $f_H = (4 + 2x)/(5 + 3x)$. Substitution for $f_H$ gave the value of $x$ as 1.039.

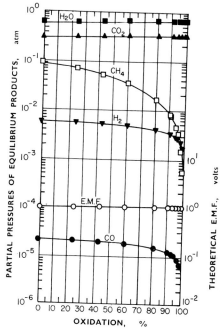

Fig. 84. Equilibrium gas compositions and cell potential as a function of per cent oxidation for a $(1CH_4 + 3(2H_2O + 1CO_2))$ fuel, 500°K, 1 atm.

As in Case I, gas phase compositions were calculated over the whole range of oxidation but a combined graphical and algebraic method was used. Open circuit potentials were again determined by substitution in the Nernst equation of partial pressures of the species in the gas phase.

*Results for Case II.* Figure 85 shows results obtained from the combined graphical and algebraic method applied in the case of the prevention of carbon deposition by the addition of 1.039 mole of water per mole of methane used as fuel. As in Case I, the open circuit potentials remain constant over nearly all the oxidation range, e.m.f. varying from 1.0697 volt at 0% to 1.0135 volt at 99% oxidation. Again the hydrogen partial pressure is sufficiently high, so that performance of such a cell using the methane–steam fuel mixture should be nearly equivalent to that of a cell using hydrogen alone. Although the partial pressure of carbon monoxide shows a maximum the general level is low so that the possibility of electrode poisoning is again very small. In contrast to Case I, partial pressures of carbon dioxide increase by about two orders of magnitude as the oxidation proceeds, and this is

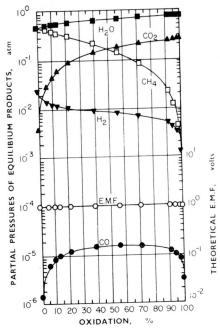

Fig. 85. Equilibrium gas compositions and cell potential as a function of per cent oxidation for a $(1CH_4 + 1.039\ H_2O)$ fuel, $500°K$, 1 atm.

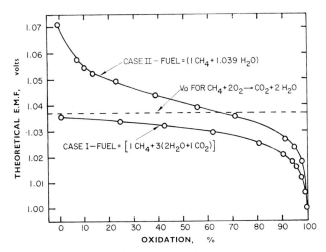

Fig. 86. Theoretical cell potentials for two fuel mixtures as a function of per cent oxidation (carbon-free at equilibrium) at 500°K.

attributed by Cairns and Tevebaugh to the fact that the fuel mixture in Case I initially contained much more (combined) oxygen than was present in Case II.

Figure 86 compares the e.m.f. values calculated for Cases I and II as a function of degree of oxidation. These potentials were calculated by substitution of the equilibrium gas phase compositions in the Nernst equation for a cell operating with 1 atmosphere of oxygen at the cathode. The dotted line shows the value of $V_0$ at 500°K for the reaction

$$CH_4 + 2\,O_2 \rightarrow CO_2 + 2\,H_2O\,. \tag{22}$$

The average partial pressures of hydrogen for Case II being about 1.7 times higher than for Case I results in correspondingly higher theoretical cell potentials when carbon deposition is suppressed by mixing water with the methane fuel.

*(c) Hydrocarbon fuels in cells using a molten carbonate electrolyte*

The detailed study of fuel cells with molten carbonate electrolytes given in Chapter 7 included some discussion of the use of hydrocarbon fuels in such cells. A typical example of this type of system is the high temperature, molten electrolyte cell of Peattie and co-workers[19]. The electrolyte is $LiNaCO_3$

held in a porous magnesia disc which has two porous electrodes pressed against it. The operating temperature is 600–650°C. Theoretical open circuit voltages could be obtained with hydrogen as fuel; when reformed propane, produced in a prereactor at a catalyst bed temperature of 500°C was used as fuel the open circuit potential was about 1 volt and a current density of 92 amp/sq.ft at 0.35 volt could be achieved. Feeding unreformed kerosine into the cell reduced the open circuit to about 0.9 volt, the current density being 30 amp/sq.ft at 0.5 volt.

Many investigators have successfully operated this type of fuel cell on hydrocarbon fuels, the main requirement being reforming with steam prior to electrochemical oxidation in the cell, although some fuels, notably kerosine, have been used alone.

*(d) Hydrocarbon fuels in a solid oxide electrolyte fuel cell*

Various types of solid oxide electrolyte fuel cells have already been discussed in Chapter 8 and some reference made to their using hydrocarbon fuels. The system devised by Binder and co-workers of the Battelle Institute, Frankfurt[10] can be considered as a typical example of a cell operating on hydrocarbon fuels; fuels used included propane and hexane. Their electrolyte consisted of a 1 mm thick disc of calcia-stabilized zirconia, prepared by sintering at 1600°C. Thin adherent platinum films coated on each face of the disc formed the electrodes. To avoid carbon deposition from the thermal

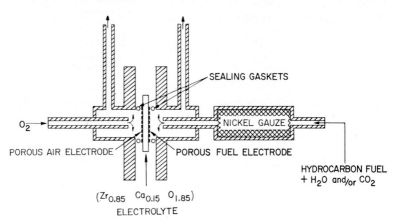

Fig. 87. Solid electrolyte fuel cell with integrated steam reformer for operation at 800–1000°C.

cracking of the hydrocarbon fuel, reforming with steam and/or carbon dioxide was performed in an integrated converter prior to the gases entering the anode compartment of the cell (Fig. 87). The converter was a simple reforming chamber packed with nickel gauze.

As shown in Fig. 88 mixtures of hexane with carbon dioxide or steam gave about the same outputs at low current densities, but reforming with steam

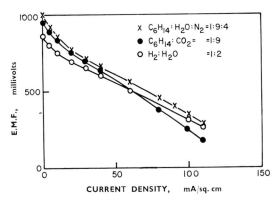

Fig. 88. Current/voltage curves for hexane reformed with various steam or carbon dioxide mixtures in a solid oxide electrolyte fuel cell at 1000°C. (The curve for a hydrogen–steam mixture is included for comparison.)

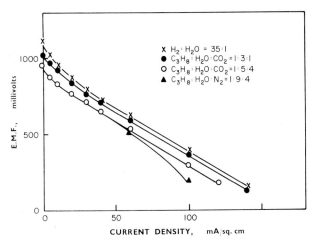

Fig. 89. Current/voltage curves for propane reformed with various steam or carbon dioxide mixtures in a solid oxide electrolyte fuel cell at 1000°C. (The curve for a hydrogen–steam mixture is included for comparison.)

gave a greater output at high current densities. Current/voltage curves obtained with propane mixtures are shown in Fig. 89. Resistances calculated from the slope $\Delta E/\Delta I$ were the same as those determined directly by a.c. resistance measurements, although as will be seen from the diagrams, some other polarization effects, apart from the ohmic drop due to electrolyte resistance, were present, mainly at low current densities. Theoretical e.m.f. were calculated as a function of the number of carbon atoms in the hydrocarbon molecule and the composition of the initial gas mixture. Good agreement was obtained between calculated and experimentally determined open circuit voltages.

## 3. ELECTROCHEMICAL OXIDATION OF HYDROCARBONS IN CELLS WITH AQUEOUS ELECTROLYTES

In recent years many investigators have been studying the electrochemical oxidation of hydrocarbons in cells using aqueous electrolytes and operating at temperatures of less than 200°C and pressures as low as atmospheric. While heat transfer problems are reduced, operation at these temperatures leads to low current densities and cell voltages owing to the electrode processes occurring more slowly than at high temperatures. Grubb[23,24] has investigated various catalyst–hydrocarbon systems, as a result of which he found platinum black to be the best simple electro-catalyst for the anodic oxidation of hydrocarbons at temperatures of less than 200°C. The nature of the electrolyte strongly affected the rate of electrochemical oxidation of the hydrocarbon tested, most hydrocarbons showing the greatest reactivity in strongly acid media.

Many of the earlier investigators into the anodic oxidation of hydrocarbons were carried out in strongly basic solutions; more recently studies have been made with alkaline carbonates and with strong acid electrolytes.

### (a) Basic electrolytes

Although many investigators had electrochemically oxidized organic fuels such as alcohols, the first published evidence of low temperature electrochemical oxidation of hydrocarbons was reported by Justi[6] in 1960; in this work some current was produced when diesel oil was oxidized at 80°C on Raney-nickel electrodes in aqueous potassium hydroxide. The work of Heath and Worsham[9] gave definite evidence for the reaction of hydrocarbons in an alkaline electrolyte. Using 27 % aqueous KOH at 205°C and 28 atmospheres pressure, they obtained almost complete electrochemical oxidation of ethane at a current efficiency exceeding 98 %, an indication that little or no side reactions occurred.

The fuel cell employed in these studies was similar to Bacon's gas diffusion cell, described in Chapter 5. A simple diagram of the system is shown in Fig. 90. The oxygen electrode consisted of a porous sintered nickel disc and

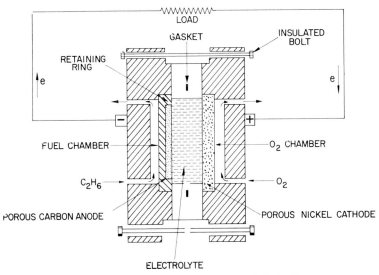

Fig. 90. High-pressure porous electrode fuel cell.

the fuel electrode was a porous carbon disc impregnated with a specially structured catalyst. No further information as to the nature of the fuel catalyst was given.

Material and electrical balances were obtained with the cell operating at a constant current density of 6.9 amp/sq.ft., highly sensitive pressure differential gauges being used to measure gaseous reactant flow rates, and differential pressure controllers to regulate the pressure drop across the electrodes and so maintain the three-phase contact between electrode, electrolyte and gaseous reactants. No gases could leave the cell except by reaction; the system responded to consumption of both fuel and oxidant by sensing the changes in pressure across the electrodes. The initial pressure differentials were then restored by admitting regulated amounts of the reactant gas feeds.

### TABLE 10

ANALYSIS OF ELECTROLYTE FROM ELECTROCHEMICAL OXIDATION OF ETHANE*

| Compounds present | Initial concentration | Final concentration |
|---|---|---|
| | (%wt.) | (%wt.) |
| Potassium hydroxide | 27.7 ± 0.5 | 23.9 ± 0.5 |
| Carbon dioxide (as carbonate) | 0.026 ± 0.01 | 3.26 ± 0.01 |
| Total carbon | | 0.86 ± 0.02 |
| Alcohols | | 0.0 ± 0.01 |
| Aldehydes | | 0.0 ± $10^{-8}$ |
| Acetic acid | | 0.0 ± 0.1 |
| Formic acid (as formate) | | 0.090 ± 0.001 |

\* due to Heath and Worsham[9]

Measurements of cell voltage, current and reactant gas flows were made; at the end of the experiment the electrolyte was analysed; the results, shown in Table 10, indicated almost complete oxidation of ethane to $CO_2$.

A detailed material and electrical balance showed that 93.3% of the oxidation of ethane was electrochemical, the remainder being chemical oxidation due to some diffusion of reactants. No other electrochemical reactions occurred since all of the current was accounted for by oxidation of ethane alone.

Initially a current of over 100 amp/sq.ft. at 0.92 volt was obtained (Fig. 91)

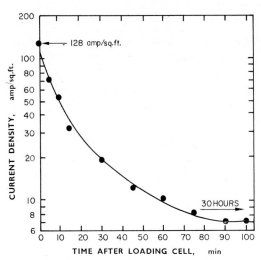

Fig. 91. Current/time decay curve for the electrochemical oxidation of ethane in a Bacon type fuel cell.

but this decayed to an equilibrium value of 6.9 amp/sq.ft. at 0.17 volt after
1½ hours. The cell output then remained constant for the duration of the
experiment.

Heath and Worsham attributed this polarization and loss of activity of the
electrodes either to flooding of the porous electrode by electrolyte, which
would reduce the active area or, alternatively, to a slow adsorption–desorption process at the fuel electrode. The chemisorption of ethane may have been
hindered by small amounts of strongly adsorbed oxidation products which
may have been sufficient to cover most of the active sites at which ethane
adsorption took place. Figure 92, in which the potentials of both fuel and oxidant electrodes are shown with respect to a bright platinum reference electrode located in the electrolyte, shows the limitation imposed on the cell by
polarization of the fuel electrode. This electrode polarized 0.7 volt at a
current density of 23 amp/sq.ft. The oxygen electrode, however, was virtually
unpolarized at the same current density.

Using 35 % wt. aqueous potassium hydroxide at 100°C and atmospheric
pressure, Schlatter found that hydrocarbons such as propane, ethylene and
acetylene were electrochemically oxidized at a platinized or palladized porous
nickel fuel electrode[8,25]. A comparison of the relative reactivities of these
three fuels on different electrodes and in various electrolyte media is shown
in Table 11.

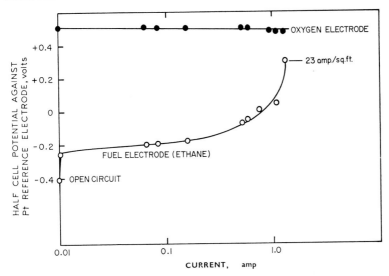

Fig. 92. Electrode polarization in a Bacon type fuel cell.

References pp. 246–247

## (b) Aqueous carbonate electrolytes

Although hydrocarbon fuels such as ethylene can be completely oxidized to carbon dioxide and water in aqueous sodium or potassium hydroxide, reaction of carbon dioxide with the electrolyte will result in the formation of carbonate and bicarbonate ions. An increase in concentration of carbonate and bicarbonate ions in solution will lead to reduced cell performance since Williams and Gregory[26] have shown that in aqueous potassium carbonate electrolyte, at low temperature, the hydrogen electrode exhibits a lower limiting current than in potassium hydroxide. The lower limiting current arises from electrolyte concentration polarization due to the lower diffusion coefficient of potassium carbonate. Additional effects may occur owing to a decrease in the electrical conductivity of the electrolyte. The low solubilities of potassium or sodium bicarbonates may cause them to precipitate out on to the fuel electrode. In a practical fuel cell the electrolyte should not react with oxidation products; if a hydrocarbon fuel is used, direct rejection of carbon dioxide is necessary.

Cairns and Macdonald[27] have shown that aqueous solutions of the carbonates and bicarbonates of caesium or rubidium are invariant electrolytes for hydrocarbon fuel cells. They form equilibrium mixtures of bicarbonate–carbonate that will reject carbon dioxide and have an alkaline pH. The

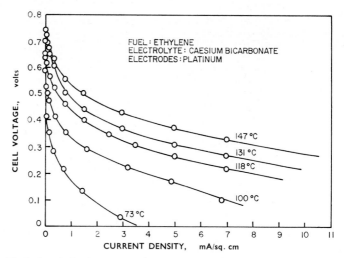

Fig. 93. Typical polarization curves (anode *vs.* cathode) for ethylene on platinum in aqueous caesium bicarbonate electrolyte.

carbonates and bicarbonates of these metals are very soluble, resulting in the following important properties.

(1) Cells can be operated up to a temperature of 200°C because of the high boiling points of the carbonate–bicarbonate solutions.

(2) Carbon dioxide rejection is improved owing to the instability of bicarbonate ions above 100°C.

(3) The ionic conductivities of the solutions are increased.

Cairns and Macdonald have carried out electrical measurements and fuel gas analyses for a number of organic fuels using platinum black electrodes in the temperature range 73–173°C. The electrolyte was contained in a pre-fired asbestos matrix.

In order to allow sampling of the fuel gas phase for analysis a circulating fuel system was used. Figure 93 shows typical polarization curves (with $IR$ losses eliminated) for ethylene, over a range of temperatures. The performance of the cell increased with temperature; individual electrode studies showed decreased polarization with increase in temperature, the fuel electrode responded to a much greater degree than did the oxygen electrode. In Fig. 94 is shown the variation in composition of the fuel gas mixture under constant current conditions. A set initial amount of ethylene was placed in the circulating fuel loop and left on open circuit overnight to allow

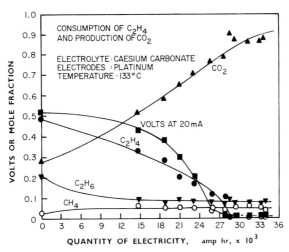

Fig. 94. Analysis of the circulating ethylene fuel against the quantity of electricity drawn from a cell with aqueous caesium carbonate electrolyte.

chemical equilibrium to be established; ethane and methane were produced under these conditions by the catalytic hydrogenation and cracking action of the anode. The ratio ethane/methane was found to be a function of temperature. It will be noticed that the cell voltage at 20 mA/sq.cm closely follows the ethylene concentration curve.

Similar experiments were performed with pure ethane as fuel; Cairns and Macdonald found a marked decrease in performance with increase in temperature which they attributed to the catalytic cracking of ethane on the platinum fuel electrode to yield large amounts of methane. At 134°C, it was found that over 30% of the fuel gas consisted of methane. In Fig. 95 are shown per-

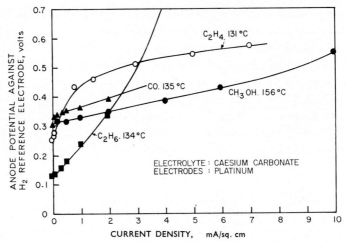

Fig. 95. Anode performance on some organic fuels in a cell with aqueous caesium carbonate electrolyte.

formance data for some other organic fuels in a fuel cell with caesium carbonate as electrolyte; the voltages are given with reference to a reversible hydrogen electrode in the same electrolyte. Methanol vapour (in nitrogen) showed the least polarization of all fuels tested, whereas ethane, although it gave the best open circuit voltage, polarized badly under load.

### (c) Aqueous acid electrolytes

In recent years there has been great interest in the use of strong acids as electrolytes for hydrocarbon fuel cells. The main advantages gained by using this type of electrolyte is the rejection of carbon dioxide and the higher conductivities obtained than with other aqueous media.

Schlatter and co-workers[8,25] have studied the activity of gaseous hydrocarbons such as ethylene, acetylene and propane in $5N$ sulphuric acid at 80°C and atmospheric pressure.

Platinized porous carbon tubes were used both as fuel and oxygen electrodes. Almost complete oxidation of propane and ethylene to carbon dioxide and water occurred. Acetylene was the least reactive of the hydrocarbons tested; propane gave the highest current/voltage characteristics–values of 2 amp/sq.ft. at 0.5 volt being obtained.

TABLE 11

COMPARISON OF RELATIVE FUEL CELL REACTIVITIES OF PROPANE, ETHYLENE AND ACETYLENE
ON DIFFERENT ELECTRODES AND ELECTROLYTES*

| Platinized porous carbon | Palladized porous nickel |
|---|---|
| 1. Ethylene > acetylene > propane (in 35% KOH > in 30% K₂CO₃) | Propane > ethylene > acetylene (in 25% K₂CO₃ and 27% KOH) |
| 2. Propane > ethylene > acetylene (in 5N H₂SO₄) | |
| 3. Acetylene (in 35% KOH > in 5N H₂SO₄) | |
| 4. Propane and ethylene (in 5N H₂SO₄ > in 35% KOH) | |

* due to Schlatter[8]

Table 11 shows the relative reactivities of propane, ethylene and acetylene on platinized porous carbon and palladized porous nickel. The influence of the nature of the electrolyte on the relative reactivities is also shown.

Griffith and Rhodes[28] of the California Research Corporation, Richmond, California, have studied the electrochemical oxidation of ethylene in $1N$ sulphuric acid on smooth and platinized platinum anodes at 80°C. Although large currents could be obtained with the latter type of electrodes there was evidence of polarization effects due to the build-up of intermediate products.

In order to obtain practical fuel cell outputs it is necessary to operate at slightly higher temperatures. Sulphuric acid, however, has the tendency to be directly reduced by the hydrocarbon fuel at temperatures of 150–200°C. Grubb[29] has shown that orthophosphoric acid should be a suitable electrolyte at these temperatures.

Vaucher and Bloch[30] have recently performed half-cell studies with hydrogen and propane using orthophosphoric acid (density 1.8) and porous carbon electrodes. The electrolyte had a specific conductivity of 0.13 mho cm in the temperature range 180–200°C. The carbon electrode was in two parts, a supporting disc rendered impermeable to the electrolyte by impregnation with a Teflon dispersion and a similar thin carbon disc impregnated with various catalysts.

The catalysts tested were platinum, rhodium, palladium and iridium, the metals being deposited on the carbon support by chemical reduction from solutions of their salts. Platinum was found to be the most active when propane was used as fuel although all catalysts tested gave good results with hydrogen.

In April 1963, General Electric Research Laboratory, Schenectady, New York, announced their high performance fuel cell suitable for electro-chemical oxidation of saturated hydrocarbons[13]. The cell used a phosphoric acid electrolyte, platinum electrodes and operated in the temperature range 150–200°C at atmospheric pressure.

The two main features of this cell are

(1) the use of a new porous gas-electrode structure, attributable to Niedrach and Aldford, which preserves the electrocatalytic properties of platinum and

(2) the employment of a phosphoric acid electrolyte at a suitable temperature and concentration.

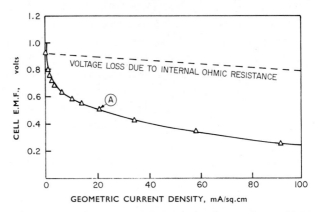

Fig. 96. Polarization curve for propane–oxygen fuel cell operating at 150°C with platinum electrodes and 85 per cent (14.6 $M$) $H_3PO_4$ electrolyte.

A number of hydrocarbons, including methane, propane, octane and cetane have been used as fuels in this cell with complete oxidation to carbon dioxide and water. More recently, Grubb and Niedrach[31] published current/voltage data for this type of cell using propane as fuel and oxygen as the oxidant. The cell operated at 150°C with 85% (14.6 $M$) phosphoric acid as electrolyte. The output obtained from the cell is shown in Fig. 96. The thin structure (0.20–0.25 mm thick) of the new electrodes eliminates the presence of any long pores which would tend to limit mass transport of fuel at relatively low current densities in the presence of inert gases such as carbon dioxide[29]. As a result of this, there is no evidence of a limiting current in the range covered by Fig. 96.

A gas-chromatographic method was used to measure the amount of carbon dioxide produced by the cell when operating at a current density of about 20 mA/sq.cm, (denoted by point A in Fig. 96). The amount measured was 98 $\pm$ 4% of that required for the complete anodic oxidation of propane, given by the equation

$$C_3H_8 + 6 H_2O \rightarrow 3 CO_2 + 20 H^+ + 20 e .\qquad(23)$$

It was assumed that the above reaction would be promoted by the presence of a high activity or high partial pressure of water at the anode. In the absence of any water vapour fed into the cell with the propane fuel mixture the electrolyte must be the source of such water. With propane as fuel the best performances[29] were obtained when the operating conditions of the cell, in terms of electrolyte concentration and temperature, were selected to give a water vapour pressure over the electrolyte of 600 mm Hg.

The foregoing information on complete cells has recently been supplemented by the results of studies on propane half-cells made by Oswin and co-workers of Leesona Moos Corporation, New York[32]. With 85% phosphoric acid at 160°C and simple platinum black electrodes, current densities of 100 to 200 mA/sq.cm were attained. Their data show a limiting current density at about 280 mA/sq.cm, due, no doubt to the electrode structure used. Grubb[33] has reported much higher limiting currents; in a complete propane oxygen fuel cell operating at 150°C, with platinum electrodes and 14.6 $M$ orthophosphoric acid, the limiting current density exceeds 500 mA/sq.cm, as seen in Fig. 97.

According to Grubb[33], the form of the voltage/current curve in Fig. 97 indicates that the current density is limited by a diffusion process, possibly involving propane or carbon dioxide. Diffusion of gaseous reactants and products in hydrocarbon fuel cells is dependent on the electrode structure; the effects of the latter on limiting current densities of fuel cells have been discussed in detail by Liebhafsky et al.[34].

Both Grubb[23] and Oswin[32] have found that with propane and higher hydrocarbons the major product of oxidation is carbon dioxide, but that methane also can be formed. It is known that at temperatures greater than 65°C propane is readily cracked on platinum and other transition metal catalysts with the production of methane[24].

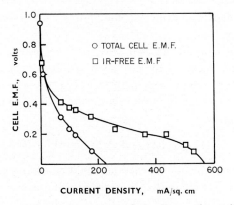

Fig. 97. Polarization curve for propane–oxygen fuel cell operating at 150°C with platinum electrodes and 85 per cent (14.6 $M$) $H_3PO_4$ electrolyte.

In the platinum-catalysed hydrocarbon fuel cell it has been found that the electrochemical oxidation reaction of propane interacts with the gas surface cracking reaction in such a way as to suppress the cracking reaction when the cell is operating under load[23]. On open circuit, however, cracking of the fuel occurs in the same way as observed by investigators of gas surface cracking processes[32,35,36].

As a fuel, methane is the least reactive of all the paraffinic hydrocarbons, this being attributed mainly to its high thermodynamic stability. In fuel cells operating at temperatures less than 100°C with strongly acidic electrolytes and platinum black electrodes Grubb[24] has observed the relative inertness of methane compared with other hydrocarbons. The performances of methane and a number of its methyl-substituted derivatives are compared in Fig. 98. The solid lines indicate regions of steady load current while the dotted lines represent regions where the load currents were unstable, falling off with time. Ethylene gave a steady load current even at very high current drain.

More recently, Grubb[37], using 14.6 $M$ orthophosphoric acid as electrolyte at 150°C and platinum black electrodes, has shown methane to be quite reactive. Figure 99 shows the current voltage characteristics of the methane–oxygen fuel cell, those of a propane–oxygen cell being included for comparison. At low current densities methane actually gave a better performance than propane. When a gas chromatographic method was used to measure the amount of carbon dioxide produced while the cell was kept at the conditions represented by point A of Fig. 99, the yield of carbon dioxide was shown to

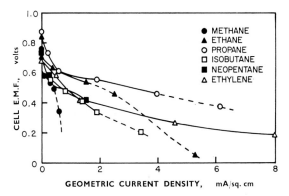

Fig. 98. Polarization curves for methane and its methyl-substituted derivatives at 65°C. (Pt black electrodes, acid electrolyte.)

be $98 \pm 4\%$ of that required for complete oxidation of methane according to equation

$$CH_4 + 2\ H_2O \rightarrow CO_2 + 8\ H^+ + 8\ e\ . \tag{24}$$

The significance of the comparatively high reactivity of methane under these conditions indicates that further detailed investigation into the methane–platinum–phosphoric acid system is needed and that previous ideas regarding the unreactivity of saturated hydrocarbons to electrochemical oxidation require drastic revision. Investigators in the field of medium temperature, phosphoric acid electrolyte cells[32], have expressed the view that although a considerable amount of work is required before such cells can be made to function in a practical and economic manner, the utilization of a direct hydrocarbon–air fuel cell is quite feasible.

Niedrach[38] has reported on the performance of hydrocarbons in ion exchange membrane cells. Some current could be drawn when propane, ethylene and methane were used as fuels and in all cases indications are

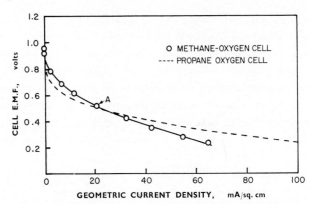

Fig. 99. Polarization curves for hydrocarbon fuel cells operating at 150°C with platinum electrodes and 85 per cent (14.6 $M$) $H_3PO_4$ electrolyte.

that at least partial oxidation of the fuel to carbon dioxide occurred. A reinforced sulphonated phenol formaldehyde casting resin in its acidic form was used as the electrolyte. Thin layers of the electrode materials (platinum or palladium blacks) were applied to the surfaces of the membrane electrolyte. All the hydrocarbon fuels tested gave higher outputs on platinum black than on palladium black, although none of the fuels performed as well

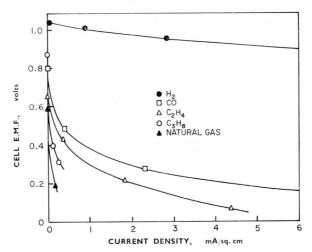

Fig. 100. Performance of several fuels in a membrane cell with platinum electrodes, sulphonated phenol formaldehyde resin; 0.018 g/sq.cm Pt/electrode; room temperature.

as hydrogen under the same conditions. Figures 100 and 101 show the performances of the fuels with both platinum and palladium catalysts. It was reported that in all cases the performance improved with increase of temperature in the range 27–85°C.

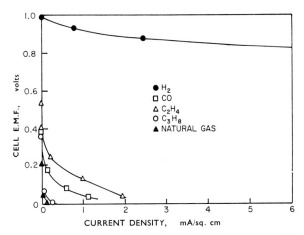

Fig. 101. Performance of several fuels in a membrane cell with palladium electrodes,
sulphonated phenol formaldehyde resin; 0.0088 g/sq.cm Pd/electrode; room temperature.

### (d) Mechanism of oxidation in aqueous electrolytes

There are four main factors which must be considered when discussing the
anodic oxidation of a hydrocarbon fuel[39], viz.:

(1) the rate of mass transport of reactants to the electrode;
(2) the rate and extent of adsorption of reactants on the electrode;
(3) the rate of surface reactions;
(4) the rate of mass transport of carbon dioxide away from the reaction
sites.

In their work on propane, Grubb and Michalske[39] considered the region
of the polarization curve well removed from that of limiting current so that
(1) and (4) were not rate-determining. While (2) or (3) may be rate-determining, there is little information available concerning them. Grubb and Michalske
explained the completeness of oxidation to carbon dioxide by the following
hypothesis. If the intermediates are more strongly adsorbed than the fuel
molecules on the electrode then steady state oxidation, if it occurs, must
proceed to completion, providing that none of the intermediates are inert to

further anodic oxidation. The final product, carbon dioxide, is not strongly adsorbed on the electrode and is easily removed.

The results indicate that propane competes poorly with the surface intermediates for reaction sites. This competitive adsorption hypothesis also predicts that more strongly adsorbed fuels might be less completely oxidized and may explain why yields of carbon dioxide when propylene and cyclopentane were used as fuels were only 82% and 91% respectively[40] whereas yields from propane exceeded 99%. Green and co-workers[41] have recently studied the electrochemical oxidation of ethylene in 1 $M$ sodium hydroxide. Oxidation to carbon dioxide was complete and they considered that the discharge of hydroxyl ions at the anode was the rate-determining step:

$$OH^- \rightarrow OH \cdot + e \qquad \text{slow} \qquad (25)$$

$$C_2H_4 \rightleftharpoons C_2H_{4ads} \qquad \text{fast} \qquad (26)$$

$$C_2H_{4ads} + OH \rightleftharpoons C_2H_4OH \cdot \qquad \text{fast} \qquad (27)$$

followed by

$$C_2H_4OH \cdot + 3 H_2O \rightarrow 2 CO_2 + 11 H^+ + 11 e. \qquad (28)$$

A fall-off in output with time was noticed, the high initial activity probably being due to the formation of hydrogen from ethylene at the platinum surface

$$C_2H_4 \rightarrow \quad \overset{\displaystyle Pt \qquad Pt}{\underset{\displaystyle Pt \qquad Pt \ Pt}{CH\text{–}CH}} \quad + 2 H.$$

The residue $\overset{}{CH\text{–}CH}$ would be less susceptible to oxidation and may lead to a decrease in surface activity with time. At limiting current the rate-determining step was found to be the mass transport of ethylene to the electrode.

Wroblowa, Piersma and Bockris[42] have studied the oxidation of ethylene over a pH range of 0.5–12.5. They found that the reaction mechanism in the Tafel region could be interpreted in terms of the formation of adsorbed hydroxyl being the rate-determining step over the complete pH range investigated.

$$H_2O \rightarrow OH_{ads} + H^+ + e \quad \text{(in acid solution)} \qquad (29)$$

or

$$OH^- \rightarrow OH_{ads} \quad +e \quad \text{(in alkaline solution)} \qquad (30)$$

Limiting currents, proportional to the ethylene pressures, were obtained for the range $10^{-4}$–$10^{-1}$ atmosphere, which indicated that the rate-controlling step under these conditions was the rate of diffusion of ethylene to the electrode. At higher pressures the Tafel region extends up to the potential where surface oxide was formed. The electrode was thereby passivated and the limiting current no longer controlled by diffusion.

Dahms and Bockris[43] have carried out a comparative study of the anodic oxidation of ethylene on some noble metal catalysts in 1 $M$ sulphuric acid at 80°C. Complete oxidation to carbon dioxide was observed on platinum, iridium and rhodium. On gold and palladium the main products of the reaction were aldehydes and ketones. The Tafel slopes as well as pH and pressure effects were different for the two groups of metals. For platinum, iridium and rhodium, water discharge was deduced as the rate-determining step, whereas for gold and palladium a mechanism involving the assumption of a $C_2H_4^+$ intermediate was proposed:

$$C_2H_4 \rightleftharpoons C_2H_{4ads} \qquad (31)$$

$$C_2H_{4ads} \rightleftharpoons C_2H_{4ads}^+ + e \qquad (32)$$

$$C_2H_{4ads}^+ + H_2O \rightarrow C_2H_4OH_{ads} + H^+ \quad \text{(rate-determining step)} \qquad (33)$$

$$C_2H_4OH_{ads} \underset{fast}{\rightarrow} C_2H_4O + H^+ + e. \qquad (34)$$

Johnson, Wroblowa and Bockris[44] have recently studied the anodic oxidation of acetylene on platinum electrodes. They proposed a reaction mechanism similar to that for ethylene but the rate-determining step in this case is the reaction between adsorbed acetylene and adsorbed hydroxyl:

$$C_2H_2 \rightleftharpoons C_2H_{2ads} \qquad (35)$$

$$H_2O \rightleftharpoons OH_{ads} + H^+ + e \quad \text{(in acid solution)} \qquad (36)$$

or

$$OH^- \rightleftharpoons OH_{ads} + e \qquad \text{(in alkaline solution)} \qquad (37)$$

$$C_2H_{2ads} + OH_{ads} \rightarrow C_2H_2OH \qquad \text{(rate-determining step)} \qquad (38)$$
$$\text{(or } C_2H \cdot H_2O)$$

$$C_2H_2OH \xrightarrow{H_2O} 2 CO_2 + 9 H^+ + 9 e. \qquad (39)$$

Evidence was also presented in these papers[42-44] regarding the state of the adsorbed organic species; in acid solution the absorbed acetylene occupied approximately four surface sites, whereas in alkali a rearrangement occurred so that the adsorbed species occupied less sites per acetylenic radical. The adsorption of ethylene, however, apparently involved four surface sites per molecule of ethylene in both acid and base media.

Studies of adsorption and reaction mechanisms obviously play an important part in understanding the electrochemical oxidation of hydrocarbons. Further studies of this type, coupled with a search for suitable catalysts, are required before a true assessment of aqueous electrolyte fuel cells can be made.

From the information presented to date it is clear that hydrocarbons can be made to react at useful current densities and potentials in fuel cells which use platinum electrodes and a phosphoric acid electrolyte in the temperature range 150–200°C. However, phosphoric acid is extremely corrosive at these temperatures and it may be difficult to develop suitable resistant materials of construction; the catalyst materials at present in use would also be very expensive and are not commercially attractive. It will be extremely interesting to see how successful the various teams working in this field are in overcoming the formidable problems associated with choice of materials and catalysts. Whether cells such as these or those with fused carbonate or solid oxide electrolytes will be most successful will depend on the outcome of research now in progress.

## REFERENCES

[1] E. BAUR AND H. PREIS, Z. Elektrochem., **43** (1937) 727.

[2] E. BAUR AND H. PREIS, Z. Elektrochem., **44** (1938) 695.

[3] O. K. DAVTYAN, Bull. Acad. Sci. URSS Classe Sci Tech., (1946) 107.

[4] H. H. CHAMBERS AND A. D. S. TANTRAM, Chap. 7 in Fuel Cells, (ed. by G. J. YOUNG), Vol. 1, Reinhold, New York, 1960, p. 94.

[5] G. H. J. BROERS AND M. SCHENKE, Chap. 2 in Fuel Cells, (ed. by G. J. YOUNG), Vol. 2, Reinhold, New York, 1963, p. 6.

[6] E. JUSTI, M. PILKUHN, W. SCHEIBE, A. WINSEL AND G. GRÜNEBERG, Hochbelastbare Wasserstoff-Diffusions-Electroden für Betrieb bei Umgebungstemperatur und Niederdruck, Franz Steiner Verlag, Weisbaden, 1960.

[7] M. J. SCHLATTER, Preprints* 145th Natl. Meeting Am. Chem. Soc., New York, Sept. 1963, Vol. 7: Div. Fuel Chem., No. 4: Symp. Fuel Cell Systems, p. 234.

[8] M. J. SCHLATTER, Chap. 15 in Fuel Cells, (ed. by G. J. YOUNG), Vol. 2, Reinhold, New York, 1963, p. 190.

[9] C. E. HEATH AND C. H. WORSHAM, Chap. 14 in Fuel Cells, (ed. by G. J. YOUNG), Vol. 2, Reinhold, New York, 1963, p. 182.

---

* Proceedings to be published by American Chemical Society as Fuel Cell Systems (Advan. Chem. Ser. No. 47).

10 H. BINDER, A. KÖHLING, H. KRUPP, K. RICHTER AND G. SANDSTEDE, *Electrochim. Acta*, **8** (1963) 781.

11 J. WEISSBART AND R. RUKA, *J. Electrochem. Soc.*, **109** (1962) 723.

12 L. W. NIEDRACH, *J. Electrochem. Soc.*, **109** (1962) 1092.

13 R. E. CARTER, W. A. ROCCO, H. S. SPACIL AND W. E. TRAGERT, General Electric Res. Lab. Press Release, December 26th, 1962.

14 W. T. GRUBB AND L. W. NIEDRACH, General Electric Res. Lab. Press Release, April 23rd, 1963.

15 J. A. A. KETELAAR AND G. H. J. BROERS, Chap. 6 in *Fuel Cells* (ed. by G. J. YOUNG), Vol. 1, Reinhold, New York, 1960, p. 78.

16 J. A. A. KETELAAR AND G. H. J. BROERS, *Ind. Eng. Chem.*, **52** (1960) 303.

17 E. GORIN AND H. L. RECHT, Chap. 5 in *Fuel Cells*, (ed. W. MITCHELL), Academic Press, New York, 1963, p. 199.

18 H. H. CHAMBERS AND A. D. S. TANTRAM, *Proc. 2nd Intern. Symposium on Batteries, Bournemouth, England, 1960*, paper 20.

19 C. G. PEATTIE, B. H. BARBEE, K. W. KREISELMAIER, S. G. PARKER, I. TRACHTENBERG AND A. WHITE, *Proc. Pacific Energy Conversion Conf., San Francisco 1962, Direct Conversion*, Am. Inst. Elec. Engrs. p. 17–1.

20 E. J. CAIRNS AND A. D. TEVEBAUGH, *General Electric Tech. Rept. 63-RL-3281C*, 1963, later published in E. J. CAIRNS, A. D. TEVEBAUGH AND G. J. HOLM, *J. Electrochem. Soc.*, **110** (1963) 1025.

21 B. J. MAYLAND AND G. E. HAYS, *Chem. Eng. Progr.*, **45** (1949) 452.

22 E. J. CAIRNS AND A. D. TEVEBAUGH, *General Electric Tech. Rept. 63-RL-322C*, 1963 (submitted to *J. Chem. Phys.*).

23 W. T. GRUBB, *Nature*, **198** (1963) 883.

24 W. T. GRUBB, *Proc. Ann. Power Sources Conf.*, **16** (1962) 31.

25 R. P. BUCK, L. R. GRIFFITH, R. P. MACDONALD AND M. J. SCHLATTER, *Proc. Ann. Power Source Conf.*, **15** (1961) 16.

26 K. R. WILLIAMS AND D. P. GREGORY, *J. Electrochem. Soc.*, **110** (1963) 209.

27 E. J. CAIRNS AND D. I. MACDONALD, *Electrochem. Technol.*, **2** (1964) 65.

28 L. R. GRIFFITH AND D. R. RHODES, in *Fuel Cells*, (Chem. Eng. Progr. Tech. Manual), Am. Inst. Chem. Engrs., New York, 1963, p. 32.

29 W. T. GRUBB, *Extended Abstr. Fall Meeting Electrochem. Soc., New York, Sept./Oct. 1963, Vol. 8: Battery Div.*, p. 98.

30 R. VAUCHER AND O. BLOCH, *Compt. Rend.*, **254** (1962) 3676.

31 W. T. GRUBB AND L. W. NIEDRACH, *J. Electrochem. Soc.*, **110** (1963) 1086.

32 H. G. OSWIN, A. J. HARTNER AND F. MALASPINA, *Nature*, **200** (1963) 256.

33 W. T. GRUBB, *Nature*, **201** (1964) 699.

34 H. A. LIEBHAFSKY, E. J. CAIRNS, W. T. GRUBB AND L. W. NIEDRACH, *Preprints* 145th Natl. Meeting Am. Chem. Soc., New York, Sept. 1963, Vol. 7: Div. Fuel Chem.*, No. 4: Symp. Fuel Cell Systems*, p. 124.

35 D. W. McKEE, *J. Phys. Chem.*, **67** (1963) 841.

36 D. W. McKEE, *J. Am. Chem. Soc.*, **84** (1962) 4427.

37 W. T. GRUBB AND C. J. MICHALSKE, *Nature*, **201** (1964) 287.

38 L. W. NIEDRACH, *J. Electrochem. Soc.*, **109** (1962) 1092.

39 W. T. GRUBB AND C. J. MICHALSKE, *J. Electrochem. Soc.*, **111** (1964) 1012.

40 W. T. GRUBB AND L. W. NIEDRACH, *Proc. Ann. Power Sources Conf.*, **18** (1963) 69.

41 M. GREEN, J. WEBER AND V. DRAZIC, *J. Electrochem. Soc.*, **111** (1964) 721.

42 H. WROBLOWA, J. PIERSMA AND J. O'M. BOCKRIS, *J. Electroanal. Chem.*, **6** (1963) 401.

43 H. DAHMS AND J. O'M. BOCKRIS, *J. Electrochem. Soc.*, **111** (1964) 728.

44 J. W. JOHNSON, H. WROBLOWA AND J. O'M. BOCKRIS, *J. Electrochem. Soc.*, **111** (1964) 863.

* See note on p. 246.

*Chapter 10*

# MISCELLANEOUS FUEL CELLS

Earlier chapters have dealt in some detail with the fuel cells that have attracted most attention and that appear to have the greatest prospects of commercial application. In addition to these, several other systems have been, or are being investigated. Most of the systems to be described are limited to potential applications in specialized fields and, in fact, are mainly sponsored by the National Aeronautics and Space Administration of the United States Government. Nevertheless, these devices must properly be regarded as fuel cells and their development has materially contributed to the expanding field of fuel cell technology.

## 1. THE BIOCHEMICAL FUEL CELL

During the past few years considerable interest has been shown in the idea of a biochemical fuel cell, that is, a fuel cell in which one or both electrode reactions are promoted or catalysed by biological processes. Research impetus stems from two considerations, firstly, the vast quantities of vegetable material which might be utilized as energy sources, and secondly, the need to eliminate organic waste material from closed environments, *e.g.* spacecraft. Biochemical processes can produce energy by the highly efficient degradation of organic matter at temperatures little removed from ambient and in neutral or nearly neutral solution, and it is possible that similar conditions may apply to a fuel cell utilizing the same processes.

### (a) General characteristics of biochemical systems

Only a very brief outline of the main processes governing biochemical processes is given here; for greater detail the reader is referred to standard biochemical texts[1].

Biochemical processes are controlled by "enzymes". Enzymes are organic catalysts of high molecular weight (10,000–200,000) which occur in, or are secreted by, living cells. They can be isolated and purified without loss of activity, in crystalline form. Structurally, they are proteins which form colloidal solutions in aqueous systems, and are unstable in strong acids or bases. They are highly specific in their catalytic ability, and are rarely capable of catalysing more than a single type of reaction; sometimes the catalytic activity is restricted to a single substance.

Enzymes, like all proteins, are sensitive to heat; hydrolysis of the interchain linkages takes place, the structure becomes disorganized and the protein is said to be "denatured". Generally, denaturation is accompanied by precipitation. Enzymes in solution can also be denatured by repeated freezing and thawing or sometimes by mechanical means, such as violent stirring.

In spite of the size of an enzyme molecule the catalytic activity is confined to a very small number of surface sites. In consequence, the activity can be completely destroyed by traces of poison, such as arsenic, mercury or silver. The catalytic power of an enzyme can, however, be considerable; the "turn-over number", defined as the number of molecules of substrate acted upon by one molecule of the enzyme in one minute, can range from about 100 to over 100,000. As with ordinary chemical reactions, enzyme-catalysed reactions follow the general rule that for every 10°C rise in temperature the reaction rate is approximately doubled, but with increasing temperature the rate of denaturation of the enzyme increases.

Enzymes are delicate substances; isolated enzymes generally have a limited shelf-life and must be stored at sub-zero temperatures if their activity is to be retained for more than a week or two. In the living organism, the enzyme balance is a dynamic one; the processes of synthesis and decomposition occur continuously.

Living organisms obtain their energy by the degradation of energy-rich substances (food) to energy-poor substances (excreta), a process known as catabolism. Most forms of life are provided with a plentiful supply of oxygen for most of the time and catabolism then takes the form of more or less complete oxidation of food to carbon dioxide and water (aerobic catabolism). In the absence of oxygen, only partial oxidation of food can be achieved (anaerobic catabolism). The two processes may be illustrated by reference to the catabolism of carbohydrates expressed schematically as follows:

$$\text{anaerobic:} \begin{cases} C_6H_{12}O_6 \rightarrow 2\ CH_3CH(OH)CO_2H & (1) \\ C_6H_{12}O_6 \rightarrow 2\ CH_3CH_2OH + 2\ CO_2 & (2) \end{cases}$$

aerobic:     $C_6H_{12}O_6 + 6O_2 \rightarrow 6\ CO_2 + 6\ H_2O.$     (3)

The biochemical route involves many steps, each controlled by a particular enzyme. Under the influence of the appropriate enzyme the reacting substance (metabolite) releases a pair of hydrogen atoms to a second substance known as a "co-enzyme". The energy released in the process is used in the manufacture of adenosine triphosphate (ATP), in which form it is readily available to the organism. The mechanism of the energy-transfer process is obscure. The released hydrogen atoms (now attached to the co-enzyme) are transferred stepwise through a sequence of comparable enzyme–co-enzyme reactions until, finally, combination with oxygen occurs. Each step is accompanied by the release of energy and the formation of ATP. Food is thus converted into excreta by the loss of successive pairs of hydrogen atoms all of which undergo oxidation by the same route. The reaction sequence is generally known as the respiratory chain.

### (b) Adaptation of biochemical processes for fuel cell purposes

To illustrate how such processes might be adapted for use in fuel cells a specific example, the biochemical oxidation of ethanol, will be considered. It should not be assumed, however, that the overall process as discussed is known to take place in some particular organism.

Under the combined influence of the enzyme *alcohol dehydrogenase* (which is found in liver and yeast) and the co-enzyme *nicotinamide-adenine dinucleotide* (NAD), ethanol is converted into acetaldehyde,

$$CH_3CH_2OH + NAD \xrightleftharpoons{alcohol\ dehydrogenase} CH_3CHO + NADH_2 \qquad (4)$$

though the equilibrium constant for the reaction is small ($K = 10^{-4}$ at pH 7)[2]. Similarly, the oxidation of acetaldehyde to acetic acid takes place under the influence of *aldehyde dehydrogenase* (also found in liver and yeast) and NAD.

$$CH_3CHO + H_2O + NAD \xrightleftharpoons{aldehyde\ dehydrogenase} CH_3CO_2H + NADH_2 \qquad (5)$$

The subsequent biochemical oxidation of acetic acid is a complicated process of at least nine steps (the Krebs "citric acid cycle"), each step involving its own specific enzyme and a co-enzyme. It is unnecessary to detail the individual steps here. The net result may be summarized in the form

$$CH_3CO_2H + 2\ H_2O + 2\ NAD + NADP + FAD$$
$$\rightleftharpoons 2\ CO_2 + 2\ NADH_2 + NADPH_2 + FADH_2 \qquad (6)$$

where NADP is *nicotinamide-adenine dinucleotide phosphate* (a compound closely related to NAD) and FAD is *flavin-adenine dinucleotide* (a co-enzyme containing the isoalloxazine group). It will be seen that hydrogen atoms have been transferred from the metabolite (ethanol) to one or other of only three different co-enzymes. At this stage, the living organism has recovered part of the energy already released and stored it in the form of ATP. More energy is released step-wise as the hydrogen atoms are transferred successively from co-enzyme to co-enzyme along the respiratory chain. Each co-enzyme can exist in an oxidized and a reduced form, and can therefore be assigned a definite standard redox potential. The standard redox potentials of the successive co-enzymes of the respiratory chain are increasingly positive, so that the electrical energy theoretically available by combination of a co-enzyme/reduced co-enzyme redox couple with, for example, an oxygen electrode will be in inverse proportion to its position in the respiratory chain. Clearly then, the respiratory chain must be interrupted at a very early stage if high electrical efficiency is to be achieved. (For the purpose of this argument it is assumed that the energy of formation of ATP is not recoverable as electrical energy.) $NADH_2$ and $NADPH_2$ are commonly found to be the starting point in the respiratory chain for many catabolic processes and have redox potentials not far removed from the standard hydrogen potential, as can be seen from Fig. 102.

The problem, then, is to arrange for $NADH_2$ or $NADPH_2$ to release a pair of ionizable hydrogen atoms to a suitable electrode rather than to the next co-enzyme along the respiratory chain. Unfortunately, neither NAD nor NADP is electroactive, that is to say, the appropriate redox potential cannot be directly established at any known electrode surface. However, the equilibrium potential can be established in the presence of certain compounds known as potential mediators, and in this way Rodkey was able to determine the redox potentials of NAD and NADP[3,4]. He found certain organic dyes that could be used as potential mediators, the most active being benzyl viologen. Even so, equilibration was unreliable unless the enzyme *xanthine oxidase* was also present. *Xanthine oxidase*, (the Schardinger enzyme) belongs to the metalloflavoprotein group of enzymes which are generally characterized by an ability to exchange hydrogen with NAD and NADP. Other workers have used quinone[5], potassium ferricyanide[6], methylene blue[7] and methyl phenazonium methosulphate[8,9] as potential mediators. It has been claimed that the last-named compound reacts directly with $NADH_2$[10] but the remainder function only in the presence of a flavoprotein enzyme such as *xanthine oxidase.* It is probable that the same limitation applies to methyl phenazonium methosulphate also, the failure to appreciate this being due to the difficulty of eliminating traces of flavoprotein from NAD of natural origin.

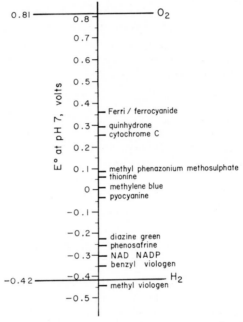

Fig. 102. Standard redox potentials at pH 7 of some compounds with possible biocell application.

If it is assumed that it is possible to establish a biochemical reaction sequence as outlined then it becomes necessary to consider what electrode potential will be realized. The final reaction may be written as

$$NADH_2 + dye \xrightleftharpoons{\text{flavoprotein}} NAD + \text{leuco-dye} \qquad (7)$$

where the dye/leuco-dye couple is the factor which will control the potential of an inert metal electrode immersed in the solution.

Reaction (7) may be divided into two parts as follows,

$$dye + 2\,H^+ + 2\,e \rightarrow \text{leuco-dye} \qquad (8)$$

and

$$NAD + 2\,H^+ + 2\,e \rightarrow NADH_2 . \qquad (9)$$

Applying the Nernst equation we have

$$E = E_1^\circ + \frac{RT}{2F} \ln \frac{C_{dye}}{C_{leuco\text{-}dye}} + \frac{RT}{F} \ln H^+ = E_2^\circ + \frac{RT}{2F} \ln \frac{C_{NAD}}{C_{NADH_2}} + \frac{RT}{F} \ln H^+$$

$$(10)$$

where $E$ is the electrode potential and $E_1^\circ$ and $E_2^\circ$ are the standard redox potentials for the dye/leuco-dye and the $NAD/NADH_2$ systems respectively. Since the two systems are at equilibrium they must be at the same potential, $E$. The equilibrium concentrations of dye, leuco-dye, NAD and $NADH_2$ will depend on the equilibrium constant $K$ for reaction (7), where

$$K = \frac{C_{NAD}\, C_{leuco\text{-}dye}}{C_{NADH_2}\, C_{dye}}$$

but provided that the quantity of dye added is small by comparison with the amount of NAD and $NADH_2$ present it will not appreciably affect the ratio $C_{NAD}/C_{NADH_2}$ which will, in fact, be governed by the rates of earlier stages in the reaction sequence. The ratio $C_{dye}/C_{leuco\text{-}dye}$ will adjust itself to the potential of the $NAD/NADH_2$ couple, which will therefore *indirectly* control the electrode potential. If the standard redox potential of the dye/leuco-dye couple is lower than that of the $NAD/NADH_2$ couple by more than about 0.2 volt it is a simple matter to show that the dye will exist virtually completely in the oxidized form. The electrode potential will then be difficult to establish since there will be no leuco-dye molecules available to produce the required electrode reaction, which is the release of protons and electrons at the electrode (reaction (8) reversed). On the other hand, if the redox potential of the dye/leuco-dye couple is greater than that of the $NAD/NADH_2$ couple by the same amount then the dye will exist almost completely in the leuco form and the rate of interaction of the dye with $NADH_2$ will be infinitely slow. If appreciable quantities of dye are added, the electrode potential will be governed by the standard redox potential of the dye rather than of the $NAD/NADH_2$ couple. For these reasons therefore, it is essential that the potential mediator (or dye) should have a redox potential as close as possible to that of the $NAD/NADH_2$ couple, and certainly within about 0.2 volt of it. This consideration alone rules out the use of quinone, potassium ferricyanide, methyl phenazonium methosulphate and methylene blue (see Fig. 102) which have redox potentials at least 0.3 volt above that of the $NAD/NADH_2$ system in neutral solution. Benzyl and methyl viologens have more negative redox potentials than NAD (at pH 7) and should have a strong tendency to reduce NAD, being themselves oxidized. However, this reaction has not been studied. At present, therefore, none of the known potential mediators would be acceptable links in the proposed biochemical/electrochemical chain, though possibly suitable alternatives might be found.

There are many incalculable factors involved in this scheme; in particular, actual reaction rates are largely unknown. A realistic estimate of possible cell performance is not possible. As a practical proposition the approach has many draw-backs, the most serious being that isolated enzymes soon lose their activity, and their use is restricted to a narrow range of temperature and pH. The scheme does, however, illustrate the principles that must govern the operation of any form of biocell.

### (c) Practical approaches to the biochemical fuel cell

Biochemical processes take place via an intricate system of enzymes and co-enzymes. In principle these reagents may be introduced into a fuel cell system in the form of (1) pure compounds, (2) cell-free, crude enzyme preparations or (3) living organisms (bacteria). Approaches (1) and (2) differ only insofar as (1) provides the opportunity of eliminating or reducing unwanted enzymatic reactions and, possibly, enables higher concentrations of the chosen enzymes to be used. Purified enzymes are difficult to prepare and expensive; on the other hand, crude extracts might be obtained quite cheaply. Both systems suffer the disadvantage that enzymatic activity cannot be retained permanently. The third approach avoids these difficulties. In living organisms enzymes are present in their natural state and function at maximum efficiency. In a suitable environment, growth and decay of the organisms can be controlled so as to ensure a constant enzyme balance. This will require a nutrient supply, but the quantity might be low by comparison with the amount of fuel (or oxidant) produced. So far as can be judged from published work, only biocells utilizing living organisms have been studied.

Following Rohrback and co-workers[11], we can divide biocells into two main types, (1) indirect and (2) direct. They are distinguished as follows.

### Indirect biocell

In the indirect biocell primary fuel fed to the organism is converted into a waste product which can be removed and utilized in a separate fuel cell. Examples of this approach are the production of hydrogen from carbohydrate by the organism *Clostridium cellobioparus*; hydrogen from formic acid by

*Escherichia coli*; ammonia from urea by, among others, *Bacillus pasteurii*; and ethanol from carbohydrate by *Saccharomyces* (yeast). In addition to these processes for producing fuel, biochemical processes can also be adapted to producing oxidant; examples are the production of oxygen from carbon dioxide by algae and plant-life in general (the photosynthetic process) and the production of oxygen (and nitrogen) from nitrate by *Micrococcus denitrificans*. As a general rule it can be assumed that fuel production is a consequence of exergonic processes (*i.e.* processes taking place with energy liberation) whilst production of oxidant takes place as a consequence of endergonic processes (*i.e.* processes taking place with energy absorption). In the first case, the organism utilizes part of the energy content of the primary fuel; in the second case the organism must be supplied with a secondary energy source, *e.g.* light. Processes leading to the production of oxygen have no possibility of application except in situations where oxygen is unavailable or in restricted supply, *i.e.* in space or in ocean waters. Since part of the energy supply— perhaps the greater part—is utilized by the organism itself, the indirect cell is unlikely to prove an efficient form of energy converter.

*Direct biocell*

The direct biocell utilizes the same basic processes as the indirect cell but in this case the organism can function two ways. It may be used to provide a continuous supply of the enzymes required by the biochemical/electro-chemical process, in which case, since the organism is allowed to derive no benefit from the process, it perishes. A portion of the population must there-fore be allowed to grow in the normal way (consuming some of the fuel in the process) so as to ensure the continued growth of the colony. Alternatively, the organism may be grown on or in the close neighbourhood of the electrode and the waste product of its metabolism (ammonia, ethanol, hydrogen, etc.) utilized directly for the production of electrical energy. Both processes can be applied in principle to biocathodes as well as to bioanodes. The direct biocell runs into the difficulty that conditions favourable to the growth of living organisms, *i.e.* neutral or nearly neutral solution, ambient or near ambient temperatures, are distinctly unfavourable for the efficient production of electrical energy in fuel cell devices.

In general, bioanodes have relatively high and biocathodes relatively low standard electrode potentials[12]. An inspection of the standard electrode potentials of possibly useful bioanodes and biocathodes (Table 12) suggests that the only biocathodes suitable for combination with a bioanode are those

TABLE 12

ELECTRODE POTENTIALS (AT pH 7) OF BIOCHEMICAL SYSTEMS

| Bioanode | $E°$ volt (pH 7) | Biocathode | $E°$ volt (pH 7) |
|---|---|---|---|
| Urea → Ammonia<br>*Micrococcus ureae,*<br>*Bacillus pasteurii* | −0.47 | Sulphate ion → Hydroxyl ion<br>*Desulphovibrio*<br>*desulphuricans* | −0.22 |
| Carbohydrate → Ethanol<br>*Saccharomyces* | −0.37 | Carbon dioxide → Methane<br>*Methanobacillus* | −0.25 |
| Carbohydrate → Hydrogen<br>*Clostridium cellobioparus* | −0.41 | Nitrate ion → Nitrogen<br>*Micrococcus denitrificans* | 0.75 |
| Formic acid → Hydrogen<br>*Escherichia coli* | −0.41 | Carbon dioxide + Water → Oxygen<br>light, algae | 0.82 |
| Sulphate ion → Hydrogen<br>*Desulphovibrio*<br>*desulphuricans*   sulphide | −0.22 | | |

involving the reduction of the nitrate ion or the regeneration of oxygen from carbon dioxide (photosynthetic process), since other combinations would not yield a useful cell voltage ($> 1$ volt).

Little is known of the way these systems would behave in practice. In the case of the sulphate biocathode the Faradaic output may or may not be in accordance with eqn. (13) for the following reason[13]. At a clean iron cathode immersed in, say, sodium sulphate solution, the normal reaction would be

$$H_2O + e \rightarrow \tfrac{1}{2} H_2 + OH^- \tag{11}$$

but in the presence of *Desulphovibrio desulphuricans* the hydrogen is consumed according to eqn. (12),

$$SO_4^{2-} + 4 H_2 \xrightarrow[\text{desulphuricans}]{\text{Desulphovibrio}} HS^- + OH^- + 3 H_2O \tag{12}$$

giving an overall reaction as follows (eqn. (13))

$$5 H_2O + SO_4^{2-} + 8 e \xrightarrow[\text{desulphuricans}]{\text{Desulphovibrio}} HS^- + 9 OH^- . \tag{13}$$

The standard electrode potential for the overall reaction is −0.216 volt at pH 7, which is close to the reported open-circuit potential of an experimental electrode[11]. If any other reducing agent is present—probably unavoidable in practice—the organism may use it as a source of hydrogen. In this case, the Faradaic output of the cell will be greater than that expected from eqn. (13)[13].

*(d) Prospects for biocells*

According to press announcements, two bacteria-utilizing biocells are commercially available. One is said to provide 1.5–3.0 mA/sq.cm at 0.5 volt from an 8 cu.cm cell. The other is described as a battery of 12 cells with an output of 40 mA at 6 volt, fuelled by powdered rice husks[14]. Taylor and co-workers[15] obtained operating data from a 2-watt urea–air cell and have predicted the characteristics of a scaled-up version. Thus, a 28-volt biocell using urea as fuel and oxygen as the oxidant would yield 0.4 volt per cell at 3 mA/sq.cm. The device would weigh 62 lb., occupy 1.2 cu.ft. and deliver 20 watts for two weeks consuming 0.0376 lb./h of urea and 0.030 lb./h of oxygen.

From the scanty details available it is not possible to assess the merits of these devices. Power outputs are, however, extremely low, and there does not appear to be any prospect for the early realization of commercially acceptable biocells. The main emphasis at present is directed towards the development of biocells to meet special needs (apart from the production of power) such as the disposal of human wastes within a closed ecology, as on extended space flights[16]. For this application it is expected that the biocell will not prove to be a net energy producer. The possibility of using biocells to produce energy from a variety of cheap organic waste products appears to be very remote.

## 2. REGENERATIVE FUEL CELLS

A regenerative fuel cell may be defined as a fuel cell in which the reactants are regenerated from the products and recycled. Regeneration can be arranged to take place within or externally to the fuel cell, the latter method being the more generally acceptable because the requirements of the regenerator and the fuel cell are frequently incompatible.

Regeneration methods may be listed as follows; (1) thermal, (2) photochemical, (3) electrical, (4) radiochemical, and (5) chemical. The so-called "redox-cell" is really a chemical regenerative cell. Potential applications of these devices are numerous; for example, thermal regenerative cells might find application where there is an abundant supply of waste heat, as in the vicinity of nuclear power plants; electrical regenerative cells have been suggested as energy storage devices, and for relieving the peak load problems of conventional electricity generating stations; photochemical regenerative devices have been proposed for earth satellite applications where sunlight provides the cheapest and most abundant form of energy;

radiochemical regenerative cells might also find an application in satellites, and might also improve the efficiency of nuclear power devices by utilizing some of the wasted radiation energy. Chemical regenerative cells alone are designed to utilize the energy of conventional fuels, in particular those fuels which offer little or no prospect of direct use in a fuel cell, *e.g.* coal.

A wide variety of working substances have been proposed for use in regenerative fuel cells, the choice being very largely dictated by the nature of the primary energy source associated with the regenerative step, but only systems which have either reached an advanced stage of development or which present novelty of approach are considered here. A comprehensive summary of the field is available elsewhere[17].

### (a) Thermal regeneration

The thermal regeneration cycle comprises the isothermal reaction of fuel A and oxidant B at the temperature $T_l$ to yield a product, AB, which is then fed into a regenerator at the higher temperature $T_h$ where it decomposes into A and B. The following steps are involved:

cell reaction: $\quad\quad$ A (at $T_l$) + B (at $T_l$) $\rightarrow$ AB (at $T_l$) $\quad\quad$ (I)

heating: $\quad\quad\quad\quad$ AB (at $T_l$) $\rightarrow$ AB (at $T_h$) $\quad\quad\quad$ (II)

regeneration: $\quad\quad$ AB (at $T_h$) $\rightarrow$ A (at $T_h$) + B (at $T_h$) $\quad$ (III)

cooling: $\quad\quad\quad$ A (at $T_h$) + B (at $T_h$) $\rightarrow$ A (at $T_l$) + B (at $T_l$) . $\quad$ (IV)

The system may be therefore properly considered as a heat engine which converts part of the energy absorbed at a high temperature $T_h$ into useful work and rejects the remainder as heat at the lower temperature $T_l$. Its efficiency can therefore be related to that of a Carnot cycle operating between the same temperatures $T_h$ and $T_l$. The maximum efficiency will be obtained only when all the steps I – IV are thermodynamically reversible. Heating and cooling steps are generally irreversible, but Liebhafsky[18] has shown theoretically that such irreversibility is of no consequence when $\Delta C_p = 0$ (where $\Delta C_p$ is the increase in heat capacity of the products over that of the reactants). The maximum efficiency of the process is then given by the integral form of the Carnot theorem, *i.e.*,

$$\text{Efficiency} = \frac{T_h - T_l}{T_h} .$$

DeBethune[19] has shown that, when $\Delta C_p$ is not zero, the maximum useful work output is given by the differential form of the Carnot theorem, provided that steps II and IV are carried out reversibly. He has also derived expressions for the maximum work output when steps II and IV are carried out irreversibly, as will inevitably be the case in practice. A consideration of these principles leads to the conclusion that the most desirable thermodynamic properties for a regenerative fuel cell cycle are

$$\Delta G \text{ (step I); negative}$$
$$\Delta S \text{ (step I); negative}$$
$$\Delta C_p; \text{ zero.}$$

Liebhafsky calculated that for a hydrogen–oxygen regenerative cycle working between the temperatures 500°K and 2000°K, the efficiency of the process would be only a few percent less than the theoretical Carnot efficiency (75 %). This favourable result is attributed to the fact that $\Delta C_p$ for this reaction is negative.

Whilst the overall efficiency of the thermal regenerative cell must be governed by these considerations, the selection of components for a working system will be governed largely by practical considerations.

An ideal working fluid should undergo appreciable decomposition at temperatures below 1000°C. It should give rise to only two products which should be readily separable, e.g. two immiscible liquids or a gas and a liquid. It should remain liquid at both the temperature of the regenerator and of the fuel cell and should be capable of yielding a useful cell voltage. A list of twenty compounds which might be recommended on the basis of these criteria has been compiled by Henderson and co-workers[20]. The list includes various sulphides, halides and hydrides. Many other possibilities could not be evaluated because of the lack of adequate data. The more important examples of thermal regenerative systems which have been studied are described below.

*The lithium–hydrogen cell*

A lithium–hydrogen regenerative cell constructed in the United States[21], consisted of a hydrogen cathode, a lithium anode and an electrolyte consisting of a lithium chloride/lithium fluoride eutectic fused at 600°C. The chemical product of the cell reaction, lithium hydride, is pumped to a regenerator operating at 900°C where it dissociates into metallic lithium and gaseous hydrogen. These are separated from the molten electrolyte and recirculated to the cell. The way in which the separation is achieved is not specifically stated, but it may be deduced from the published flow diagram that lithium and hydrogen together with some of the electrolyte are first evaporated from the bulk electrolyte and then cooled. Hydrogen gas readily separates; lithium and the remaining electrolyte are, apparently, partly or totally immiscible and separate into two liquid layers which can be separated and recycled. Simple gas electrodes were constructed taking advantage of the fact that some metals at the cell temperature are permeable to hydrogen. Thin sheets of iron or preferably, niobium were used. Catalytic activity is not required of the electrode. A laboratory cell yielded 1400 mA/sq.cm at a cell voltage of 0.325 volt. The open circuit voltage was 0.45 volt. The overall efficiency (on an undefined basis) of this device was stated to be 6–10%.

Severe engineering problems will have to be solved in developing cells of this type, which may ultimately find a use as nuclear power plant boosters, particularly in view of the likely development of liquid-metal-cooled reactors.

*Liquid metal cells*

The principles governing the operation of liquid metal cells have been described by Agruss[22]. The cell is really a concentration cell which may be depicted as

$$A/A^+/A(B)$$

where A(B) consists of a solution of metal A in metal B (or perhaps an actual compound AB), and $A^+$ represents a molten salt electrolyte. The cell voltage will depend on the activity of the metal A in A(B), which in turn will depend on the free energy change for the net process, *i.e.*

$$A + B \rightarrow A(B) \, .$$

In these cells the liquid metals themselves constitute the electrodes, a feature offering certain advantages over other systems. The exchange current can be very high, (in the region of 200 mA/sq.cm), permitting high current densities to be drawn at low levels of activation overpotential. Concentration polarization cannot occur within the electrolyte but may do so within the alloy A(B) if the current drawn causes metal A to be deposited at the surface of A(B) at a rate faster than it can diffuse into the bulk; even so, polarization will be slight (a few millivolts at up to 1 A/sq.cm). The principal source of voltage loss is in the resistance of the electrolyte, but even this is small by comparison with that in aqueous systems. For thermal regeneration, metals A and B should ₗave widely different vapour pressures so that A can be evaporated from B ₜt the higher temperature and recycled. These conceptions have been con-ᵢrmed by a study of the cell

$$Na/Na^+/Na \ (Sn)$$

ᵥhere the electrolyte consisted of sodium iodide, 62.5 mole % and sodium ₕloride 37.5 mole %, a eutectic mixture melting at 526°C[23]. Tests were ᵦonducted at 625°C in an atmosphere of nitrogen. At this temperature ᵢome decomposition of the electrolyte took place and caused a decline in ₑll voltage. As predicted, the only significant polarization measured was ₕat due to the electrolyte resistance. The main problems associated with ₕis cell are due to the corrosive nature of the metals at high temperatures. ˙he best constructional material was found to be low-silica-content alumina. ₗ later version of this cell used the system

$$K/K^+/K \ (Hg)$$

ᵥhere the electrolyte was a eutectic mixture of potassium iodide, potassium ₕloride and potassium hydroxide, m.p. 250°C[24]. This cell had the advantage ᵢf a lower regeneration temperature than that of the Na–Sn cell, but pre-ₑnted comparable corrosion problems.

*₁cid concentration cells*

˙he e.m.f. of a concentration cell with transference, *i.e.* of the type

$$H_2/H_2SO_4 \text{ aq. } (C_1) \ | \ H_2SO_4 \text{ aq. } (C_2)/H_2 \ ,$$

ₛ given by the formula

$$E = 2t_a \frac{RT}{F} \ln \frac{C_1}{C_2}$$

ᵥhere $t_a$ is the transport number of the $HSO_4^-$ ion, and activity coefficients ₗre assumed to be unity. The electrodes of such a cell are reversible with ₑspect to the $H^+$ ion; $HSO_4^-$ and $H^+$ ions migrate in opposite directions ₗcross the boundary dividing the two acid electrolytes, the net result being ₕe dilution of the more concentrated of the two. Since the e.m.f. of the cell ₛ proportional to the transport number of the ion which is not reversible ᵥith respect to the electrodes, *i.e.* $HSO_4^-$ in the example given, the transport ₗumber of this ion should be as large as possible. Generally, concentration ₑlls yield small cell voltages ($< 0.4$ volt) which are not attractive to fuel cell designers, but when considered as part of a regenerative cell system they have the advantage that regeneration is readily accomplished by evaporating water from the concentrated to the more dilute electrolyte, thus obviating the need for very high temperatures and eliminating reactant separation problems. Cells of this type are claimed to have given outputs of 20 mA/sq.cm at 0.3 volt[25].

### (b) Photochemical regeneration

Photoregenerative systems embodying inorganic as well as organic photo-sensitive materials have been proposed. As the two systems differ somewhat in principle they will be discussed separately.

#### Inorganic photo-electrochemical cells

These devices depend on the photodissociation of the fuel cell product into reactants which can subsequently be removed and recycled. Operating criteria are similar to those governing thermal regenerative devices, that is to say, in addition to the normal requirements of fuel cell operation, the product must readily decompose into reactants which can be separated by practicable processes. It should absorb light (preferably sunlight) over a broad spectral range with a high quantum yield of reactants. The reaction must be reversible and preferably free from side-reactions. Since the fuel cell product must be amenable to photodissociation, the cell voltage will necessarily be limited, since otherwise most of the incident light energy could not possibly be effective. Calvert[26] has derived an aproximate eqn. (14) expressing the efficiency of the process for converting light into chemical energy of a form suitable for use in a fuel cell, i.e.,

$$\% \text{ Efficiency} = \frac{100 \, \Delta G^\circ \, \Phi}{E\lambda} \qquad (14)$$

where $\Delta G^\circ$ is the standard free energy of the reaction, $\Phi$ is the quantum yield and $E\lambda$ the energy of light in kcal/mole of quanta at wavelength $\lambda$. The maximum power theoretically available from a photolysis cell can be calculated from eqn. (14) and takes the form of eqn. (15)[27];

$$\text{Power (watts/sq.cm)} = \frac{\Phi I \, nFE}{N} \qquad (15)$$

where $I$ is the light intensity in quanta absorbed (sq.cm/sec) and $N$ is Avogadro's number; $n$, $F$ and $E$ have their usual significance.

The spectral band of photochemically useful solar energy lies in the region 1500–8000 Å. Higher energy regions cause ionization; lower energy regions merely heat the system. The usable energy range represents about 58 % of the total solar energy[27].

Few suitable inorganic systems appear to be available. A system which has been studied[27] is based on nitrosyl chloride which photodissociates with a quantum yield of 2 into nitric oxide and chlorine

$$2 \, NOCl \xrightarrow{hv} 2 \, NO + Cl_2 \; ; \quad \Delta G = 4.9 \, kcal \,. \tag{16}$$

From the standard free energy change for the reaction, the standard cell voltage is found to be 0.21 volt. Regeneration in the liquid phase is attractive because of the compactness of the absorbing layer and because the nitric oxide separates as a gas. However, it appears that the back reaction is then so rapid that only small quantum yields are actually obtained. Gas phase regeneration is possible but separation of the reactants is then more difficult. It involves the absorption of chlorine and nitrosyl chloride in a non-volatile solvent (thus separating nitric oxide) followed by evaporation of the chlorine and unchanged nitrosyl chloride from the solvent. Nitrosyl chloride is itself non-conducting but acts as an ionizing solvent for the electrolyte, in this case, aluminium chloride

$$NOCl + AlCl_3 \rightarrow NO^+ + AlCl_4^- \,. \tag{17}$$

Operated at temperatures between $-10°$ and $-20°C$ (to maintain liquidity) the cell gave the expected open circuit voltage (0.21 volt) but actual currents were "vanishingly low". An alternative version operated at room temperature and 30 lb./sq.in. gave slightly better outputs[27]. Both cells present considerable engineering difficulties associated with the corrosive nature of the working fluid and it appears that development of this system has now ceased.

An alternative proposal involves the use of the hydrogen–iodine system[28]. Hydrogen iodide absorbs radiation in the region 2000–4000 Å with a quantum yield of 2. No practical details have been made available.

*Organic photo-electrochemical cells*

Proposals for utilizing organic materials in photo-electrochemical devices depend for their success on the fact that certain organic dyes absorb light and are thereby promoted to an active state. In this state they are capable of reacting with a suitable reducing agent towards which they are normally unreactive. The reaction may be utilized in a regenerative cell process by a scheme such as the following, proposed by Eisenberg and his associates[29,30].

Cell A (Fig. 103) is a twin-compartment regenerative cell, one compartment containing the organic dye D and a reducing agent RH, the other compartment containing a redox couple $M^{2+}/M^{+}$. Under influence of light reaction (18) takes place:

$$\text{anode compartment: } D + RH \;\xrightarrow{hv}\; DH + R. \tag{18}$$

When the external circuit is completed a current flows, and reactions (19) and (20) take place:

$$\text{anode compartment: } \qquad DH \rightarrow D + H^{+} + e \tag{19}$$

$$\text{cathode compartment: } M^{2+} + e \rightarrow M^{+}. \tag{20}$$

The reaction products are then transferred to a dark cell B also comprising twin compartments where reactions (21) and (22) take place:

$$\text{anode compartment: } \qquad M^{+} \rightarrow M^{2+} + e \tag{21}$$

$$\text{cathode compartment: } R + H^{+} + e \rightarrow RH. \tag{22}$$

The net result is the conversion of light energy to electrical energy. Power

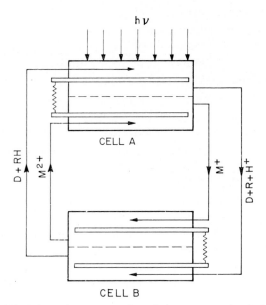

Fig. 103. Schematic representation of photoregenerative fuel cell.

can be derived from both cells; for complete chemical reversibility the same quantity of current must be drawn from both cells.

The system proflavine/ascorbic acid coupled with the stannic/stannous fluoride redox couple has been studied in greatest detail[30], alternative systems having proved on examination to be largely irreversible. The stannic/stannous couple was chosen because its potential is intermediate between the "dark" potential and the photo-induced potential of the photosensitive chemical system. Thus in the regenerator (cell A) the photosensitive electrode acts as the anode whilst in the fuel cell (cell B) where the chemical processes are reversed it acts as the cathode. The maximum power obtained from this system was 20 $\mu$W and the open circuit potential was 0.175 volt. Limitations on the performance appear to be imposed by (1) the low quantum yield and (2) concentration polarization. Doubtless other systems embodying these principles are possible but, on the present evidence, commercial prospects are remote. However, as specialized power-producing devices for use in space applications they may prove to have some advantages over other forms of solar cells.

### (c) Electrical regeneration

Electrical regenerative cells have been developed chiefly around the hydrogen–oxygen system. Since these devices are not net producers of electricity their main application must be as storage systems, in which role they compete with conventional storage batteries. The main interest centres around their use in satellite systems, when electrical energy generated during the sunlit part of the orbit can be stored for use during the dark transit.

### The hydrogen–oxygen regenerative cell

There are three main types of hydrogen–oxygen regenerative cell. One design[31,32] uses separate electrolysis and generator cells. When solar energy is available electrolysis takes place, hydrogen and oxygen gases are generated and removed for storage until such time as they are required by the fuel cell. The same electrolyte is used in both cells and, to eliminate the admittedly difficult problem of water separation in an environment of zero gravity, both must be made to function efficiently over a wide range of electrolyte concentrations. Most of the special features of this particular design are a result of the anticipated operation at zero gravity. Thus it is necessary to impress a vortex motion on the electrolyte in the electrolysis cell to facilitate gas/liquid separation. A semipermeable membrane prevents mixing of the regenerated gases. A pressurized system is essential for space application; advantage can be taken of this, however, since higher temperatures can be used and the output improved. Laboratory tests have shown that the main losses in this cell arise from activation polarization. Polished nickel electrodes have yielded the best performance and current densities as high as 1600 mA/sq.cm have been reported.

The second design utilizes a single cell to carry out the twin functions of generator and fuel cell[33,34]. For zero gravity applications, the ion exchange membrane fuel cell with no free-flowing electrolyte (Chapter 5) possesses a clear advantage over systems using fluid electrolytes. Operation of the cell on continuous discharge would, however, result in a slow leaking of the electrolyte from the membrane and a possible drowning of the electrodes. The test cell used platinum black electrodes with an alkaline electrolyte; short-cycle operations were carried out successfully although the regeneration efficiency was only about 50%. Most of the losses were considered to be caused by the relatively high resistance of the ion exchange membrane. The main problem in this system is to develop ion exchange membranes of greater chemical stability. In other respects the inherent simplicity of construction and freedom from moving parts makes this design particularly attractive for space applications.

The third design[35] resembles the previous one in its simple construction and absence of moving parts. The electrodes consist of platinized porous Raney nickel plates and the electrolyte is aqueous potassium hydroxide absorbed in asbestos. The possibility of hydrogen and oxygen storage within the electrodes offers possible improvements in the energy/weight ratio but practical development has not been successful. No performance details are available.

Justi[36] has described a modified "DSK electrode" for use in a regenerative cell. The DSK electrode comprises active fine-pore Raney nickel embedded in a macro-porous nickel skeleton (for the hydrogen electrode) or similarly active fine-pore Raney silver in a macro-porous nickel skeleton (for the oxygen electrode). This arrangement provides electrodes gas-tight at low pressures and needing no waterproofant. To make these electrodes suitable for use in a regenerative process, the electrolyte face of the electrode is coated with a fine-pore inactive metal such as copper. Regenerated gas is formed on the active catalyst behind the inactive metal film and can escape only via the gas-side of the electrode provided that the capillary pressure within the inactive metallic film is sufficiently high. Regeneration and compression of the gas is thus achieved simply and economically. A working model has been operated successfully.

## The hydrogen–halogen regenerative cell

There have been many proposals over the years for the use of hydrogen and halogens together in fuel cells. Earlier suggestions were principally concerned with the economies and improvements that might be realized in the manufacture of the hydrogen halides, notably hydrogen chloride. More recently, it has been suggested that the hydrogen/halogen system could form the basis of a regenerative fuel cell system[28]. The advantages claimed are the high degree of reversibility of the electrodes, the potentially high power outputs, (e.g. 80 mA/sq.cm at 1.05 volt for hydrogen/bromine can be achieved with no appreciable polarization), and the high regeneration efficiency, i.e. 80–90%.

## (d) Radiochemical regeneration

Radiochemical regenerative cells may become of importance in the future as the use of nuclear power increases. Discharged fuel elements from nuclear reactors are highly radioactive and represent a source of energy for which, at present, little commercial application can be visualized. The conversion of at least some of this waste energy to electrical energy may prove to be economically worthwhile even though the overall efficiency of the process may be low.

Rosenblum and English[37] proposed a cell which utilized radiation energy to decompose water into hydrogen and hydrogen peroxide, the latter being subsequently decomposed into oxygen and water in a separate decomposition chamber containing a suitable catalyst. The separated hydrogen and oxygen gases were then used to power a fuel cell. The "overall power efficiency" of this system was said to be about 3%.

An improved arrangement has been studied by Yeager and co-workers[38]. They used an acidified oxygen-free ferrous sulphate solution irradiated by a high-energy source (e.g. cobalt-60), a system which has been thoroughly studied in connection with radiation dosimetry. The radiation-induced reaction under anaerobic conditions is complex but may be simply represented by

$$2\,Fe^{2+} + 2\,H^+ \rightleftharpoons H_2 + 2\,Fe^{3+}\,, \tag{23}$$

where the yield of ferric ion is 8.2 ions/100 eV absorbed energy[39]. If it is assumed that reaction (23) can be reversed in a fuel cell working at 100%

efficiency it can be readily shown that the overall efficiency, calculated as electrical output/absorbed radiation energy, is about 15%. As the concentration of ferric ion and hydrogen in solution increases, the reverse of reaction (23) takes place and the oxidation yield per unit of absorbed radiation diminishes. Ultimately an equilibrium condition is reached when the effective oxidation yield is zero. It is therefore necessary to work with low ferric ion concentrations for optimum radiation yields, a situation likely to increase the fuel cell problems because of the attendant lower open-circuit voltage and higher degree of concentration polarization.

The cell constructed by Yeager and his associates to study this system consisted of separate regenerator and fuel cell compartments. This system avoided radiation damage to the fuel cell electrodes but made the equipment bulky and introduced pumping losses. A micro-porous polyvinyl chloride separator minimised diffusion of ferric ion to the anode where chemical reaction with hydrogen would lower the Faradaic efficiency of the process. In laboratory tests with an electrolyte consisting of 0.25–0.5 $M$ ferrous sulphate and 0.025–0.05 $M$ ferric sulphate in 1 $M$ sulphuric acid, current densities of 11 mA/sq.cm were obtained at a cell voltage of about 0.5 volt.

Other redox systems comparable to the ferrous/ferric system could doubtless be proposed. Much more research will be needed to assess the potentialities of such devices.

### (e) Chemical regeneration

The chemical regenerative fuel cell, also known as the redox cell, was conceived as a means of utilizing cheap and readily available (but electrochemically inactive) fuels in a low temperature fuel cell. In the redox cell, the electrode reactions are ionic reactions which can be chosen on the basis of high reaction rates and suitability of redox potential. Regeneration of the electroactive species can be arranged to take place internally or externally. A schematic diagram of a regenerative cell by Austin and co-workers[40] is given in Chapter 1, Fig. 1.

A theoretical treatment of redox fuel cells was given by Austin and co-workers[40]. Let the fuel regenerator reaction be represented by

$$A + B \underset{k_2}{\overset{k_1}{\rightleftharpoons}} C + D \tag{24}$$

where A and C are the oxidized and reduced forms of the redox couple and

B and D are respectively fuel and waste product. The succeeding fuel cell reaction is then represented by

$$C \rightleftharpoons A + n\,e\,. \tag{25}$$

Assume that the concentrations of B and D can be kept constant by controlling the supply of fuel B and the removal of waste product D, and that circulation of products is rapid enough to ensure that A and C are at the same concentration in both regenerator and fuel cell. When current is drawn the concentration of A increases by $\Delta C_A$ and that of C decreases by $\Delta C_C$ ($\Delta C_A \equiv \Delta C_C$) until the net forward rate of reaction (24) is equal to the rate at which current is drawn. From the Nernst equation we can then derive

$$\eta = \frac{RT}{nf} \ln \frac{(C_A + \Delta C_C)C_C}{(C_C - \Delta C_C)C_A} \tag{26}$$

where $\eta$ is the polarization of the electrode due to the departure from equilibrium conditions, and $C_A$ and $C_C$ represent the concentrations of A and C at equilibrium.

The net forward reaction rate, $r$, is given by

$$r = k_1 (C_A + \Delta C_C)C_B - k_2(C_C - \Delta C_C)C_D = \frac{i}{nF} \tag{27}$$

and since

$$k_1 C_A C_B = k_2 C_C C_D \tag{28}$$

$$r = \Delta C_C (k_1 C_B + k_2 C_D)\,. \tag{29}$$

Substituting for $\Delta C_C$ in eqn. (26) gives

$$\eta = \frac{RT}{nF} \ln \left[ \frac{1 + \dfrac{r}{(k_1 C_A C_B + k_2 C_A C_D)}}{1 - \dfrac{r}{(k_2 C_B C_C + k_2 C_C C_D)}} \right]. \tag{30}$$

Now the maximum current, $i_l$, will be passed when $C_C \to 0$. Then $\Delta C_A = C_A + C_C$ and

$$i_l = nFk_1 (C_A + C_C)C_B\,. \tag{31}$$

Now let

$$C_A = KC_C$$

where

$$K = \frac{k_2\, C_{\mathrm{D}}}{k_1\, C_{\mathrm{B}}}. \tag{32}$$

By combining eqns. (30), (31) and (32) and using the relationship $i/nF = r$, we can derive

$$\eta = \frac{RT}{nF} \ln\left[\left(1 + \frac{i}{K i_l}\right)\Big/\left(1 - \frac{i}{i_l}\right)\right]. \tag{33}$$

In deriving eqn. (33) homogeneous reactions have been assumed and conventional rate constants have been used. The current is, therefore, in units of amp/litre.

The system will be 100% efficient only if the fuel cell voltage corresponds to the free energy change of the net chemical process, e.g. for the system depicted in Fig. 1 the overall process is the oxidation of hydrogen, for which the standard cell voltage is 1.23 volt. In this cell high efficiency can only be achieved when the standard potentials of the anolyte redox couple and the catholyte redox couple are approximately the same as those of hydrogen and oxygen respectively. Most fuel cell reactions of any importance are combustion reactions, and most carbonaceous fuel–oxygen reactions give theoretical cell voltages close to that of the hydrogen–oxygen cell. Thus in general, an anode couple is required with a standard redox potential close to zero and a cathode couple with a standard redox potential close to 1.2 volt[41]. Systems that appear to fulfil these requirements are:

*Catholyte*: bromine/bromide (1.07 volt); chlorine/chloride (1.36 volt)

*Anolyte*: stannic/stannous (0.15 volt); cupric/cuprous (0.17 volt); sulphate/sulphur dioxide (0.2 volt); mercurous/mercury (0.27 volt).

Posner[41] investigated the reactions of the above anolyte couples with active chars, coke, and a low rank coal. Partial oxidation of the fuels was achieved with all except the stannous/stannic couple. A more detailed investigation of the reduction of cupric ions in hydrochloric acid by coal showed that 15% of the coal reacted. Posner also studied redox reactions in a fuel cell, using for this purpose stannous/stannic and bromine/bromide couples. His results showed that whereas the bromine/bromide couple reacted favourably with little polarization, the stannous-stannic couple exhibited a high degree of activation polarization (porous carbon electrodes).

Austin and co-workers[40] discussed the kinetics of the reduction of cupric ion by hydrogen as in

$$2 \, Cu^{2+} + H_2 \rightleftharpoons 2 \, Cu^+ + 2 \, H^+ \tag{34}$$

using Halpern's data[42] and applying eqn. (31). The calculated limiting current was 8 mA/l, *i.e.*, the regenerator volume would have to be about 100 litres per ampere of current drawn, or for a cell voltage of one volt, about $10^5$ litres per kilowatt. Similar calculations applied to the reduction of titanic ions by hydrogen catalysed by palladium or platinum gave the somewhat better figure of 50 litres per kilowatt. Even if this latter figure were acceptable for practical applications the long term instability of the titanous/titanic couple would make the use of this particular couple impracticable. Further experiments showed that the rate of reduction of stannic or titanic ion by various oxygenated hydrocarbons was so slow as to give undetectable concentrations of products even after many hours of reaction. Even if a catalyst were found to increase the reaction rate it is questionable whether the rate would exceed that of the platinum- or palladium-catalysed reduction of titanic ion by hydrogen which, as shown, is of doubtful utility. Austin and his co-workers therefore conclude that no known redox couple reacts sufficiently fast with carbonaceous fuels to enable it to be used in a fuel cell, and doubt whether improved catalysis can lead to a sufficiently increased reaction rate.

Although it appears that the redox anode will prove to be an impracticable proposition, a measure of success has been achieved with the redox cathode, where air or oxygen is used as the regenerative substance.

Merton-Bingham and Posner[43] studied the kinetics of the nitrogen/peroxide-catalysed regeneration of the bromine/bromide couple with oxygen. Some of their results have since been disputed[44] and it is doubtful whether this system is practicable. The nitric acid/air-regenerated electrode is said to give better outputs than direct oxygen electrode[45]. The mechanism is believed to be in accordance with the equations

$$H^+ + NO_3^- \rightarrow HNO_3 \tag{35}$$

$$HNO_3 + 2 \, NO + H_2O \rightarrow 3 \, HNO_2 \quad \text{(slow step)} \tag{36}$$

$$HNO_2 + H^+ + e \rightarrow H_2O + NO \tag{37}$$

the overall reaction being represented by

$$4 \, H^+ + NO_3^- + 3 \, e \rightarrow 2 \, H_2O + NO \, . \tag{38}$$

The potential of the electrode is governed by the electron transfer reaction, eqn. (37). The rate of reaction (35) is increased by using a large excess of sulphuric acid in the system.

Regeneration is accomplished by oxidizing nitric oxide with oxygen, a process well-known in the nitric acid industry and represented by

$$2\ NO + O_2 \rightarrow 2\ NO_2 \tag{39}$$

$$3\ NO_2 + H_2O \rightarrow 2\ HNO_3 + NO . \tag{40}$$

Some loss of nitric acid occurs in the regenerative cycle, though the amount of make-up nitric acid can be minimized by careful control of operating conditions. It has yet to be shown whether these losses can be kept within acceptable limits.

### 3. AMALGAM CELLS

The sodium amalgam–oxygen cell has been developed by Yeager and his associates[46]. The complete cell is of the form

$$Na/Na^+ \quad OH^-/O_2$$
$$\text{(aqueous)}$$

but the sodium fuel is applied in the form of a mercury amalgam in order to eliminate the direct reaction of sodium with the aqueous electrolyte. The anodic half-cell reaction is

$$Na^+ + e \rightleftharpoons Na$$

but, whereas the standard electrode potential of sodium is $-2.71$ volt, the standard electrode potential of sodium in amalgam form is $-1.96$ volt. Although this is lower than the reversible hydrogen potential in alkaline solution, hydrogen evolution does not take place at an appreciable rate because of the high hydrogen evolution overpotential on sodium amalgam.

The half-cell potential of the sodium amalgam electrode is given by

$$E = -1.96 + 0.059 \log \frac{a_{Na^+}}{a_{Na}} \quad (25°C) \tag{41}$$

where $a_{Na^+}$ and $a_{Na}$ refer to the activity of sodium ions in the electrolyte and of sodium in the amalgam respectively. The activity coefficient of sodium in the amalgam $(\gamma_{Na})$ is given by

$$\log \gamma_{Na} = 16.4\ X_{Na} \tag{42}$$

where $\gamma_{Na} = a_{Na}/X_{Na}$ and $X_{Na}$ is the mole fraction of sodium in the amalgam[46]. Yeager's cell is illustrated in Fig. 104. Sodium amalgam is directed by a set of capillary tubes to the top edge of a vertical steel plate where, by virtue of its "wetting" ability, it flows down in a continuous film. The back of the steel plate is protected by a plastic film. The oxygen electrode consists of a hollow block of porous graphite coated with a silvered active-carbon prepara-

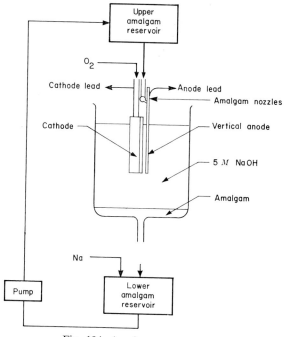

Fig. 104. Amalgam–oxygen cell.

tion, non-active surfaces being masked by a plastic film. The anode is characterized by the almost total absence of activation polarization and suffers only slightly (a few millivolts) from concentration polarization at current densities up to 1000 mA/sq.cm. Polarization characteristics of the complete cell can be attributed to polarization of the cathode and to the electrolyte resistance. The self-discharge rate with 4 moles % of sodium amalgam and 4 $M$ sodium hydroxide was found to be equivalent to less than 0.5 mA/sq.cm or even better if stringent purification procedures were adopted. Particles of carbon or graphite substantially increase the self-discharge rate because the hydrogen evolution overpotential on these substances is much lower than on the amalgam itself. Since the oxygen electrode is constructed from these substances, great care is required in assembly. In operating this type of cell it is essential not to exceed the solubility limit of sodium in mercury (about 0.55% wt. at room temperature) since the solid phases which may then form redissolve only with difficulty and may cause blockages in the amalgam feed lines. For similar reasons, air must be excluded from contact with the amalgam or solid sodium oxide or carbonate may be formed. Single cells of the type described gave outputs of 100 mA/sq.cm at 1.66 volt and 200 mA/sq.cm at 1.42 volt with 0.52% wt. sodium amalgam and 5.1 $M$ sodium hydroxide at 25°C. The output could be maintained for long periods with no appreciable increase in polarization. Termination of the test was generally the result of a mechanical failure. A series-connected 450-watt five-cell unit was designed to produce about 150 mA/sq.cm at 1.5 volts per cell, but output fell short of expectation. When a battery of such cells is operated from a common fuel reservoir it is essential to ensure electrical isolation of the individual cells. In an early arrangement this was accomplished by a series of solenoid-operated valves placed in the feed line and in the discharge line from each individual anode. Only one pair of valves was open at any instant. Later work showed that adequate insulation could be obtained if the amalgam was fed to the anode in the form of a fine spray, and allowed to fall dropwise from the anode into a sump.

The specific advantages claimed for this type of cell are (1) a high cell voltage, (2) operation at atmospheric pressure, (3) low temperature operation, (4) absence of explosion hazard, and (5) fuel stored at ambient temperatures and atmosphere pressure. Its disadvantages are (1) the high cost of sodium, (2) the high toxicity of mercury, (3) the complexity of the auxiliary equipment, and (4) the need for a continuous water supply.

A modified form of the sodium amalgam cell has been described by Smatko[47]. This cell used a halogen (chlorine or bromine) as the oxidant. The anode consisted of a sintered glass disc the back face of which formed one wall of a chamber into which the amalgam was admitted with an upward flow to eliminate voids. The cathode was a porous, waterproofed-graphite disc forming a wall of a second chamber into which the halogen was admitted. The electrolyte, brine, was pumped through a third chamber between the two electrodes. Outputs of 100 mA/sq.cm at 2.5 volt (sodium–bromine) and 100 mA/sq.cm at 2.0 volt (sodium–chlorine) were obtained, the chief problem being the gradual loss of the hydrophobic character of the cathode. It is claimed that this type of cell should be capable of providing twice the energy per unit volume of a sodium amalgam–oxygen cell.

Neither of these designs offers any real hope of commercial application as a power producer. They have been developed primarily for undisclosed military purposes, probably as replacements for submarine storage batteries, in which case regeneration of the fuel and oxidant from the used electrolyte (or from sea-water) would be necessary. A possible commercial application is in the caustic soda manufacturing industry. Currently, sodium amalgam, produced by the electrolysis of brine, is decomposed by water. By carrying out the decomposition in a sodium–oxygen cell the net power consumption for the process could be reduced. Yeager considers that this application will require improved cathodes which must be capable of operating for several years at high power densities and low polarization.

Womack[48] suggested using zinc amalgam in a regenerative fuel cell device. The merit of zinc is that it can be recovered from spent electrolyte by precipitation with lime followed by reduction of the precipitate with coal or coke. Both lime and electrolyte (alkali metal hydroxide) are recoverable from the process. The idea does not appear to have been developed.

### 4. LOW TEMPERATURE CARBON MONOXIDE FUEL CELLS

The use of carbon monoxide as a fuel in high temperature fuel cells with molten carbonate or solid oxide electrolytes has been considered in earlier chapters, and its use in low temperature fuel cells will now be considered. It is important that the electrochemistry of carbon monoxide at ambient temperature should be studied for two reasons; firstly, because carbon monoxide is a product of steam reforming reactions, and secondly, because carbon monoxide may occur as an intermediate product in the electro-oxidation of a variety of organic fuels.

Historically, the possibility of using carbon monoxide in a fuel cell dates back to 1874 when Grove[49] presented results on a number of fuels including carbon monoxide. In 1896 Borchers[50] described a carbon monoxide–air fuel cell which used an electrolyte consisting of a mixture of cuprous chloride and hydrochloric acid. In 1918 Hofmann[51] showed that carbon monoxide could be oxidized to carbon dioxide by hydrated cupric oxide in an alkaline solution and this observation led him to set up the cell

$$O_2 \ Cu/alkali/Cu \ CO$$

for which he claimed an open circuit potential of 1.32 volt at 20°C compared with a calculated value of 1.34 volt. Similar cells with copper or platinum-on-carbon as carbon monoxide electrodes combined with platinum–air electrodes gave potentials between 1.05 and 1.14 volts at 18°C. Auerbach[52] pointed out that in alkaline solution carbon monoxide would be oxidized, not to carbon dioxide, but to carbonate ion and therefore Hofmann's calculated open-circuit potential was incorrect. It is of interest to calculate the theoretical open circuit potentials for carbon monoxide half-cell reactions and for complete carbon monoxide–oxygen cells in both alkaline and acid electrolytes.

### (a) Electrode potentials and cell e.m.f.

Standard electrode potentials, $E°$, of carbon monoxide electrodes and standard e.m.f., $V°$, for carbon monoxide–oxygen cells in both alkaline and acid media may be calculated from the equation

$$E° = \frac{-\Delta G°}{nF}$$

where $\Delta G°$ is the free energy change for the reaction when the reactants are in their standard states of unit activity, $n$ is the number of electrons involved in the reaction and $F$ is the Faraday. The following free energy data for 25°C will be used

| Reacting species | $\Delta G°$ (kcal) |
|---|---|
| $OH^-$ (aq.) | $-37.6$ |
| $H_2O$ (liq.) | $-56.7$ |
| $CO$ (g) | $-32.8$ |
| $CO_3^{2-}$ (aq.) | $-126.2$ |
| $CO_2$ (g) | $-94.3$ |

Table 13 gives the standard potentials and e.m.f. for the assumed reactions.

### (b) Carbon monoxide electrodes in alkaline electrolyte

Young and Rozelle[53] measured half-cell potentials for carbon monoxide electrodes on a number of catalysts in an electrolyte of 40% aqueous potassium carbonate and obtained the values shown in Table 14.

These results are of interest in that they show that in passing from the metals

TABLE 13

STANDARD ELECTRODE POTENTIALS ($E°$) OF CARBON MONOXIDE ELECTRODES AND STANDARD
E.M.F. ($V°$) OF CARBON MONOXIDE–OXYGEN CELLS IN ACID AND ALKALINE ELECTROLYTES

| Electrolyte | Electrode or cell reaction | Standard potentials (or e.m.f.), at 25°C (volt) |
|---|---|---|
| Alkali | $CO_3^{2-} + 2\,H_2O + 2\,e \rightleftharpoons CO + 4\,OH^-$ | −1.22 |
| Alkali | $2\,CO + 4\,OH^- + O_2 \rightleftharpoons 2\,CO_3^{2-} + 2\,H_2O$ | 1.62 |
| Acid | $CO_2 + 2\,H^+ + 2\,e \rightleftharpoons CO + H_2O$ | −0.10 |
| Acid | $2\,CO + O_2 \rightleftharpoons 2\,CO_2$ | 1.33 |

of Group VIII of the Periodic Table to those of Group IB there is a sharp increase in the value of the half-cell potential indicating that transition metals are needed to set up the required equilibrium. These workers give no indication of the performance of their carbon monoxide electrodes under current drain.

Justi and co-workers[54] have shown that carbon monoxide can be activated in alkaline solution using the DSK or double skeleton type of electrode. Grüneberg[55] investigated the electrochemical oxidation of carbon monoxide on Ni and Cu–DSK electrodes in alkaline solution and proposed the following mechanism:

$$CO + OH^- \rightarrow HCOO^-$$

$$HCOO^- + OH^- \rightarrow CO_3^{2-} + 2\,H_{ads}$$

$$2\,H_{ads} \rightarrow 2\,H^+ + 2\,e\,.$$

TABLE 14

HALF-CELL POTENTIALS IN MILLIVOLTS (STANDARD HYDROGEN SCALE) FOR CARBON MONOXIDE
ELECTRODES IN 40% AQUEOUS $K_2CO_3$ AT 27°C

| Period \ Group | VIA | VIIA | VIII | | | IB |
|---|---|---|---|---|---|---|
| 4 | | | | Co −440 | Ni −495 | Cu −190 |
| 5 | | | Ru −475 | Rh −540 | Pd −570 | Ag −225 |
| 6 | W −462 | Re −469 | Os −520 | Ir −510 | Pt −545 | Au −150 |

This mechanism accounts for the observed electrode potential being close to the hydrogen potential despite the fact that the standard electrode potential for carbon monoxide in alkaline solution is about 400 millivolts more negative than the reversible hydrogen potential.

Justi has proposed that the reversible carbon monoxide potential should be approached on metals which possess a high hydrogen overpotential. A number of different electrode catalysts of the DSK type have been tried as carbon monoxide electrodes and Fig. 105 shows some typical results obtained with copper, molybdenum and tungsten electrodes.

The use of KOH as electrolyte is, however, unrealistic from the point of view of long term operation of a fuel cell using carbon monoxide, since the electrolyte will gradually become converted to carbonate. Cairns and Mac-Donald[56] have recently described invariant electrolyte systems of rubidium and caesium carbonates or bicarbonates which have an alkaline pH and operate at temperatures in excess of 100°C. These electrolytes have already been discussed in Chapter 9 in connection with the oxidation of hydrocarbon fuels and have also been used for the anodic oxidation of carbon monoxide

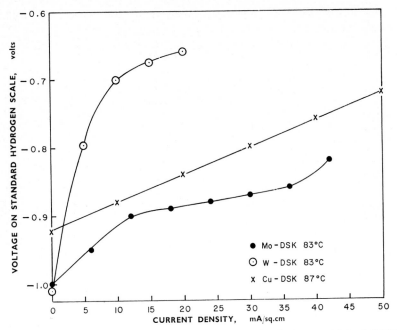

Fig. 105. Polarization curves for the anodic oxidation of carbon monoxide in 5 N KOH.

at a platinum black electrode. Whilst outputs obtained with this system were originally low[56], Cairns and Bartosik[57] have recently described a carbon monoxide electrode operating in caesium carbonate electrolyte at 130°C, using a teflon-bonded platinum black catalyst, which could sustain 40 mA/sq.cm at an anode polarization of 0.3 volt. This system shows considerable promise for the direct utilisation of carbon monoxide in a fuel cell.

### (c) Carbon monoxide electrodes in acid electrolytes

Gilman[58–61] has recently studied the electrochemical oxidation of carbon monoxide on smooth platinum in $N$ perchloric acid by a potential sweep method whereby it was possible to relate the observed current–voltage characteristics to the amount of adsorbed material on the surface of the electrode. He measured the fraction of the surface covered with carbon monoxide ($\theta_{CO}$) and with oxygen ($\theta_O$) as a function of potential during a periodic triangular voltage sweep of 0.04 volt/sec. During the ascending sweep the surface was found to be 75% covered with carbon monoxide up to 0.9 volt when a steep fall in coverage was observed and then $\theta_{CO}$ remained at zero up to 1.8 volt. The oxygen coverage on the electrode rose gradually from $\theta_O = 0$ at about 0.8 volt to $\theta = 1$ at 1.6 volt. Knowing the amount of adsorbed material on the surface of the electrode at different potentials, Gilman calculated the fraction of free surface $\theta_F$. Figure 106 gives a comparison between current density and fraction of surface free of adsorbed material as a function of voltage during a 0.04 volt/sec triangular sweep up to 1.2 volt.

Gilman concluded that large currents due to carbon monoxide oxidation

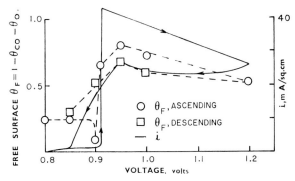

Fig. 106. Comparison of current with free surface, $\theta_F$, during 0.04 volt/sec triangular sweep to 1.2 volt.

occur at low coverages; at high coverages carbon monoxide tends to poison its own electrochemical oxidation. Two possible reasons were proposed for these observations. Either the electrochemical rate constant for the oxidation of adsorbed carbon monoxide may decrease with increasing coverage or the currents which flow at low carbon monoxide coverages may be considered to be due to "unadsorbed" carbon monoxide which is not tightly bound to the surface and is therefore more easily oxidized. It is clear that Gilman's work is of fundamental importance in relating the current–voltage character-istics for the oxidation of carbon monoxide to the adsorption data for carbon monoxide and oxygen on the electrode surface.

There are few data available on the current–voltage characteristics of gas electrodes fed with carbon monoxide in acid solutions under approximately steady state conditions. Gilman[58] has indicated that fuel cell polarization values have been obtained by Niedrach of General Electric Company but the results are as yet unpublished. In the author's own laboratory, half-cell polarization measurements have been made with an anode of platinum black supported on a gold-plated, microporous polyvinyl chloride substrate which was fed with carbon monoxide at slightly greater than atmospheric pressure. The electrolyte was 6 $N$ sulphuric acid and the anode voltage was measured with respect to a hydrogen reference electrode in the same medium. The anodic polarization curve is shown in Fig. 107.

The carbon monoxide was converted to carbon dioxide in accordance with the reaction

$$CO + H_2O \rightleftharpoons CO_2 + 2 H^+ + 2 e .$$

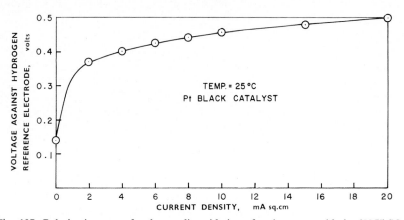

Fig. 107. Polarization curve for the anodic oxidation of carbon monoxide in $6N$ $H_2SO_4$.

Figure 107 shows that there was considerable overvoltage associated with the oxidation of carbon monoxide on a platinum black catalyst at ambient temperature. In addition, at any given current density the voltage drifted during operation to more positive values, a phenomenon which has been observed for fuels such as methanol, formic acid and hydrocarbons. On the basis of this polarization curve one might expect a $CO-O_2$ fuel cell with an acid electrolyte at 25°C temperature to have a terminal voltage of about 0.4 volt at a current density in the region of 20 mA/sq.cm, these characteristics becoming less favourable with time.

Binder, Köhling and Sandstede[62] have studied the oxidation of carbon monoxide on a Raney platinum electrode both in 3 $N$ $H_2SO_4$ and 28 $N$ $H_3PO_4$ at 100°C. At an electrode potential of 500 mV measured against a hydrogen reference electrode in the same medium the carbon monoxide electrode sustained a current density of 220 mA/sq.cm in sulphuric acid and 90 mA/sq.cm in phosphoric acid. Binder and co-workers showed that the carbon monoxide reacted with water vapour to produce carbon dioxide and hydrogen at the electrode, and that current arose from the oxidation of hydrogen. The rest potentials of the carbon monoxide electrode in these experiments were close to those obtained with hydrogen as fuel, which provides additional information that it is not the carbon monoxide which is directly oxidized but the hydrogen resulting from conversion.

## REFERENCES

[1] E. O'F. Walsh, *An Introduction to Biochemistry*, English Univ. Press, London, 1961.
[2] H. Theorell, A. P. Nygaard and R. Bonnichsen, *Acta Chem. Scand.*, **8** (1954) 1490.
[3] F. L. Rodkey, *J. Biol. Chem.*, **213** (1955) 777.
[4] F. L. Rodkey and J. A. Donovan, *J. Biol. Chem.*, **234** (1959) 677.
[5] W. D. Wosilait and A. Nason, *J. Biol. Chem.*, **206** (1954) 255.
[6] J. H. Quastel and A. H. M. Wheatley, *Biochem. J.*, **32** (1938) 936.
[7] H. S. Corran, D. E. Green and F. B. Straub, *Biochem. J.*, **33** (1939) 793.
[8] F. Dickens and H. McIlwain, *Biochem. J.*, **32** (1938) 1615.
[9] H. G. Du Buy and J. Showacre, *J. Histochem. and Cytochem.*, **7** (1959) 370.
[10] H. A. Ells, *Arch. Biochem. Biophys.*, **85** (1959) 561.
[11] G. H. Rohrback, W. R. Scott and J. H. Canfield, *Proc. Ann. Power Sources Conf.*, **16** (1962) 18.
[12] M. Shaw, *Proc. Ann. Power Sources Conf.*, **17** (1963) 53.
[13] H. P. Silverman and C. Albright, *Extended Abstr. Fall Meeting Electrochem. Soc., New York, Sept./Oct. 1963, Vol. 1: Electro-organic Div.*, p. 33.
[14] *Financial Times*, 22nd Nov., 1963, 13; 13th Sept., 1963, 11.
[15] J. E. Taylor, W. Fatica and G. H. Rohrback, in *Fuel Cells*, (Chem. Eng. Progr. Tech. Manual), Am. Inst. Chem. Engrs., New York, 1963, p. 11.

16 E. M. COHN, *Preprints\* 145th Natl. Meeting, Am. Chem. Soc.*, New York, Sept. 1963, Vol. 7: Div. Fuel Chem., No. 4: Symp. Fuel Cell Systems, p. 1.

17 *Status of Regenerative Fuel Cells*, Fuel Cell Corp., St. Louis, 1963

18 H.A. LIEBHAFSKY, *J. Electrochem. Soc.*, **106** (1959) 1068

19 A. J. DEBETHUNE, *J. Electrochem. Soc.*, **107** (1960) 937.

20 R. E. HENDERSON, B. AGRUSS AND N. G. CAPLE, *Prog. Astron. Rocketry*, **3** (1961) 411.

21 J. E. TAYLOR, N. FATICA AND G. H. ROHRBACK, in *Fuel Cells*, (Chem. Eng. Progr. Tech. Manual), Am. Inst. Chem. Engrs., New York, 1963, p. 13.

22 B. AGRUSS, *Extended Abstr. 120th Meeting Electrochem. Soc.*, Detroit, Oct. 1961, Battery Div., p. 97.

23 R. D. WEAVER, S. W. SMITH AND N. L. WILLMAN, *Extended Abstr. 120th Meeting Electrochem. Soc.*, Detroit, Oct. 1961, Battery Div., p. 99.

24 R. E. HENDERSON, in *Fuel Cells*, (Chem. Eng. Progr. Tech. Manual), Am. Inst. Chem. Eng., New York, 1963, p. 17.

25 J. KING, F. A. LUDWIG AND J. J. ROWLETTE, *Progr. Astron. Rocketry*, **3** (1961) 387.

26 J. G. CALVERT, *Ohio J. Sci.*, **53** (1953) 293.

27 W. E. MCKEE, E. FINDL, J. D. MARGERUM AND W. B. LEE, *Proc. Ann. Power Sources Conf.*, **14** (1960) 68.

28 R. M. LURIE AND C. BERGER, *Extended Abstr. 120th Meeting Electrochem. Soc.*, Detroit, Oct. 1961, Battery Div., p. 71.

29 H. SILVERMAN, W. MOMYER AND M. EISENBERG, *Proc. Ann. Power Sources Conf.*, **14** (1960) 72.

30 H. SILVERMAN, W. MOMYER AND M. EISENBERG, *Proc. Ann. Power Sources Conf.*, **15** (1961) 53.

31 W. H. PODOLNY, *Proc. Ann. Power Sources Conf.*, **14** (1960) 64.

32 J. M. LEE AND R. M. HANDLEWICH, *Proc. Ann. Power Sources Conf.*, **15** (1961) 43.

33 J. S. BONE, *Proc. Ann. Power Sources Conf.*, **14** (1960) 62.

34 J. S. BONE, S. GILMAN, L. W. NIEDRACH AND M. D. READ, *Proc. Ann. Power Sources Conf.*, **15** (1961) 47.

35 F. A. LUDWIG, D. H. MCCLELLAND AND H. A. FRANK, *Proc. Ann. Power Sources Conf.*, **15** (1961) 33.

36 E. W. JUSTI, in *Fuel Cells*, (Chem. Eng. Progr. Tech. Manual), Am. Inst. Chem. Engrs., New York, 1963, p. 79.

37 L. ROSENBLUM AND R. E. ENGLISH, *Advanced Energy Sources and Conversion Techniques*, Vol. 1, U.S. Dept. Comm. Office Tech. Serv. PB151461, p. 243, (ASTIA No. AD209301).

38 J. F. YEAGER, R. J. BENNETT AND D. R. ALLENSON, *Proc. Ann. Power Sources Conf.*, **16** (1962) 39.

39 A. J. SWALLOW, *Radiation Chemistry of Organic Compounds*, Pergamon, Oxford, 1960, p. 52.

40 L. G. AUSTIN, R. D. CHAMBERLIN AND A. R. SCHLEICHER, Final Rept. on redox fuel cells: The fuel regenerator, *U.S. Dept. Comm. Rept. AD 289,559*, 1962.

41 A. M. POSNER, *Fuel*, **34** (1955) 330.

42 J. HALPERN, E. R. MACGREGOR AND E. PETERS, *J. Phys. Chem.*, **60** (1956) 1455.

43 B. E. MERTON-BINGHAM AND A. M. POSNER, *J. Am. Chem. Soc.*, **77** (1955) 2634.

44 W. E. RENEKE, *M. S. Thesis*, Univ. Florida, 1961.

45 J. A. SHROPSHIRE AND B. L. TARMY, *Preprints\* 145th Natl. Meeting Am. Chem. Soc.*, New York, Sept. 1963, Vol. 7: Div. Fuel Chem., No. 4: Symp. Fuel Cell Systems, p. 158.

46 E. YEAGER, in *Fuel Cells*, (ed. by W. MITCHELL), Academic Press, New York, 1963, p. 299.

\* Proceedings to be published by American Chemical Society as *Fuel Cell Systems* (Advan. Chem. Ser. No. 47).

[47] J. S. SMATKO, *Proc. Ann. Power Sources Conf.*, **15** (1961) 52.

[48] G. J. WOMACK, *Fuel Soc. J. Univ. Sheffield*, (1963) 35.

[49] W. R. GROVE, *The Correlation of Physical Forces*, Longmans Green and Co., London, 6th edn. 1874.

[50] W. BORCHERS, *U.S. Patent 567,959* (1896).

[51] K. A. HOFMANN, *Ber.*, **51B** (1918) 1576; **52B** (1919) 1185; **53B** (1920) 914.

[52] F. AUERBACH, *Z. Elektrochem.*, **25** (1919) 82.

[53] G. J. YOUNG AND R. B. ROZELLE, Chap. 3 in *Fuel Cells*, (ed. by G. J. YOUNG), Vol. 1, Reinhold, New York, 1960, p. 23.

[54] E. JUSTI, M. PILKUHN, W. SCHEIBE AND A. WINSEL, *High Drain Hydrogen–Diffusion Electrodes Operating at Ambient Temperature and Low Pressure*, Franz Steiner, Wiesbaden, 1959.

[55] G. GRÜNEBERG, *Dissertation*, Tech. Hochschüle Braunschweig, 1958.

[56] E. J. CAIRNS AND D. I. MACDONALD, *Electrochem. Technol.*, **2** (1964) 67.

[57] E. J. CAIRNS AND D. C. BARTOSIK, *J. Electrochem. Soc.*, **111** (1964) 1205.

[58] S. GILMAN, *J. Phys. Chem.*, **66** (1962) 2657.

[59] S. GILMAN, *J. Phys. Chem.*, **67** (1963) 78.

[60] S. GILMAN, *J. Phys. Chem.*, **67** (1963) 1898.

[61] S. GILMAN, *J. Phys. Chem.*, **68** (1964) 70.

[62] H. BINDER, A. KÖHLING AND G. SANDSTEDE, *15th CITCE Meeting, London, 1964*.

*Chapter 11*

# COMPLETE POWER SOURCES

## 1. BATTERIES

As we have seen, fuel cells supply electricity as direct current at low voltage, commonly less than one volt. This is unsuitable for most practical applications, and multiple fuel cells, or fuel batteries, must be constructed in which groups of cells are connected electrically in series and/or in parallel to give usable outputs.

In order to understand the problems of constructing fuel batteries it is first necessary to review the requirements of a single fuel cell. In its simplest form a fuel cell consists of two electrodes separated by electrolyte. Fuel is supplied to one electrode and oxidant to the other. Provision must be made for the removal of the reaction products from the electrodes and for the removal of any impurities present in the fuel and oxidant feeds. There must be electrical connections from the electrodes to the exterior of the cell and the heat produced owing to the inefficiency of the system must be removed in some way. Thus all the cells, in a fuel battery must (1) be suitably interconnected electrically, (2) receive adequate supplies of fuel and oxidant, and (3) be provided with exhaust systems for both impurities and products, including heat. In addition to these physico-chemical requirements the cells must be engineered into a mechanically sound battery. This implies adequate structural support for the various components and freedom from leaks. For most applications there is also a demand for lightness and compactness; this is particularly true for present-day military or space applications.

While these requirements must all be considered in constructing a fuel battery from a given electrode system, the difficulty of meeting any particular requirement varies considerably from one type of cell to another. Thus heat removal might be difficult from a large fuel battery operating on hydrogen and oxygen at low temperatures but would be no problem at all in a medium-sized solid oxide battery operating at 1000°C. Indeed the problem in the

latter case would be to provide adequate thermal insulation to keep the
battery self-sustaining and to provide adequate heat exchange between exhaust and incoming air. Moreover, many of the requirements are interrelated
and often require conflicting solutions. For example, heat removal from a low-
temperature cell can be accomplished by circulating the electrolyte through
the battery and then through a radiator. Adequate circulation without excessive pressure drops requires large electrolyte spaces and galleries and these
not only increase the bulk of the battery but give rise to undesirable electrical
properties, namely high internal resistance of the cells and increased parasitic
currents. Thus the heat removal, electrical and volume requirements are
conflicting and a compromise must be reached or another method adopted
for heat removal.

Section 1 discusses some of the problems in making batteries from established fuel cell electrodes and describes several of the batteries which have
been constructed.

### (a) Electrical connection

Since fuel cells are low voltage, high current devices it is very important to
minimize both the internal resistances of individual fuel cells and the electrical resistances which are inevitably introduced when a number of cells are
connected together to make a battery. The case of ohmic polarization within
the electrolyte was considered in section 3 of Chapter 3 and may be summarized as follows.

The voltage drop $\Delta V$ introduced by the internal resistance of a fuel cell
electrolyte depends on the inter-electrode spacing $l$ (cm) and the specific
resistance of the electrolyte $\rho$,

$$\Delta V = \frac{Il\rho}{A}$$

where $I$ is the current (amp) and $A$ is the geometrical area of the electrodes
(sq.cm). $l$ is not simply the geometric separation but is the effective thickness
of free electrolyte between the two electrodes. Where, for example, the electrolyte is retained in a porous material such as asbestos or glass fibres a
tortuosity factor is introduced and the effective value of $l$ may be several
times the geometrical separation of the electrodes. Since $\rho$ is very dependent
on electrolyte concentration, this must be controlled.

A further contribution to the internal resistance of an individual cell
comes from the electrodes themselves, which are not perfect conductors.

If current is collected from the periphery of the electrode, then the larger the electrode, the larger will be this effect of the electrode resistance. For example, for two circular electrodes of area $A$ (sq.cm) with edge collection it may be shown that for specific resistance of the electrode conductor $\mu$, thickness $d$ (cm) and current density $i$ (mA/sq.cm) the maximum voltage loss $\Delta V$ is

$$\Delta V = i\left(\frac{\mu A}{4\pi d} + \rho l\right).$$

There are two different arrangements of the cells in a battery, these being known as homopolar or unipolar and bipolar.

In the homopolar arrangement fuel is supplied to the spaces between a pair of electrodes insulated from each other. Each electrode is in contact with electrolyte separating it from another pair of electrodes

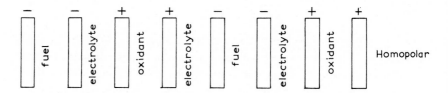

supplied with oxidant. Thus adjacent electrodes are of the same polarity.

In the bipolar arrangement fuel and oxidant electrodes alternate, the fuel and oxidant being separated by an impermeable diaphragm. Thus adjacent electrodes are of different polarity.

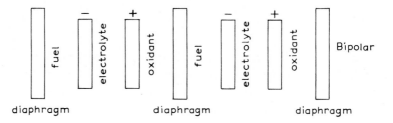

The homopolar arrangement is the more compact and simplifies the supply of fuel and oxidant within the battery. However, the series electrical interconnection of the cells requires the connection of alternate electrodes. This can only be done outside the main body of the battery.

− Electrolyte +   + Electrolyte −   − Electrolyte +

In bipolar construction the distribution of reactants within the battery is more complex but series electrical connection of the cells is much simplified, the contact being made through the impermeable diaphragms. Bipolar construction has been the more widely used in recent batteries.

When the basic fuel cell uses a circulating liquid electrolyte to remove heat the series connection of cells to form a battery can lead to electrical losses through the electrolyte system. For reasons discussed later the cells are normally fed with electrolyte in parallel flow. Under these conditions the electrolyte provides a conducting path between the various cells comprising the battery, and parasitic or shunt currents flow through the electrolyte system. These reduce the efficiency of the battery, produce heat and also, if sufficient cells are interconnected, form gas in the electrolyte stream by electrolysis.

The magnitude of the parasitic currents, may be calculated by applying Kirchoff's laws to the network of resistances[1]:

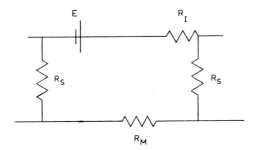

where $R_I$ is the internal resistance of one cell, $R_s$ is the resistance of the electrolyte ports into a cell, $R_m$ is the resistance of the electrolyte manifold between cells and $E$ is the e.m.f. of one cell.

It can than be deduced that $R_s$ and $R_m$ must be as high as possible and $R_s$ should be much greater than $R_m$ to reduce the shunt currents to a minimum. This means in practice that the electrolyte inlet and outlet ports to each cell must be as long and narrow as is compatible with acceptable pressure losses in the electrolyte circulating system. Furthermore, the electrodes and current-carrying components must be effectively insulated from electrolyte manifolds, for example Bacon[2] has used O-ring insulating inserts.

The alternative procedure is to eliminate the shunt currents by using a "trapped" electrolyte, in which the electrolyte is retained between the electrodes in the capillaries of an inert insulating matrix such as asbestos (or glass) paper. There is then no electrical connection through the electrolyte system to adjacent cells. Trapped electrolyte systems require careful control to maintain invariance of the electrolyte. Thus it is usually necessary to humidify incoming gases to prevent concentration of the electrolyte, and all traces of carbon dioxide must be removed if air is used with a trapped potassium hydroxide electrolyte. Circulating electrolyte systems are normally more tolerant.

### (b) Supply of fuel and oxidant

The choice of the system for the supply of fuel and oxidant to a battery depends to a large extent on the nature of the reactants. When the reactants are gases, or are fed to the battery in a gasified condition, the feeds to the individual cells may be in series, in series-parallel or in parallel. The choice is mainly dependent on the purity of the feed gases, the nature of the products, the sizes of the individual cells and the tolerance of the particular electrode systems to reduced concentrations of reactive species.

Parallel gas flow is the simplest to arrange and results in the minimum pressure losses within the gas spaces. However, it may be difficult to ensure uniform distribution to a large number of individual cells from a common manifold. Furthermore, distribution difficulties can arise if two phases (for example, gas and electrolyte) are present in parallel channels or if components of the feed gases and products differ substantially in density or viscosity. Parallel flow is essential if the concentration of the reactive species is low (for example, if air is used as oxidant) so that high gas flows must be used to ensure removal of the inert gases.

Series flow ensures that all cells receive a stream of gas but each cell operates at a slightly lower pressure than the previous one. This is partly because some reactive species will have been removed in the upstream cells but more particularly because of the accumulation of pressure losses at the inlets, exits and across each cell. The limit to the number of cells in a series bank with pure gases and with a liquid electrolyte is normally reached when the pressure in the last cell is below that required to maintain the gas/liquid interface in the correct position within the electrode. The number can be increased by reducing the pressure losses in each single cell but this normally means increasing the size of the various gas passages resulting in an increased overall volume for the battery.

When feed gases are impure, or when solid electrolytes are used, the limit for series flow is reached when the concentration of reactive species falls below that required for adequate output. This varies appreciably with the type of electrode, thick electrodes normally being less tolerant than thin ones.

Chambers and Tantram[3] have shown that for a hydrogen–air battery at 550°C the theoretical cell voltage falls appreciably with the proportion of the gas oxidized. Consequently, it is claimed that most efficient utilization of energy will be obtained by multi-stage oxidation, that is by series fuel flow. The data are:

| 97% gas utilization | Energy obtained |
| --- | --- |
| Single pass | 83% |
| Four-stage (series) | 94% |
| Eight-stage (series) | 96% |

Unfortunately, this means that in theory successive cells in the series bank should operate at different voltages, within the range 1.2 volt to about 0.8 volt.

Cairns, Tevebaugh and Holm[4] have shown that this fall in voltage is much less significant for a methane system at 227°C in which carbon deposition is prevented by recycling oxidation products (carbon dioxide and water) or by adding steam. This is probably because an equilibrium concentration of hydrogen is reached rapidly. The voltage falls by only 0.03 volt for 0–99% oxidation when oxidation products are recycled, and by 0.06 volt when steam is added. For this system it is possible to operate with fuel flow in series without an appreciable fall in voltage in successive cells.

For large batteries it may be necessary to connect, in parallel, blocks of cells in which feed gases are supplied in series.

Where the fuel is a liquid two methods have been used. Fuels such as methanol or hydrazine which are soluble in the liquid electrolyte are normally supplied to the electrodes dissolved in the electrolyte and, for reasons to be considered later, in parallel feed. Liquid fuels which are insoluble in the electrolyte are not normally suitable for use in low temperature batteries. When used in high temperature batteries they vaporize and/or crack before the electrochemical reaction occurs so they can then be treated as gaseous feeds.

### (c) Exhaust system for products

The most usual products to be removed from the battery are water, heat, carbon dioxide (from carbonaceous fuels) and nitrogen (from hydrazine).

Water removal will not be a problem in high temperature batteries since the water will be present entirely in the gas phase and can be removed by venting of the appropriate gas stream.

In low temperature cells the water is formed below its boiling point and will tend to condense. With a liquid electrolyte the water tends to dissolve in the electrolyte and can thus be removed from the battery by circulating the electrolyte. If this procedure is adopted the electrolyte becomes progressively more dilute and eventually the performance of the battery deteriorates. To eliminate dilution it is possible to re-concentrate the electrolyte by evaporation outside the battery, possibly by supplying external heat, which is wasteful in terms of the overall efficiency of the fuel battery system. As an alternative in space applications only, it has been proposed[1] that the water vapour should be rejected to the vacuum of space by transpiration through a porous diaphragm or through a thin plastic membrane.

The alternative to rejecting water to the electrolyte is to reject the surplus water to the gas streams by feeding one or both of the gases at a rate sufficient to remove the excess water. The rate of gas feed required to maintain an invariant electrolyte depends on the operating temperature of the cell and on the composition of the electrolyte. For batteries operating on air the excess air and water vapour can be vented to atmosphere. For batteries operating on relatively pure gases (e.g. oxygen or hydrogen) this procedure would be wasteful. In these circumstances it is usual to recycle the gas to which the water is rejected over a cooler to condense the water[1].

In batteries with an alkaline electrolyte water is formed at the fuel electrodes and in order to minimize concentration polarization at high current densities it is preferable to remove excess water by recirculating the fuel gas, as was done by Bacon[5]. With an acid electrolyte the water forms at the oxidant electrodes and it is then preferable to remove the water in the oxidant stream. This has been done by Chapman and Oster[6,7].

The waste heat produced in the battery can be removed by one or more of the following methods:

(1) Cooling the external surface of the battery[5].

(2) Circulating the fuel and/or oxidant gases through an external cooler[1,5,9]; with air as oxidant the excess air can be vented to atmosphere[6].

(3) Circulating the electrolyte through an external cooler[1,8,9].

(4) Circulating a separate coolant through galleries in the battery[7].

(5) Cooling the system by an endothermic reaction carried out within the battery[9].

Cooling the external surfaces of the battery is likely to be of most value in cells operating at relatively high temperatures. (If the temperature differential is relatively low a large surface area will be required for heat transfer.) This procedure results in temperature gradients within the battery which will increase as the size of battery (particularly the cross section) increases. For a particular design of battery there is likely to be a maximum size above which the temperature gradients become unacceptable; this was less than ten inches diameter in the medium temperature Bacon battery[5].

Increasing the circulation rate of the gas feeds has the advantage that water vapour is also removed and thus the latent heat of water is rejected at the same time. In most practical batteries this amounts to about one-third of the total heat to be rejected. The objection to removing all the remainder of the heat by gas recirculation is the relatively low specific heat of most gases. This necessitates high mass flows with consequent increases in the dimensions of the gas passages to give acceptable pressure drops. The exception to this is hydrogen which has a relatively high specific heat and low viscosity. Consequently, adequate heat removal can be achieved by recirculating the hydrogen in a hydrogen battery through an external cooler[5].

Recirculation of a liquid electrolyte is probably the method most commonly used to remove heat from a battery. This system requires careful compromises in the design since large electrolyte passages are needed to keep the pressure losses in the system low while long narrow electrolyte passages are needed to minimize electrical losses. Except for very small batteries parallel flow of electrolyte must be used since series flow leads to excessive pressure losses.

Circulating a separate coolant through the battery has the advantage that the external cooler need not be resistant to the electrolyte, but the method does result in increased bulk in the battery. Nonetheless, this procedure has been used in at least one of the batteries designed for use in the Gemini spacecraft[7].

Heat removal by an endothermic reaction as proposed by Liebhafsky and Cairns[9] has not so far been reported as a practical achievement. Nonetheless it is potentially interesting for high temperature batteries. The basic idea is to feed to a fuel battery a fuel mixture which undergoes endothermic reforming or reaction within the battery, the products of the endothermic reaction then reacting electrochemically at the fuel cell electrodes. The battery would be operated at such a voltage that the heat produced because of the inefficiency of the electrochemical reaction would balance that taken up by the endothermic reaction plus the heat losses from the battery. Steam–methanol and steam–hydrocarbon reforming are potentially interesting for this system.

The removal of carbon dioxide from a low temperature battery with an acid electrolyte does not present any difficulties. The gas is not particularly soluble in the electrolyte and, once the electrolyte has become saturated, the gas bubbles out with the circulating electrolyte and may be separated outside the battery. It may be necessary to increase slightly the electrolyte exit ports from each cell to cope with the increased volume of gas–liquid mixture. Fortunately, the gas bubbles tend to break the electrolyte stream within the ports and the parasitic currents do not increase significantly. Nitrogen can be removed from hydrazine batteries by the same method.

The removal of carbon dioxide from alkaline hydroxide batteries is much more difficult because reaction occurs in the electrolyte to form carbonate, the hydroxide ion concentration falls and with it battery output. It is uneconomic to discard the electrolyte and thus some method must be found for economically reconverting the carbonate to hydroxide. Various methods have been proposed by Murray and Grimes[10], including the use of ion exchange resins (adversely affected by the alkaline medium) and precipitation with lime (causing problems of calcium carbonate disposal). Justi[11] has proposed electrodialysis and has claimed that this method can operate on a power consumption of about 10% of the total power produced but has published no details of the technique. At present a satisfactory method of removing carbon dioxide from alkaline hydroxide electrolytes has not yet been established.

There would be no problem in removing carbon dioxide from alkali carbonate electrolytes, where the gas could bubble out of the circulating electrolyte. Unfortunately, the output of cells with such electrolytes has not yet reached attractive levels. A further disadvantage is that crystals of relatively insoluble bicarbonate might form on the fuel electrode at low temperatures with consequent fall in output.

### (d) Materials of construction

One problem which is concerned with fuel cell engineering rather than with physico-chemical matters is the selection of materials of construction. In low

temperature batteries the main problem is to select materials which are unaffected by the strongly acid or alkaline electrolytes. Plastics can be used for
many of the main components, depending on the temperature of operation,
but metal structural components are necessary at the higher end of the "low"
temperature range (100–120°C), and also for current collection and transport.
The main materials suitable for low temperature cells are summarized in
Table 15.

TABLE 15

| Material | Acid electrolyte | Alkaline electrolyte | Remarks |
|---|---|---|---|
| Platinum | √ | √ | |
| Palladium | x | √ | |
| Rhodium | √ | √ | |
| Gold | √ | √ | |
| Silver | x | √ | Dissolves slowly in alkali |
| Nickel | x | √ | May anodize to non-conducting surface |
| Lead | √ | x | Heavy, and slowly attacked in acid |
| Stainless steels | Some √ | √ | Satisfactory for structure but not for current collection |
| Titanium | √ | x | Anodizes; must be platinum-plated for current collection |
| Tantalum | √ | √ | |
| Polyolefins | √ | √ | Temperature-limited; high density material has greater range |
| Polymethacrylates (Perspex, Lucite) | √ | √ | |
| Polystyrene | √ | √ | Temperature-limited |
| Polyvinylchloride (PVC) | √ | √ | Temperature-limited |
| Polyamides (Nylon) | x | √ | |
| Epoxy resins | √ | √ | Usefulness depends on composition |
| Fluoro-plastics (Teflon, Fluon) | √ | √ | |
| Chlorinated polyether (Penton) | √ | √ | |
| Rubbers | √ | √ | |

Low temperature fuel batteries normally contain substantial quantities of plastics which differ widely in coefficient of expansion and in creep characteristics from the metals. Temperature cycling of such batteries tends to cause leaks and it is usual to spring-load the battery to overcome the problem[1,12].

### (e) Developed batteries

Now that some of the features to be considered in designing fuel batteries have been described, it is interesting to review several of the various types of battery which have been built. These include:

The Bacon battery: medium temperature, hydrogen–oxygen, alkaline electrolyte.

General Electric ion exchange battery: low temperature, hydrogen–oxygen or air, cation exchange membrane.

Hydrazine batteries (Allis-Chalmers): low temperature, hydrazine–oxygen, alkaline electrolyte.

Chloride Electrical Storage: low temperature, hydrazine–oxygen, alkaline electrolyte.

"Shell" Research: low temperature, hydrazine–air, alkaline electrolyte.

### The Bacon battery

The Bacon cell, which has been described in Chapter 5, is a high-pressure (600 lb./sq.in.) hydrogen–oxygen cell operating at medium temperatures (200°C) with potassium hydroxide solution as electrolyte. The essential feature is the use of bi-porous nickel electrodes to control the gas/liquid interface. Bacon has described a battery of forty cells with electrodes about ten inches in diameter[2,5]. The battery is of homopolar construction, with series electrical connections made outside the battery. The gases and electrolyte are fed to the individual cells in parallel. The electrodes are insulated from the electrolyte manifolds by O-rings of polytetrafluoroethylene. Heat and water are removed by recirculating the hydrogen from the battery through a cooler/condenser. The rate of circulation required to remove the heat at high outputs removes too much water from the battery and the electrolyte tends to concentrate. This is adjusted by automatically returning some of the condensate to the electrolyte system as necessary.

Pratt and Whitney have refined the techniques used in the Bacon battery and have developed two batteries for use in the Apollo Project for a moon landing. The batteries (Fig. 108) are a 2-kW unit for the spacecraft itself and a 1-kW unit for the Lunar Excursion Module which is intended to make a brief journey on the surface of the moon. Little detailed information is available on the construction of these batteries. The large battery is understood

Fig. 108. Hydrogen–oxygen fuel cell powerplants designed and built by the Pratt and Whitney Aircraft Division of United Aircraft Corporation at East Hartford, Connecticut, U.S.A. in 1964. (A), 2 kW closed cycle fuel cell powerplant designed to supply on-board electrical power and potable water for the Command and Service Module of the NASA Apollo Project; (B), 1 kW open cycle fuel cell powerplant designed to provide on-board electrical power for the Lunar Excursion Module (LEM) of the NASA Apollo Project.

to consist of Bacon bi-porous nickel electrodes operating at about 200°C with trapped, molten, (85%) potassium hydroxide as electrolyte. Pure oxygen and hydrogen are preheated and fed to the cells at about 60 lb./sq.in. The hydrogen is recirculated rapidly by a hydrogen pump through a cooler to remove the heat. Product water also condenses and some is recycled with the feed gases to maintain invariance of the electrolyte. The remainder of the product water is available in potable form for the astronauts. The cells are fed with gases in parallel with separate feed pipes to each cell and electrical connections are then in series. A feature of this construction for space equipment is that each individual fuel cell may be tested separately before installation into the fuel battery.

*General Electric Company ion exchange battery*

The General Electric ion exchange batteries are based on the firm's cationic exchange membrane electrolyte (see page 103). These have been built into batteries operating on hydrogen and air (a 200-watt portable back-pack) for military use[6] and hydrogen and oxygen for use in spacecraft (two 25-watt batteries for the HOPE project[7] and a 2-kW battery (Fig. 109) for the Gemini two-man spacecraft[7]).

All three designs of battery are bipolar, giving internal series electrical connections. As the electrolyte is solid there is no circulation of electrolyte. The gases are fed to the cells in parallel flow, the air in the back-pack being continuously exhausted. The pure gas feeds (hydrogen and oxygen) can be purged as necessary to remove impurities which accumulate.

Heat and water are removed from the back-pack battery partly by the air stream which also cools by evaporating the product water and partly by passing additional convective cooling air through the battery. The air stream tends to remove more water than is produced in the reaction and this has a deleterious effect on the electrolyte membrane. To overcome this, the battery is provided with a water reservoir and a system of wicks to distribute water to the surfaces of the membrane to maintain the desired membrane humidity.

In the HOPE battery the bipolar current collector is also a cooling fin connected to an external heat sink and thence to a space radiator. Product water then condenses on the surface of the bipolar collector where it is absorbed in wicks from which it is withdrawn by capillary action for collection.

In the Gemini battery heat is removed by circulating coolant through tubes in the bipolar current collector to a space radiator. Wicks are again provided

Fig. 109. General Electric ion exchange fuel battery for Gemini mission.

for collecting the condensed product water which is removed from the battery for use as drinking water.

*Hydrazine batteries*

Hydrazine batteries with alkaline electrolyte have been exhibited by Allis-Chalmers Manufacturing Company[8], Chloride Electrical Storage Company Ltd.[13] and "Shell" Research Ltd., hydrazine–oxygen batteries by the first two and hydrazine–air by the last named.

The Allis-Chalmers battery is the largest, about 3 kW, and has been used to power a golf-cart. It is of bipolar construction with series electrical connections. Oxygen and electrolyte are fed in parallel, the electrolyte stream containing the hydrazine fuel. Heat is removed by circulating the electrolyte through an external radiator, and nitrogen is removed with the electrolyte. There is no provision for the removal of water.

The Chloride Electrical Storage battery is of unusual construction in that it is similar in appearance to a storage battery (Fig. 47). The electrodes are connected electrically in parallel. Oxygen feed is also in parallel while electrolyte and dissolved hydrazine are fed through the hollow porous anodes in parallel. Nitrogen is vented from the electrolyte. Methods of removing water and heat have not been described.

The "Shell" Research battery (Fig. 110) consists of twenty-five cells with bipolar construction and series electrical connections. Air and electrolyte containing dissolved hydrazine are supplied in parallel. Excess air is vented from the air electrodes and the nitrogen is removed in the electrolyte stream.

Fig. 110. "Shell" Research hydrazine–air fuel battery.

The heat is removed in the circulating electrolyte. There is no provision for water removal other than that lost in the air stream when running at elevated temperature. Output from the electrodes, the area of which is 0.7 sq.ft., is 20 amp at 18 volts at 15°C and increases at higher temperatures.

The battery was exhibited at the World Petroleum Congress, 1963, demonstrating a fuel battery operating on a liquid fuel and air. The battery was self-sustaining, providing its own services (circulation of air and electrolyte) and also powered a demonstration illustrating the electrochemical reaction between hydrazine and air.

## Methanol batteries

Allis-Chalmers and "Shell" Research Ltd. have produced methanol batteries. The Allis-Chalmers battery[10] operates on methanol and oxygen with an alkaline electrolyte while the "Shell" Research battery uses methanol and air with acid electrolyte. Precise details of the construction and of the removal of products are not available but some data are given on pages 114 and 119. Both supply the fuel dissolved in the electrolyte and are of bipolar construction with series electrical connections.

## High temperature batteries

The development of high temperature batteries has not proceeded as rapidly as that of low temperature batteries. Indeed, no substantial high temperature battery has yet been described, the largest recorded[14,15] so far having an output of about 100 watts. In this particular system the fuel is partially pre-oxidized to give a fuel gas which is fed to the fuel anodes. The spent fuel from the anodes is mixed with excess air, thus supplying the carbon dioxide needed with oxygen at the cathode.

In general, the battery designs proposed are similar to those for low temperature batteries but different constructional materials are used. In particular, parallel plate electrodes are the most common with either homopolar or bipolar construction. Normally, both fuel and oxidant are supplied in parallel, but Hardy and McCallum[16] have proposed series feed of both fuel and oxidant in a molten carbonate battery. In this system fuel passes in series flow through the anode chambers of a six-cell module to a combustion chamber where the excess fuel is mixed with air and catalytically burnt. The excess air and combustion gases are then returned in series flow through the cathode chambers. A serious disadvantage of this design is the excessive pressure drop (15 lb./sq.in.) through the battery which leads to considerable power losses in pumping the air.

Several workers who have developed tubular cells (see Chapter 7) have proposed batteries of cells in the form of shell-and-tube heat exchangers in which one of the reactants passes up the tubes while the other passes around the outside of the tubes. In such a battery it is necessary for series electrical connections to join the current collector from the inside of one tube to that from the outside of the next.

Workers at Westinghouse Electric Corporation have proposed a form of construction which simplifies the series electrical connections for a battery with an oxide electrolyte. In this the electrolyte is in the form of thin cylindrical tubes ground into thin-walled bell-and-spigot segments which nest together to form a continuous tube (Fig. 79). Electrodes are applied to the inner and outer surfaces of the segments and a conducting seal is used to join the segments together. In this way the inner electrode of one cell is electrically connected to the outer electrode of the next, thus giving series electrical connections down the continuous tube. So far, only small batteries have been described.

## 2. PRODUCTION OF HYDROGEN

There is no doubt that the easiest and most efficient type of fuel cell to develop and manufacture is one designed to use hydrogen as fuel. Unfortunately, hydrogen as such is not a convenient fuel because it is not readily stored or transported. It can be stored or carried at high pressure or as liquid hydrogen in cryogenic containers. In both cases, considerable power is needed to compress or liquefy the gas and the containers are heavy or bulky and relatively expensive. Furthermore, the use of liquid hydrogen is still not sufficiently commonplace for routine commercial or automotive applications. Thus hydrogen is an expensive fuel and its use as primary fuel can only be envisaged for highly specialized applications.

Nevertheless, the hydrogen-fuelled cell is sufficiently attractive to make it worthwhile considering using hydrogen as a secondary fuel by generating the gas as required from a more convenient primary fuel. To a large extent this is what happens inside a high temperature fuel cell (see Chapter 9) when the hydrocarbon feed reacts with added steam or water of reaction to produce hydrogen and carbon monoxide, which then react at the electrode. The present section discusses ways of providing hydrogen by reaction outside the cell.

Hydrogen can be produced from both organic and inorganic materials, by a large number of reactions, most of which are unsuitable for making hydrogen outside the laboratory and thus need not be discussed. Of the others, one, hydrolysis of borohydride, is extremely expensive but has been used for a highly specialized military application by General Electric[6]. The others to be described have all been used in hydrogen production outside the laboratory although the outputs have varied from a few hundred standard cubic feet (scf) per day to about 50 million scf per day. In view of the importance of hydrogen as an industrial chemical many reviews have been published[17,18].

### (a) Hydrogen purification

When any processes for making hydrogen for fuel cells are considered it is essential to decide how pure the product gas should be. Low temperature cells need the purest product, since they are based on active catalysts which are likely to be poisoned readily by such impurities as carbon monoxide and sulphur compounds. When low temperature cells use an alkaline electrolyte the carbon dioxide content of the hydrogen must also be low. High temperature cells will consume carbon monoxide and reject carbon dioxide but, in general, sulphur compounds are likely to cause difficulties with the materials of construction.

The total quantity of inert impurities which the hydrogen may contain will vary with the design of electrode, but the more inert material present the greater must be the rate of venting and consequently the greater the wastage of unused hydrogen from the cell.

### Complete purification by diffusion

Diffusion through palladium or palladium–silver alloys produces hydrogen containing no detectable impurities. The hydrogen may then be used in any type of fuel cell without wastage. The palladium–silver alloys are more stable than palladium itself, which undergoes phase transformation in the presence of hydrogen at temperatures below $300°C$[19]. The palladium–silver diffusers are expensive and thus are only attractive for relatively small throughputs (up to about 30,000 scf/h)[20] or for highly specialized applications. They cannot be used for gases containing sulphur or certain halogen compounds.

### Removal of carbon dioxide

Carbon dioxide may be removed by scrubbing the hydrogen with mono-ethanolamine, "Sulfinol"[21] (a mixture of sulpholane and alkanolamines), water, or solutions of potassium carbonate or potassium hydroxide. The carbonated liquid is normally regenerated by heating (although, when water is used, this is not usually recycled).

### Removal of carbon monoxide

When carbon monoxide is present in large quantities it is usual to convert it to carbon dioxide by the water gas shift reaction over promoted iron oxides or proprietary catalysts containing copper, zinc and chromium:

$$CO + H_2O \rightleftharpoons H_2 + CO_2 .$$

The carbon dioxide is then removed by scrubbing. Depending on the initial concentration of carbon monoxide, more than one stage of water gas shift may be required with intermediate removal of the carbon dioxide. Removal of the last traces of carbon monoxide may be accomplished by scrubbing with ammoniacal copper solutions, by conversion to methane over a nickel or ruthenium catalyst,

$$CO + 3\ H_2 \rightarrow CH_4 + H_2O$$

by selective oxidation over platinum catalyst at relatively low temperatures (60–160°C, depending on the pressure), by molecular sieves, or cryogenically. These two last processes will also remove carbon dioxide and nitrogen.

### (b) Hydrogen generation

The principal methods which are likely to be of interest for making hydrogen for fuel cells are as follows.

#### Hydrolysis of borohydrides

The hydrolysis of borohydrides may be represented by

$$NaBH_4 + 2\ H_2O \rightarrow NaBO_2 + 4\ H_2 .$$

The reaction occurs readily at normal ambient temperatures and produces hydrogen of high purity which may be used in fuel cells without purification. Furthermore, the weight of hydrogen obtained from a given weight of material is very high. These factors combine to make sodium borohydride a very convenient source of pure hydrogen when the hydrogen generator must be highly portable. The price of sodium borohydride is so high that such generators are unlikely to find wide applications in fuel cells. However, General Electric Company[6] have developed a 200-watt portable power source which weigts only 60 pounds and which combines a sodium borohydride/sulphuric acid hydrogen generator with an air-breathing ion exchange fuel battery.

#### Cracking or reforming methanol

The steam reforming of methanol may be represented by

$$CH_3OH + H_2O \rightarrow CO_2 + 3\ H_2$$

and cracking by

$$CH_3OH \rightarrow CO + 2 H_2 .$$

The main impurity in addition to carbon dioxide in the first reaction is carbon monoxide from the reaction

$$CO_2 + H_2 \rightleftharpoons H_2O + CO$$

while carbon and carbon dioxide may be formed in the second reaction. The quantities of the impurities vary with the catalyst, temperature, pressure and molar ratio of reactants.

The reforming process was used during World War II in portable hydrogen plants which were manufactured by the Girdler Corporation and produced about 4000 scf hydrogen per hour.

More recently, the Girdler Corporation[22] and The M. W. Kellogg Company[23] have separately made design studies for hydrogen generators to produce up to 70 lb. of hydrogen per hour by the steam–methanol reaction. The object was to provide a hydrogen supply for a submarine powered by fuel cells. Both proposed plants were to use palladium–silver diffusers to purify the product gas, since weight and volume were at a premium and, in addition, liquid scrubbers were considered undesirable for ship-board use.

Methanol represents a readily handled liquid fuel for hydrogen generation. While not particularly cheap in comparison with hydrocarbon fuels methanol is readily available in adequate purity; the methanol–steam reaction occurs at relatively low temperatures, process control is simple and the product gas can be purified without great complication. The steam–methanol reaction is probably the most attractive for use in small hydrogen generators for fuel cells for special applications.

*Cracking ammonia*

Ammonia cracks over a nickel catalyst at 900–1000°C to form hydrogen and nitrogen:

$$2 NH_3 \rightarrow 3 H_2 + N_2 .$$

Undissociated ammonia is readily removed from the products by water scrubbing. The main disadvantage of the method for low temperature fuel cells is the high concentration of nitrogen as an impurity in the hydrogen, and this nitrogen is relatively difficult to remove. Lummus[24] has proposed that diffusion be used to remove the nitrogen in a design for a hydrogen fuel cell plant for a submarine. Liquid ammonia is not as easy to handle as some other liquid fuels. Nonetheless, ammonia cracking is already widely practised in small plants for the production of reducing atmospheres for some metallurgical processes.

*Electrolysis of water*

It may seem paradoxical to suggest that hydrogen required to make electricity in a fuel cell should be made by electrolysis, *i.e.* by consuming electricity. However, hydrogen and oxygen are more easily stored than electricity and the combination of electrolyser, gas storage and fuel cell can function as a reservoir for electricity. The hydrogen and oxygen obtained by electrolysis of alkaline solutions are relatively pure and, for fuel cell use, should require no further purification.

This process is only likely to be used with fuel cells to form, in effect, a storage battery.

*Steam reforming of hydrocarbons*

Hydrocarbons react with steam, the reactions occurring being exemplified as follows for propane

$$C_3H_8 + 3 H_2O \rightarrow 3 CO + 7 H_2$$

$$CO + H_2O \rightleftharpoons CO_2 + H_2 .$$

The hydrocarbon feed must be desulphurized before being reformed. This is normally done catalytically over bauxite or a metal oxide to give hydrogen sulphide which is then washed out by alkali. The reforming reaction occurs over a nickel catalyst at 750–1000°C. At this stage the product contains a high proportion of carbon monoxide so it is subjected to a first stage of water gas shift before further purification.

The advantage of steam reforming of hydrocarbons is that it can be operated with light distillate fuels. Reformer plants have been reported supplying hydrogen for a 10-kW fuel cell (150–250 scf/h). A design for a submarine hydrogen plant generating hydrogen from light petroleum distillate for fuel cells has been prepared by Chemical Construction Corporation[25]. The proposed plant uses hydrodesulphurizing of the feed followed by palladium–silver diffusion purification of the product.

*Other methods*

For hydrogen production on the very large scale there are processes such as the steam–iron process

$$Fe + H_2O \rightarrow FeO + H_2$$

$$3 FeO + H_2O \rightarrow Fe_3O_4 + H_2 \ .$$

The oxide is then reduced by treatment with water gas ($H_2 + CO$) or producer gas ($H_2 + CO + N_2$) so that the process presupposes a ready source of water gas or producer gas. No new plants have been built in recent years because of improvements in other processes.

The water–gas process is also widely used

$$H_2O + C \rightarrow CO + H_2$$

$$CO + H_2O \rightarrow CO_2 + H_2 \ .$$

More recently, partial oxidation processes, such as the Texaco and Shell Gasification Processes have been introduced which can accept a wide range of petroleum fuels, including cheap heavy fuels. To simplify purification for fuel cells these plants need to operate with liquid (tonnage) oxygen and hence are only used on a very large scale.

Finally, hydrogen is produced as a by-product from the catalytic reforming of hydrocarbons. This hydrogen is normally used for processes within the refinery.

### (c) Economics of hydrogen generation for fuel cells

If theoretical current efficiency is assumed, 1000 scf of hydrogen will produce 67,800 cell-amp-h. The probable operating voltage for commercial cells operating at low pressure on hydrogen and air will be in the region of 0.6–0.8 volt/cell so that 1000 scf of hydrogen corresponds to a gross power output of 40–55 kW hour of electricity, excluding power consumed by auxiliaries such as blowers and cooling systems which will absorb at least 5% of the gross power.

It has been claimed that partial oxidation processes become more attractive than steam–hydrocarbon reforming for hydrogen production when the hydrogen requirement exceeds about $15 \times 10^6$ scf/day[26]. This corresponds to electricity production at the rate of about 30,000 kW/h, which is well into the range of central power generation where fuel cells are never likely to complete economically with steam turbines, whether supplied by coal, oil or nuclear reactors. Thus partial oxidation processes are unlikely to be used to supply hydrogen for fuel cells.

On the smaller scale, steam–hydrocarbon reforming covers the widest range of plant capacities. Unfortunately, the reaction requires considerable process energy. It is not possible to be very precise but the energy input, including the energy content of the hydrocarbon feedstock, to prepare 1000 scf of hydrogen not less than 99.8% pure is in the range 140–175 kW. This results in overall efficiencies for the hydrogen generation, fuel cell and auxiliary system of 22–37%. A large diesel electric generator can be expected to give an overall efficiency of about 34%. Thus, at best the hydrogen generator and fuel cell will only just exceed a diesel generator in overall efficiency, while at worst the fuel cell system will be much less efficient.

Bacon has reviewed[5] the allowable capital for the combination of fuel cell and hydrogen generator, in comparison with the capital cost of a diesel electric generator which is about £50 per kilowatt hour for plants of several hundred kilowatts in the United Kingdom. He assumes that the hydrogen generators and fuel batteries will be about equal in cost and that the overall efficiency will be 55–60%. (As indicated above, other figures for steam––methane reforming give much lower results.) Even then, Bacon concludes that a plant of about 250 kW hour capacity will only be competitive with a diesel generator if the use of impure (77%) hydrogen can be tolerated. If pure hydrogen (98%) must be used, he suggests that the minimum plant capacity must be of the order of 10,000 kW hour.

All in all, it must be concluded that a hydrogen generator/fuel cell system is unlikely to be a commercial competitor of the diesel electric generator, unless economics are not the sole consideration. One possible exception is the combination of a high-pressure electrolyser and a vehicle powered by fuel cells. This is only likely to be economic in special circumstances, for example if the electric vehicle is required for full-time (24 h/day) operation. The fuel cell vehicle could be rapidly recharged with hydrogen and oxygen from storage fed by the electrolyser. It might be less costly in capital and operation than three conventional battery-powered vehicles or one such vehicle with three sets of batteries so that two could be charging while the third was operating.

If other considerations outweigh economics then the hydrogen generator and fuel cell may find applications. The design studies for submarine plants (in which liquid oxygen is used) suggest that military applications are being seriously considered.

*(d) Combined hydrogen producer and fuel cell*

"Shell" Research Ltd. have described[27] what is claimed to be the first substantial integrated hydrogen producer and low temperature fuel battery. The unit (Fig. 111) delivers 5 kW net which is produced indirectly from methanol and air and has been demonstrated mounted in the back of a Land-Rover 15 cwt. utility vehicle.

Methanol is converted to hydrogen by the methanol–steam reaction, heat being supplied to the reactors by burning methanol. The hydrogen is freed from the carbon dioxide, steam and carbon monoxide by means of a palladium–silver diffuser. The purified hydrogen is then fed to a low-temperature fuel battery. When hydrogen becomes available, air is supplied from a low pressure blower and the fuel battery becomes operational.

Operation of the unit is completely automatic. After switching on, start-up power is supplied from small lead–acid batteries until the fuel battery takes over. Thereafter, the lead–acid batteries are recharged while the fuel battery is running.

Fig. 111. "Shell" Research 5 kW hydrogen producer and fuel battery.

The fuel battery is based on the "Shell" microporous plastic electrodes (see page 100) with potassium hydroxide as electrolyte. Substantial quantities of plastic are also used as structural materials to obtain a light battery. The fuel battery is arranged as two modules, each containing 62 individual fuel cells. Each module is supplied with hydrogen and air at 1–2 lb./sq.in. and electrolyte. The hydrogen is in series/parallel flow and the air and electrolyte in parallel. The batteries are of bipolar construction with series electrical connection. Heat is removed in the circulating electrolyte and dissipated to the atmosphere through a conventional radiator, while water is removed in the air. The overall efficiency of the whole unit is 20–22%.

## REFERENCES

1 Union Carbide Consumer Co., *U.S. Govt. Res. Rept. AD 403,890*, 1963.
2 F. T. BACON, Chap. 5 in *Fuel Cells*, (ed. by G. J. YOUNG), Vol. 1, Reinhold, New York, 1963, p. 74.
3 H. H. CHAMBERS AND A. D. S. TANTRAM, Chap. 7 in *Fuel Cells*, (ed. by G. J. YOUNG), Vol. 1, Reinhold, New York, 1960, p. 105.
4 E. J. CAIRNS, A. D. TEVEBAUGH AND G. J. HOLM, *J. Electrochem. Soc.*, **110** (1963) 1025.
5 F. T. BACON, in *Fuel Cells*, (Chem. Eng. Progr. Tech. Manual), Am. Inst. Chem. Engrs., New York, 1963, p. 66.
6 L. E. CHAPMAN AND E. A. OSTER, *Proc. Ann. Power Sources Conf.*,**15** (1961) 21.
7 E. A. OSTER, *Proc. Ann. Power Sources Conf.*, **16** (1962) p. 22.
8 S. S. TOMTER AND A. P. ANTONY, in *Fuel Cells*, (Chem. Eng. Progr. Tech. Manual), Am. Inst. Chem. Engrs., 1963, p. 22.
9 H. A. LIEBHAFSKY AND E. J. CAIRNS, in *Fuel Cells*, (Chem. Eng. Progr. Tech. Manual), Am. Inst. Chem. Engrs., 1963, p. 50.
10 J. N. MURRAY AND P. G. GRIMES, in *Fuel Cells*, (Chem. Eng. Progr. Tech. Manual), Am. Inst. Chem. Engrs., 1963, p. 57.
11 E. W. JUSTI, in *Fuel Cells*, (Chem. Eng. Progr. Tech. Manual), Am. Inst. Chem. Engrs., 1963, p. 79.
12 K. R. WILLIAMS, J. W. PEARSON AND W. J. GRESSLER, *Proc. 4th Intern. Symp. on Batteries, Brighton, 1964*, (ed. by D. H. COLLINS), Pergamon, Oxford, in press.
13 M. I. GILLIBRAND AND G. R. LOMAX, *Proc. 3rd Intern. Symp. on Batteries, Bournemouth, 1962*, (ed. by D. H. COLLINS), Pergamon, Oxford, 1963, p. 221.
14 J. K. TRUITT, in *Fuel Cells*, (Chem. Eng. Progr. Tech. Manual), Am. Inst. Chem. Engrs., 1963, p. 1.
15 G. FRYSINGER, J. K. TRUITT AND C. G. PEATTIE, *Proc. Ann. Power Sources Conf.*, **18** (1964) 00.
16 R. W. HARDY AND T. MCCALLUM, in *Fuel Cells*, (Chem. Eng. Progr. Tech. Manual), Am. Inst. Chem. Engrs., 1963, p. 45.
17 W. C. FAITH, D. B. KEYES AND R. L. CLARK, *Industrial Chemicals*, Wiley, London, 1957, p. 440.
18 G. R. JAMES, *Chem. Eng.*, **67** (1960) 161.
19 J. B. HUNTER, *Preprints 144th Natl. Meeting Am. Chem. Soc., Los Angeles, April 1963*, *Vol. 8: Div. Petrol. Chem.*, p. B-49.

20 J. P. Derrig, *49th Natl. Meeting, Am. Inst. Chem. Engrs., March 1963.*

21 M. N. Papadopoulos, C. C. Williams and K. E. Zarker, *Preprints 144th Natl. Meeting Am. Chem. Soc., Los Angeles, April 1963, Vol. 8: Div. Petrol. Chem.,* p. B-35.

22 Girdler Corp., *U.S. Govt. Res. Rept. AD 292,273,* 1962.

23 The M. W. Kellog Co., *U.S. Govt. Res. Rept. AD 292,134,* 1962.

24 The Lummus Co., *U.S. Govt. Res. Rept. AD 292,139,* 1962.

25 Chemical Construction Corp., *U.S. Govt. Res. Rept. AD 292,252,* 1962.

26 C. W. Ertel, *Hydrocarbon Process. Petrol. Refiner,* **40** (1961) 163.

27 Anon., *Engineer,* **218** (1964) 1002.

*Chapter 12*

# THE STATUS, PROBABLE DEVELOPMENT AND APPLICATIONS OF FUEL CELLS

## 1. THE CURRENT STATUS OF FUEL CELLS

While the principles of operation of fuel cells may be considered to be established, their state of development as useful power sources is changing rapidly. It is nevertheless worthwhile at the end of this book to recapitulate some of the points that have emerged from the detailed consideration of different fuel cells. Undoubtedly some types of fuel cell will be developed quite rapidly and the ease of development may exert a strong influence on whether or not a particular system finds useful application. While the nature of progress cannot be predicted, certain generalizations may be made.

It is clear that the efficiency of the fuel cell itself is independent of the size of the cell. Considerations of, for example, heat loss and heat exchange may, however, set a lower limit to the size of self-sustaining high temperature fuel cells. Similarly, since minute air blowers are inefficient, there is a limit to the smallest size of air-breathing fuel cell that can be made. Nevertheless, the minimum rating of self-sustaining air-breathing low temperature fuel cells is unlikely to be more than a few hundred watts. Similarly, high temperature cells of no more than a kilowatt or two should be self-sustaining. While overall efficiencies should rise slightly with the size of the fuel cell power plant, further improvements above a power level of a few kilowatts are likely to be marginal. This contrasts with conventional steam generating sets which give improved efficiency as their size increases, up to at least 500 megawatts.

Another difference between the fuel cell and heat engines is that, whereas with a given heat engine the efficiency increases with increasing power output, the reverse is true of a fuel cell. This means that a compromise between initial cost and efficiency must be made for the fuel cell. When this point is borne in mind it seems probable that for fuel cell power plants overall efficiencies of 50% or even less will be much more common than the figures of 70% or 80% which were spoken of a few years ago.

Before making any further assessment of the possible uses of fuel cells the state of development of a number of fuel cells will be recapitulated.

### (a) Hydrogen–oxygen (air) fuel cells

The two most highly developed hydrogen–oxygen fuel cell systems are the General Electric ion exchange membrane cells and the Bacon type of fuel cells built by Pratt and Whitney. Both of these systems have provision for water removal. As they have been developed for use in space, high standards of reliability have been achieved and single fuel cells with lives greater than 5000 hours have been tested for both systems.

Other hydrogen–oxygen fuel cell systems include those constructed by Chloride Electrical Storage Company Ltd. and "Shell" Research Ltd. in England, the "Quadrus" cell of ASEA in Sweden, the Justi cell as developed by Varta A.C. in Germany, the Brown Boveri cell in Switzerland, and cells made by Union Carbide and Allis-Chalmers in the U.S.A. Batteries of all of these cells have been built and given lives of at least 2000 hours and, in many cases, longer, with powers ranging from 20 watts to 15 kW. The best power/weight ratios are about 20 watts/lb., coupled with power/volume ratios of about 1 kW/cu.ft. or slightly more. As many of the electrode systems can be used at much higher power densities than these, it is doubtless only a matter of time before better ratios are attained. Figures of 100/watts/lb. and 5 kW/cu.ft. represent the order of performance that should be expected within a few years but considerable engineering development will be required before these are achieved.

The hydrogen–air fuel cells which are most highly developed at the time of writing are probably the ion exchange fuel cells of General Electric and the "Shell" Research fuel cells. Both systems have been run with full water removal for long periods. The power outputs of individual batteries have exceeded 4 kW, power/weight and power/volume ratios being similar to those for hydrogen–oxygen cells.

### (b) Electrolyte-soluble fuels

So far the only complete fuel cell power units employing soluble fuels which have been built use hydrazine hydrate as the fuel and, as mentioned in Chapter 6, comprise both hydrazine–air and hydrazine–oxygen cells. Power/weight and power/volume ratios are of the same order as those for hydrogen–

oxygen cells. Unfortunately, hydrazine hydrate is both toxic and very expensive; additionally, having a molecular weight of 50 and a yield of only four electrons per molecule it compares unfavourably with methanol (molecular weight 32 and six electrons per molecule). There appears to be no point in further elaborating the details of these cells which, although technically interesting, are unlikely to find widespread use.

Although electrode studies have been made with ammonia as a dissolved fuel, there are no indications that complete power sources are being built to operate on ammonia.

While methanol–air and methanol–oxygen fuel batteries have been constructed with an invariant electrolyte (sulphuric acid) complete power sources with full water removal have not yet been demonstrated, but there is every reason to suppose that they will be built in the near future. Power/weight and power/volume ratios initially are likely to be slightly poorer than those for hydrogen–air cells, but power densities of 50–100 watts/lb. and 3–5 kW/cu. ft. might reasonably be expected within the next five years.

It has been suggested that alkaline electrolytes might be used with methanol as the fuel. For the reasons advanced in Chapter 6 this is not a very satisfactory proposition. The use of an electrodialytic device to remove carbon dioxide from the electrolyte has been proposed, but in the absence of fuller details one is led to believe that use of acid electrolytes results in simpler and probably more acceptable systems.

Although there is no doubt that useful methanol-consuming fuel cells will be built with platinum metals as catalysts, their really widespread application awaits the development of catalysts made from non-precious metals. Apart from cost, world supplies of platinum are insufficient for this metal to be used in millions of fuel batteries.

### (c) Medium temperature (100–200°C) hydrocarbon fuel cells

Individual hydrocarbon–oxygen fuel cells have been constructed which use electrodes containing high concentrations of platinum black catalysts and operate with phosphoric acid as the electrolyte. There has been no indication that practical power units based on these cells are under construction; not only is the performance of these cells rather low but their cost would be prohibitive for all but the most exceptional applications.

## (d) High temperature (500–1000°C) hydrocarbon fuel cells

Although no complete high temperature fuel cell batteries have been made, it is probable that completely self-sustaining units will shortly be in operation. Power/weight ratios are unlikely to exceed 10 watts/lb. initially, although marked improvements should eventually be made; power/volume ratios may well be poor initially (less than 1 kW/cu.ft.) because of the thermal insulation required. At the moment, fused carbonate cells are the most highly developed and so are likely to be used in the first units. On the other hand, if a reduction in the operating temperature of solid oxide fuel cells from 1000°C to 700°C or so could be associated with a robust type of construction, the greater simplicity of the oxide cells would probably ensure their ultimate success at the expense of the fused carbonate cells.

## 2. PROBABLE DEVELOPMENT AND APPLICATIONS OF FUEL CELLS

Because they present fewer engineering problems and are easier to start, low temperature fuel cells with aqueous solutions or ion exchange resins as electrolytes are at a higher state of development than high temperature fuel cells are. These low temperature cells require special fuels, such as hydrogen, methanol or hydrazine, which are more expensive than hydrocarbon fuels; this limits their possible field of application.

The chief advantage of the hydrogen–oxygen fuel battery is that, when power is required for more than a few hours, the weight of the battery and the associated stored gases is less than that of secondary cells (Fig. 112). For this reason they are being developed for space applications. There have also been reports that such units are being considered to power vehicles, such as fork-lift trucks, at present powered by storage batteries. The main difficulty is likely to be in ensuring freedom from hydrogen leaks. It must also be borne in mind that the overall efficiency of an electrolyser–fuel cell system is unlikely to be greater than 50%, a figure which is considerably inferior to that for lead–acid accumulators. On the other hand, much greater vehicle utilization should be possible with the fuel battery since hydrogen and oxygen cylinders can be recharged in a matter of minutes, compared with several hours to recharge lead–acid batteries.

It has also been suggested that the hydrogen–oxygen cell in conjunction with an electrolyser could be used to store electricity generated in off-peak periods by nuclear power stations. However, the overall efficiency of 50%,

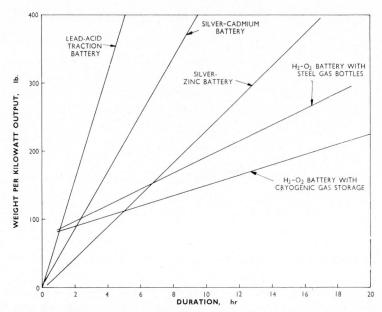

Fig. 112. Comparison of different electrical storage systems (assuming 75 lb./kW fuel battery).

coupled with the expense and the fact that the fuel cell generates direct current which would have to be inverted before use, appear to make the over-all economics unattractive. A widely discussed possibility is the use of hydrogen–oxygen fuel cells to power submarines. Hydrogen would be generated from suitable hydrocarbons, methanol, or liquid ammonia while oxygen would be carried as liquid oxygen or obtained from the decomposition of hydrogen peroxide. For smaller submarines this type of system offers very much greater performance and range than can be obtained with storage batteries. Contracts have been placed both in the U.S.A. and Sweden to study the possibilities.

Hydrogen–air batteries are, at present, the most suitable candidates for replacing some small generators. The hydrogen must be generated from a suitable fuel and this is quite possible, as discussed in the last chapter. However, the overall equipment is expensive and likely to remain so, particularly when the complexity of completely automatic, portable, hydrogen generators is considered. The advantages which such units offer in comparison with existing gasoline- and diesel-powered generators are: relative silence, greater reliability, possibly lower weight and lower fuel consumption. The overall cost of such systems is likely to be such that they will be used only for military applications.

The inherent simplicity of fuel cells using dissolved methanol or hydrazine makes them very attractive from an engineering standpoint. Hydrazine cells are at present cheaper to construct than methanol cells and may be useful in special applications where fuel cost is not the dominant factor. As direct methanol cells are developed they may be expected to displace the combination of hydrogen–air cell, and hydrogen generator. Because of the present high cost of the catalysts in direct methanol cells, they are likely to be limited to relatively low power applications, say, up to 10 kW. Until catalyst costs are reduced the chief uses of direct methanol fuel cells will probably be military, although a compact quiet power unit of one or two hundred watts could well be useful for a variety of civilian purposes. In a small unit such as this the cost per kilowatt is not the dominant factor that it is when larger power units are considered.

Subsequent development of a cheap, direct methanol cell would undoubtedly result in much more widespread use. Such a cell might best be used in electric vehicles of advanced performance but until such a cell is developed, it is unwise to speculate too widely on its possible application. The review by Poulston and Kirtley[1] is rather sobering when cars powered by methanol fuel cells are considered. Even if, as is probable, these authors are conservative in their views on electric motors, and the electric transmission problems of a fuel cell-powered car can be solved by the introduction of cheap lightweight motors, there remains the problem of making a fuel cell of suitable power/weight ratio.

On a cost and weight basis the methanol fuel cell would seem better placed to compete with the diesel engine than with the gasoline engine. Because of the relatively low calorific value of methanol (9,758 B.Th.U./lb. compared with about 19,500 B.Th.U./lb. for light hydrocarbons) the methanol fuel cell is unlikely to be cheaper to operate than a diesel engine. In these circumstances, it could only be secondary factors, such as silence and reduced atmospheric pollution, which would cause the adoption of the fuel cell in preference to the diesel engine in transport. A marked reduction in the cost of methanol might alter this situation. There is no doubt that electrical transmission is very smooth and with the power controlled by silicon-controlled rectifiers it should not be difficult to match the fuel cell to the electric motors. Also it should not be difficult to ensure that the electrical transmission weighed no more than a conventional one; this means that on a weight and volume

*Reference on p. 318*

basis, the fuel cell would have to be comparable with the diesel engine alone. It is not the case, as is sometimes assumed, that the fuel cell plus electric motor must compete with the diesel engine either on a weight or cost basis.

Hydrocarbon-burning fuel cells are in many ways the least developed and are correspondingly the most difficult to assess. All cells which have so far worked successfully have to be heated before starting. The medium temperature (150–200°C) cells are much more expensive, but are less subject to carbon deposition and are easier to engineer than those operating at higher temperatures.

There seems little doubt that all hydrocarbon fuel cells will require relatively clean fuels which vaporize completely leaving no deposits. Nickel and its alloys are subject to sulphide corrosion and if these materials are used in the construction of a high temperature fuel cell sulphur compounds in the fuel will have to be maintained at satisfactorily low concentrations. When these facts are borne in mind, the economic justification for large central power stations does not appear strong. This is particularly so when it is recalled that fuel cells are unlikely to give very much higher efficiencies than steam generating plants and that the direct current generated will have to be inverted to alternating current. If supplies of a clean fuel such as natural gas were readily and cheaply available, very large fuel cell plants delivering direct current for electrolytic processes might be attractive.

On the other hand, since fuel cells of a few kilowatts output are as efficient as larger ones, there seems to be a better chance of the fuel cell, combined where necessary with a solid-state inverter, competing in the market at present held by electric generators powered by diesel or gasoline engines. This presupposes that the laboratory fuel cells now running can be developed into reliable practical power sources. Applications where instant starting is not essential are most suitable for all the hydrocarbon cell systems so far demonstrated. This would suggest static power plants and locomotives as logical outlets for high temperature fuel batteries. In the U.S.A. there is great interest in domestic power sources fuelled by natural gas. In view of the widely fluctuating loads in a home it is not clear that, in areas where electricity is already distributed, the fuel cell would be attractive. However, in many remote places a simple, efficient, silent source of electricity would be very valuable and as standards of living increase the potential markets for such a device would increase. These are not in the main, however, in N. America or Europe.

It is clear that, while military applications for fuel cells seem probable, no fuel cells have yet appeared that have immediate commercial possibilities. Until economically viable fuel cells are at least in the prototype stage it is rash to make predictions about the extent to which fuel cells will be applied. Neither for that matter is it safe to make precise calculations of the performance that will be required of a fuel cell to make it competitive with existing power units. On the one hand, development of the fuel cell may spur manufacturers to develop further the equipment with which it competes. This has happened in the case of nuclear power; conventional steam generators have progressively improved and the newer form of power has had to compete with progressively lower costs. On the other hand, its silence and the reduced atmospheric pollution arising from lower fuel consumption and more complete oxidation of the fuel may make the fuel cell attractive even when it is no cheaper to operate.

What can be asserted is that marked reductions in fuel cell costs will have to be achieved before commercial applications are achieved. If the cost to manufacture a fuel cell (not its selling price) is, say, £100 a kilowatt and its life a few thousand hours, a limited commercial market may be possible. At a price of £10 a kilowatt it should reach a widespread market. Passenger cars would probably need a power unit costing no more than two or three pounds sterling per kilowatt for the fuel cell to be acceptable to the motor industry. Indeed, this figure may well be too high.

There is no doubt too that fuel costs will play a dominant part in determining the acceptance of fuel cells. Hydrocarbon fuels used at an efficiency of 50% would certainly be a very attractive proposition in such applications as railway locomotives which use direct current for their propulsion. High temperature fuel cells should be acceptable for this purpose. Once the cells had reached operating temperature, if adequately insulated thermally, they should remain operable after being shut down for many hours.

In applications where load factors are low and instant starting is important it appears at present that methanol fuel cells are likely to be needed. The user would have to accept the more expensive fuel as the price for added convenience; power units for electric delivery vehicles and the like would fall into this category.

As said before, these statements are of necessity imprecise and may even give a pessimistic view of the prospects for the fuel cell. This is not, however, the writer's intention. At the beginning of the book it was said that if the problems of the fuel cell were easy they would have been solved before. However, with the resources of modern organizations the problems are now being solved. Of the so-called newer forms of energy converters—fuel cells, thermoelectric and thermionic converters, and MHD (magnetohydrodynamic) generators—fuel cells have made much more progress towards their target than the other systems. The thermoelectric and thermionic devices are very inefficient, efficiencies being a few percent at most—and only low-power units producing a few hundred watts at most have been made. MHD generators are limited to very large outputs and lives to date have been measured in minutes rather than hours. Fuel cells having quite high efficiencies (50 % or more) have been built, lives of more than five thousand hours obtained and outputs of 10 kilowatts or more attained. The progress made in the last five years is such that there are strong grounds for believing that the fuel cell will eventually occupy a significant position as an energy converter.

## REFERENCE

[1] B. V. POULSTON AND J. G. KIRTLEY, Paper presented at an *Ordinary Meeting of the Automobile Div. Inst. Mech. Engrs.*, *10th March 1964*.

# AUTHOR INDEX

AGRUSS, B., 260
AIKAZIAN, E. A., 87
ALLMAND, A. J., 25
ANTONY, A. P., 147
ARMSTRONG, G., 128
AUERBACH, F., 276
AUSTIN, L. G., 44, 268, 270
AZZAM, A. M., 56

BACON, F. T., 6, 91, 94, 161, 174, 287, 290, 294, 306
BAKER, B. S., 179
BALACEANU, J. C., 76
BARD, A. J., 150
BARNARTT, S., 56
BARTOSIK, D. C., 279
BAUR, E., 3, 6, 156, 185, 214
BERL, W. G., 17, 89
BERZINS, T., 67
BEUTNER, R., 4, 46
BEWICK, A., 76
BINDER, H., 215, 228, 281
BIRCUMSHAW, L. L., 281
BLOCH, O., 76, 160, 180, 238
BOCKRIS, J. O'M., 16, 24, 33, 35, 36, 56, 90, 244, 245
BOIES, D. B., 120, 132
BORCHERS, W., 275
BREITER, M. W., 34, 69, 80, 81, 87, 121, 132, 140, 141, 143, 145
BRODD, R. J., 62, 71
BROERS, G. H. J., 156, 157, 160, 163, 167, 168, 170, 176–178, 181, 214, 216
BRUMMER, S. B., 144–146
BRUNNER, R., 3
BUCK, R. P., 68, 80, 126, 137–139, 140
BUTLER, J. A. V., 128

CAIRNS, E. J., 88, 93, 159, 202, 220–227, 234, 278, 279, 289, 291
CALVERT, J. G., 262
CARNOT, S., 1, 14
CARTER, R. E., 195, 196, 200, 209
CHAMBERS, H. H., 159, 168, 170, 174, 214, 218, 219, 289
CHAPMAN, L. E., 290
CHODOSH, S. M., 88, 101
CLARK, M., 89
CLEARY, J. G., 197
COHN, G., 130
CONWAY, B. E., 35, 36

DAHMS, H., 245
DAMASKIN, B. B., 82
DAVIES, M., 89
DAVTYAN, O. K., 156, 167, 214
DAY, R. J., 90
DE BETHUNE, A. J., 259
DEGOBERT, P., 160, 180
DELAHAY, P., 38, 67, 68, 74, 75, 78, 80, 82, 137
DE WHALLEY, C. H., 181
DIXON, J. M., 194–199
DOLIN, P., 82
DONNAN, F. G., 25
DOUGLAS, D. L., 104, 161, 175, 178
DRAVNIEKS, A., 120, 132
DUDDY, J. C., 95
DZIECIUCH, M., 35

EHRENBURGH, H., 3
EISENBERG, M., 44, 63, 263
EISS, R., 91
ENGLISH, B., 267

ERSCHLER, B., 82
EVANS, M. G., 74
EVANS, U. R., 6

FERREL, D. T., 95
FICK, A., 38, 65
FICK, L., 44
FLEISCHMANN, M., 76
FRICK, G., 139
FRUMKIN, A. N., 81, 82, 87

GALIOTTO, R. J., 23, 151
GARNER, P. J., 10, 102
GENTILE, R. G., 125, 127, 130, 131
GILLIBRAND, M. I., 147, 149–151
GILMAN, S., 69, 80, 121, 126, 140, 143, 279, 280
GINER, J., 75, 126, 143, 144
GLASSTONE, S., 110
GLICKSMAN, R., 62
GORIN, E., 44, 159, 170, 216
GRAY, T. J., 91
GREEN, M., 244
GREGER, H. H., 4, 157
GREGORY, D. P., 40, 83, 87, 88, 93, 100, 115, 234
GRIFFITHS, L. R., 68, 80, 126, 137–140, 237
GRIMES, P. G., 114, 292
GROVE, W. R., 275
GRUBB, W. T., 10, 93, 103, 230, 237, 239, 240, 243
GRÜNEBERG, G., 277
GUTBIER, A., 150

HABER, F., 3, 4
HACKERMAN, N., 71, 72
HALDEMAN, R. G., 101
HALPERN, J., 271
HARDY, R. W., 299
HART, A. B., 165, 181
HEATH, C. E., 214, 230–233
HENDERSON, R. E., 259
HICKLING, A., 62, 68, 76, 110, 128, 132, 135
HOAR, T. P., 90
HOARE, J. P., 16
HOFMANN, K. A., 275

HOLM, G. J., 289
HORIUTI, J., 87
HOVORKA, F., 62, 89
HUND, F., 187, 190
HUNGER, H. F., 113
HUNGER, J., 105
HUSH, N. S., 74
HUQ, A. K. M. S., 16, 90

IVES, D. J. G., 24

JABLOCKOFF, P., 2
JACQUES, W. W., 3
JAFFE, S. S., 89
JANZ, G. J., 24, 158, 159, 161, 178
JEFFES, J. H. E., 20
JOHANSEN, H. A., 197
JOHNSON, J. W., 245
JUDA, W., 105
JULIARD, A. L., 80, 144
JUNGNER, E. W., 6, 102
JUSTI, E., 88, 91, 96, 112, 115, 130, 214, 230, 266, 277, 278, 292

KABANOV, B. N. K., 82
KARP, S., 150
KATAN, T., 23, 151
KAY, R. M., 62
KETELAAR, J. A. A., 157, 163, 216
KHOLPANOV, L. P., 83
KINGERY, W. D., 188, 190
KIRKLAND, T. G., 96
KIRTLEY, J. G., 315
KIUKKOLA, K., 188, 190
KNORR, C. A., 80, 87
KÖHLING, A., 281
KORDESCH, K., 62, 91, 112, 174
KOZAWA, A., 90
KRONENBERG, M. L., 173
KRUPP, H., 132
KUTSCHKER, A., 144

LANGER, C., 3, 4, 10, 99
LANGMUIR, I., 33
LATIMER, W. M., 149
LEE, J. M., 19
LEVICH, B., 82

LIEBHAFSKY, H. A., 93, 159, 202, 258, 259, 291
LINGANE, J. J., 75, 90
LOMAX, G. R., 147, 149–151

MACDONALD, D. I., 234–236, 278
MAKRIDES, A. C., 144–146
MARKO, A., 62, 112, 174
MARTINYUK, G. A., 146
MCCULLUM, T., 299
MEGGLE, R., 87
MEITES, L., 150
MERTON-BINGHAM, B. E., 271
MICHALSKE, C. J., 243
MOND, L., 3, 4, 10, 99
MOREHOUSE, C. K., 62
MOSER, A., 4
MÜLLER, E., 120, 128, 134, 135, 143
MUNSON, R., 68, 87
MURRAY, J. N., 114

NERNST, W., 6, 14, 183
NEUDLINGER, K., 150
NIEDRACH, L. W., 93, 103, 215, 239, 241, 280
NODDACK, W., 194

OKAMOTO, G., 87
OSTER, E. A., 104, 290
OSTWALD, W., 1
OSWIN, H. G., 88, 101, 239, 240
OTTO, D., 87

PAL'QUEV, S. F., 194
PARSONS, R., 33, 35, 36, 82
PAVELA, T. O., 23, 41, 109, 118, 124–128, 132, 136–140, 149
PEATTIE, C. G., 218, 227
PERRY, J., 105
PIERSMA, B. J., 24, 244
PLUST, H. G., 95
POLLNOW, G. F., 62
POSNER, A. M., 270, 271
POULSTON, B. V., 315
POWELL, J. H., 165, 181
PREIS, H., 3, 185
PRIGENT, M., 75, 139, 140

RANDLES, J. E. B., 77, 82
RECHT, H. L., 44, 159, 170, 216
REED, A., 3
RUETSCHI, P., 91, 95
RHODES, D. R., 237
RICHARDSON, F. D., 20
RICHESON, W. E., 63
RIDDIFORD, A. C., 38, 83, 90
RIDEAL, E. N., 6
RINEY, J. S., 72
RODKEY, F. L., 251
RODWELL, F., 128, 132, 135
ROE, R. M., 16, 71
ROHRBACK, G. H., 254
ROSENBLUM, L., 267
ROTH, W. L., 195, 200
ROZELLE, R. B., 276
RUFF, O., 186
RUKA, R., 193, 194, 202, 204, 206, 208, 215

SAEGUSA, F., 161
SAND, H. J. S., 66
SANDLER, Y. L., 173
SANDSTEDE, G., 281
SAWYER, D. T., 90
SCHENKE, M., 176, 178, 214
SCHLATTER, M. J., 24, 109, 118, 134, 214, 233, 237
SCHMID, A., 97
SCHMID, G. M., 72
SCHULDINER, S., 16, 71, 87
SCHWABE, K., 120, 121
SEVCIK, A., 77
SHALIT, H., 80, 144
SHAW, M., 139
SHLYGIN, A. I., 121, 146
SHROPSHIRE, J. A., 102
SIEGL, K., 4
SIVER, Y. G., 82
SLOTT, R., 121, 144
SMATKO, J. S., 274
STAICOPOULOS, D., 62
STRASSNER, J. E., 74
SUBCASKY, W. J., 139

TAFEL, J., 30
TAITELBAUM, J., 3, 6
TANAKA, S., 130, 133
TANATAR, S., 150

TANTRAM, A. D. S., 159, 168, 170, 174, 214, 218, 219, 289
TARMY, B. L., 102
TEVEBAUGH, A. D., 220–227, 289
TOBLER, J., 6
TOMTER, S. S., 147
TRACHTENBERG, I., 63, 159, 161, 170, 171–173
TREADWELL, W. D., 156
TRUITT, J. K., 168, 173
TRUMPLER, G., 156

URBACH, H. B., 43

VAUCHER, R., 238
VETTER, K. J., 87
VIELSTICH, W., 80, 128, 136, 144
VON FRIEDERSDORFF, C. G., 181

WADANO, M., 120
WAGNER, C., 187, 188, 190
WEISS, R. S., 89
WEISSBART, J., 193, 194, 202, 204, 206, 208, 215
WILL, F. G., 80
WILLIAMS, K. R., 10, 40, 87, 88, 92, 100, 102, 115, 234
WINSEL, A. W., 91, 112
WOMACK, G. J., 275
WORSHAM, C. H., 214, 230–233
WROBLOWA, H., 24, 244, 245
WYNN, J. E., 110, 113
WYNVEEN, R. A., 10, 96, 151

YEAGER, E., 62, 89, 90, 272
YEAGER, J. F., 267, 268
YOUNG, G. J., 276

# SUBJECT INDEX

Acetylene,
  as fuel, 233, 237
  mechanism of anodic oxidation of, 245
Activation
  free energy of, 28, 31, 33
  polarization (see Polarisation)
A.C. Methods, 80
Adenosine triphosphate, 250
Air,
  as oxidant in fuel cells, 98, 100, 104
Alcohol dehydrogenase, 250
Aldehyde dehydrogenase, 250
Allis-Chalmers,
  ammonia–oxygen cells, 151
  hydrazine–oxygen cells, 147, 294, 297
  hydrogen–oxygen cells, 311
  methanol–peroxide cells, 112
  methanol–oxygen cells, 114, 299
American Cyanamid, 101
Ammonia,
  as fuel, 9, 23, 111, 151, 312
  cracking, 303
Anode, definition, 2
Apollo battery, 95, 294
Armour Research Foundation, 112
Asbestos fibres to immobilize electrolyte,
  10, 96
ASEA, 311
Atmospheric pollution, 315, 317

Bacteria, in biochemical cells, 254
Batteries,
  amalgam, 274
  Bacon, 294
  bell-and-spigot, 210, 300
  biochemical, 257
  fuel, 2, 284

high temperature, 173, 179, 299
hydrazine, 297
hydrogen, 7, 294–297, 311
ion exchange, 294, 296
methanol, 111–116, 153, 299, 312
segmented tube construction, 210, 300
Benzyl viologen, 251–253
Bioanodes, 255
Biocathodes, 255
Biochemical
  fuel cells, 9, 248
  oxidation of ethanol, 250
  processes, 248
Biporous electrodes, 93
Borax, as electrolyte, 3
Brown-Boveri, 311

Caesium,
  bicarbonate electrolytes, 234, 278
  carbonate electrolytes, 234, 278
Carbon,
  as fuel, 2
  deposition, 166, 217–227
  deposition, prevention of, 218, 223
  dioxide, reduction of, 122, 143
    removal from hydrogen, 301
  rejection, 115, 234, 235, 237, 278, 280,
    292
  electrodes, 97, 99, 106
  monoxide, as fuel, 3, 4, 8, 11, 157, 167,
    169, 173, 177, 215, 216, 236, 242, 243
Catalysis, 36, 129
  and free energy of adsorption of hy-
    drogen, 35, 36
Catalysts,
  for ethylene glycol, 130
  for formaldehyde, 131

Catalysts (continued)
  for formic acid, 130, 131
  for hydrocarbons in aqueous electrolytes, 230, 237
  for hydrogen, 88
  for methanol, 130–132
  for molten carbonate cells, 160
  for oxygen, 91, 92
  testing, 50, 129–132, 160, 168, 238
Catalytic hydrogenation, 236
Cathode, definition, 2
Cetane, as fuel, 239
Chemisorption, as rate-determining step, 33
Chloride Electrical Storage Co. Ltd.
  hydrazine–oxygen battery, 147, 294, 297, 311
Chronoamperometry, 74–80, 137
  experimental techniques, 76
  linear, 77–80, 143
  in stirred solutions, 75
Chronopotentiometry, 65–74, 137
  experimental techniques, 72–74
Concentration polarization (see Polarization)
Conductance, 42
Conductivity,
  electronic, in solid oxides, 189–194
  ionic, in molten carbonates, 159
  ionic, in solid oxides, 187, 188
Consecutive electrochemical reactions, 32, 67
Copper D.S.K. electrode for CO, 278
Costs,
  fuel, 317
  fuel cell, 317
Cracking, thermal, 216–218
Current–voltage curves, 46–50
  measurement of, 50–63
Cyclopentane, as fuel, 244

Deacon process, 6
Delivery vehicles, electric, 317
Diaphragm, ceramic, 3, 161, 166, 167
  plaster of Paris, 3
Diffusion coefficient, 38, 75
  effective, 40, 163
  of methanol, 124
  of oxygen, 92
Diffusion control, 36–41, 87
Diffusion layer, 38

  in stirred solution, 38, 124
  in unstirred solution, 38, 124
Double layer capacitance, 70, 71
D.S.K. electrodes, 88, 96, 266, 278

Economic considerations, 313–318
Economics of hydrogen generator/fuel battery, 305–306
Efficiency, 11, 20–23, 180, 310
  comparative thermal, 22
  current, 21
  current, measurement of, 23
  free energy, 22
  of hydrogen generator/fuel battery, 305
  thermal, 1
  voltage, 21, 180
Electric motors, 315
Electrical connections, 285
Electrode, poisoning of, 75
Electrode potential,
  definition of, 14
  open circuit, 116–123, 148, 151, 276, 277
  reversible, 14–20
  standard, 117
    ammonia, 151
    bioanodes, 255, 256
    biocathodes, 255, 256
    carbon monoxide, 277
    formaldehyde, 119
    formic acid, 119
    hydrazine, 148
    methanol, 119
    oxygen, 15
    redox couples, 270
Electrode processes,
  at hydrogen electrodes, 86–89
  at oxygen electrodes, 17, 89–90
  in molten carbonates cells, 157–159, 172
  in solid oxide cells, 184, 202
  involving pre-electrochemical steps, 67
Electrode surfaces, study of, 68–70, 79
Electrodes,
  air, 3, 97, 98
  biporous, 93
  carbon, 97–99, 106
  D.S.K., 88, 96, 266, 278
  for ion exchange cells, 103
  for molten carbonate cells, 160, 161
  for solid oxide cells, 205
  gas diffusion, 97–98

homoporous, 95
membrane diffusion, 5, 88, 101, 179
microporous plastic, 99
molten silver, 3, 4, 209
redox, 5, 101, 268
reference, 24–26
    for molten carbonate cells, 161
solid, 87
sintered metal, 95, 105, 160, 217
thin, 99
three-phase, 10, 92
two-phase, 10
Electrodialysis, 312
Electrolysers, 313
Electrolysis of water, 304–306
Electrolyte insulation, 287
Electrolytes, 1
    aqueous, 8
    aqueous bicarbonates and carbonates, 234–236, 278
    fused, 3, 4
    gelled, 10
    immobilized, 10, 96
    ion exchange, 10, 103
    molten carbonate, 4, 157–160
    non-aqueous, 11
    solid oxide, 11, 183–200
E.M.F., effect of,
    electrolyte concentration on, 19
    pressure on, 17
    temperature on, 19
    of carbon monoxide cells, 276
    of molten carbonate cells, 162
    of ammonia cells, 152
    of hydrazine cells, 149
    of hydrogen cells, 15
Enzymes, 9, 248
Ethane as fuel, 215, 231–233, 236
Ethylene,
    as fuel, 215, 233–237, 242
    mechanism of anodic oxidation of, 244–246
Exchange current,
    definition of, 29
    significance of, 31

Flavin–adenine dinucleotide, 251
Formaldehyde,
    hydration of, 118
    oxidation of, 132

Formic acid,
    oxidation of, 122, 143, 144
    reduction of, 122
Free energy, 116
Fuel,
    supply as a gas, 288
    supply as a liquid, 289
Fuel cells,
    current status of, 310
    definition of, 2
    economics of, 180, 313
    prospects for, 153, 180, 313
    high temperature, with molten carbonate electrolytes, 156–181, 228, 313
    high temperature, with solid oxide electrolytes, 183–212, 313, 316
    low temperature,
        amalgam, 272
        ammonia, 111, 151
        biochemical, 9, 248
        carbon monoxide, 275
        chemical regenerative, 5, 268
        concentration, 261
        hydrazine, 9, 111, 147
        hydrocarbon, 237, 240, 312
        hydrogen–air, 86, 311
        hydrogen–halogen, 267
        hydrogen–oxygen, 86, 311
        lithium–hydrogen, 259
        liquid–metal, 260
        methanol, 110–116
        photoelectrochemical, 262
        regenerative, 2, 257
        redox, 5, 268
    medium temperature, 231–241, 312
Fuels,
    inorganic, 111
    organic, 109

Gas recycle, 218, 223, 290
Gemini battery, 291, 296
General Electric Co.
    batteries, 296
    ion exchange electrolyte cells, 311
    low temperature hydrocarbon cells, 238
    molten carbonate cells, 175
    solid oxide cells, 209
Gibbs–Helmholtz equation, 2, 20, 219
Gold,
    electrodes, 99, 100, 205, 210, 293

Gold, electrodes (continued)
    for formaldehyde, 128
    for high temperature cells, 158, 160,
        161, 210
    for hydrocarbons, 245
    for methanol, 131, 132
    formation of surface films on, 80


Half cells, 51–53
Heat exchange, 310
Heat loss, 310
Heat removal, 290
    by electrolyte circulation, 291
    by endothermic reaction, 291, 292
    by gas recirculation, 290, 291, 294
    by separate coolant, 291
Hexane as fuel, 215, 228
High temperature batteries, 173, 179, 299
High temperature fuel cells (see Fuel cells)
Homopolar construction, 286
HOPE battery, 296
Hydrazine, 2, 111, 147–151, 311, 315
    batteries, 292, 297, 298
    mechanism of anodic oxidation of, 149
Hydrocarbon fuels,
    in aqueous electrolyte cells, 230–246
    in ion exchange cells, 241
    in molten carbonate cells, 169, 173, 179,
        227
    in solid oxide cells, 228
Hydrocarbon reforming, 304
Hydrogen,
    economics of production, 305
    producer and fuel cell, 307
    production, 300–307
        from ammonia, 303
        from borohydrides, 302
        by catalytic reforming, 217, 305
        by electrolysis, 304
        by hydrocarbon–steam reforming,
            216–219, 228, 304
        from methanol, 302
        by partial oxidation, 305
        by steam–iron process, 305
        by water gas process, 216, 305
    purification,
        cryogenically, 302
        by diffusion through Pd–Ag, 301
        by molecular sieves, 302
        by scrubbing, 301

        by water gas shift, 216, 302
    use of impure, 106
Hydrogen–oxygen cells, 86, 311
    comparison of various types, 105
Hydrogen peroxide, 89, 112, 314


Interrupter methods for cell resistance,
    57–63
    in molten carbonate cells, 170
Inverters, 316
Ion exchange
    batteries (see Batteries)
    membranes, 10, 88, 103, 114, 313
Ionic conductivity (see Conductivity)
Iridium,
    electrodes,
        for air, 91
        for hydrocarbons, 238, 245
        for methanol, 130–132
    formation of surface films on, 80
Kerosine as fuel, 169, 173, 214, 218, 228
Kinetics,
    of electrode processes, 27–50, 65–83
    of methanol oxidation, 123–146
    in molten carbonate cells, 162
Kirchoff's laws, 287


Langmuir isotherm, 34
Lattice vacancy,
    model for oxide ion conductance, 187
Lead, 293
Limiting current, 36–41, 82, 123–126
    at hydrocarbon electrodes, 239
    at hydrogen electrodes, 87
    at methanol electrodes, 41, 124
    in molten carbonate cells, 163
    at oxygen electrodes, 93
Low temperature batteries (see Batteries)
Luggin capillaries, 52, 55–57


Manganese,
    as catalyst, 3
    dioxide, 3
Materials of construction, 293
Matrix cells, 161, 167–174, 180, 228
    ohmic effects in, 164
Methane as fuel, 214, 217, 239, 241

in high temperature cells, 166, 208, 209
Methanol, 8, 111–146, 312, 315
  acid fuel cells, 115, 312
  alkaline fuel cells, 112–114
  fuel batteries, 2, 284
  mechanism of anodic oxidation of, 34, 41, 134–146
    in acid solution, 140–146
    in basic solution, 135–140
    oxidation intermediates of, 132–134
    reforming and cracking of, 302, 307
    vapour in molten carbonate cells, 169, 176
Methyl phenazonium methosulphate, 252, 253
Methyl viologen, 253
Methylene blue, 252, 253
Methylene glycol,
  formation of, 118
  ionization of, 118
  oxidation of, 122
  reduction of, 122
Microporous plastic electrodes, 99
Molybdenum D.S.K. electrode for CO, 278

Nernst
  equation, 14, 117, 253
  glower, 184
  mass, 184
Nickel boride, 88
Nickel, 293
  alloys with silver (see Silver)
  ammonia cracking with, 303
  corrosion of,
    in molten carbonate cells, 160, 177
    by sulphides, 316
  electrodes,
    for high temperature cells, 160, 167, 168, 170, 173, 176–178, 209, 217, 294
    for low temperature cells,
      for hydrocarbons, 230, 233, 237
      for hydrogen, 87, 93–97
      for methanol, 129–132
      for oxygen, 231
Nickel oxide electrodes, 91, 94
  lithiated, 94, 170
Nicotinamide–adenine dinucleotide, 250
Nitric acid, 101, 271
Nitrogen,
  blanketing, 40, 97

removal, 292
Nitrous acid, 101, 271

Octane as fuel, 239
Ohmic polarization (see Polarization)
Oscillations, 128
Osmium, as oxygen electrode, 91
Overpotential, 28 (see also Polarization)
Oxidant supply, 288
Oxide electrolytes, 11, Chapter 8
  ions in, 11
  ion diffusion in, 187–194
Oxygen concentration cell, 157, 184, 191
Oxygen electrodes, 2, 15–17
  reversible potential of, 15–17, 89

Palladium, 293
  alloys with silver, 11, 101, 180, 301
  electrode catalysts,
    for high temperature cells, 178
    for hydrocarbons, 237, 243
    for hydrogen, 101, 104
    for methanol, 131
    for oxygen/air, 91, 98
  formation of surface films on, 80
Palladium–silver
  diffuser, 301
  diffusion electrodes (see Electrodes, membrane diffusion)
Parasitic currents, 287
Paste electrolyte cells, 166, 175
Perhydroxyl ion, 17, 89
Phase diagram of $Li_2CO_3$–$Na_2CO_3$, 158
Plastics as constructional materials, 293
Phenolsulphonic acid–formaldehyde co-polymers, 104
Platinized
  carbon, 4, 98, 112, 237
  nickel, 91, 233
  Raney nickel, 112, 132
Platinum, 293
  alloys with gold, 91, 210
    with iridium, 91, 98, 160
    with palladium, 114
    with rhodium, 160
    with ruthenium, 115
  electrode catalysts,
    for carbon monoxide, 276–281
    catalytic cracking on, 236, 240

Platinum, electrode catalysts (continued)
  for hydrazine, 147
  for hydrocarbons, 236–246, 312
  for hydrogen, 4, 87–89, 99–105, 160,
    167, 205, 209
  for methanol, 129, 312
  for other organic compounds, 130
  for oxygen/air, 89–91, 115, 228
  formation of surface films on, 68–70,
    78–80, 140–146
  platinized, 25, 52, 99, 126, 129
  surface area of, 32, 129
  Raney, 130, 281
  surface area determination, 71, 80
  world supplies of, 312
Phosphoric acid electrolytes, 9, 238–241,
  246, 312
Polarization,
  activation, 27–36, 126, 165, 203, 233
  activation and concentration, 48–50
  activation and ohmic, 47–49
  concentration, 36–41, 123, 163, 203, 207,
    234, 239, 244
  gas transport, 40, 163
  ohmic, 42, 43, 123, 164, 203, 285
    elimination of, 55–63
  in porous electrodes, 43–45
Polyfluorocarbon–polystyrene sulphonic
  acid copolymers, 104
Porosity,
  influence on ohmic polarization, 43
Porvic (microporous plastic) electrodes,
  99
Potassium hydroxide as electrolyte, 9, 278
  (also Chapters 5, 6, 9, 11)
Potassium ferricyanide, 252, 253
Potential, reversible electrode, 14–20
  effect of pressure on, 17, 18
  measurement of, 24–26, 50–63
  mediators, 251
Potentiostat, 76
Potentiostatic sweep methods (see Chronoamperometry)
Power
  systems, 11
  –volume ratio, 311, 313
  –weight ratio, 311, 313
Pratt and Whitney fuel battery, 294
Pressure operation, 94
Propane as fuel, 215, 218, 228, 233, 237–
  240, 244

Propylene as fuel, 244

Quadrus, 311
Quinone, 252, 253

Reforming,
  catalytic, 305
  of hydrocarbons, 216, 217, 304
  of methanol, 303
Resistivity of oxide electrolytes, 194–199
  of calcia–zirconia systems, 195
  of yttria–zirconia systems, 197
  variation with composition, 194, 199
  variation with temperature, 196, 198
Respiratory chain, 250
Rotating disc electrodes, 82
Rhodium, 293
  electrodes,
    for hydrogen, 87, 238
    for hydrocarbons, 238, 245
    for methanol, 130–132
  formaldehyde decomposition on, 120
  formation of surface films on, 80
Rubidium,
  bicarbonate, 234, 278
  carbonate, 234, 278

Sand equation, 66, 137
Schardinger enzyme (see Xanthine oxidase)
Shell Gasification process, 305
"Shell" Research Ltd., 311
  electrodes, 100
  hydrazine battery, 147, 298
  hydrogen producer and fuel battery, 307
  methanol battery, 115
Shunt currents, 287
Silicon controlled rectifiers, 315
Silver, 293
  alloy with nickel, 91
  electrodes with zinc, 96
  for high temperature cells, 3, 4, Chapter 7
  for low temperature cells, 90, 91, 96, 98,
    100
  for methanol, 130
Sodium borohydride, 111
Spinels, 91, 98
Spring loading, 294
Stainless steel, 160, 293

Steam reforming, 217–219, 304
  catalyst for, 217
Storage of gases, 7
Submarines, 314
Surface areas, 129
  determination of, 70–72, 80
Surface coverage,
  with carbon monoxide, 279
  with formic acid, 144
  with methanol, 34, 140
Surface reactions, 34, 35
Surface roughness factor, 32

Tafel equation, 30, 122, 126, 137, 142, 165
Tantalum, 293
Temkin isotherm, 34, 141
Texaco hydrogen process, 305
Thermodynamics, 14–20, 116–120, 258
  of the carbon–hydrogen–oxygen system, 219
  of carbon monoxide cells, 276
  of molten carbonate cells, 161
  of solid oxide cells, 200
Three-phase contact, 92
Tin, 6
Titanium, 293
Tortuosity,
  effect on ohmic polarization, 43, 164
Transference number, 40
  of oxide ion in oxide electrolytes, 189–194

of electron in oxide electrolytes, 189–194
Transition time, 66–68, 73, 138
Tubular battery, 300
Tungsten D.S.K. electrode for CO, 278
Turnover number, 249

Union Carbide fuel cells, 99, 311
Unipolar construction, 286

Vacuum deposition of electrodes, 100, 165, 178, 205
Vanadium, 6
Vehicles, 313, 315

Water removal, 101, 103, 290, 294
  by wicking, 296
Westinghouse bell-and-spigot battery, 210, 300
Wet proofing of electrodes, 98

Xanthine oxidase, 251

Yttria, 3, 184, 187, 197

Zirconia stabilization for electrolyte, Chapter 8

# DATE DUE

| | | | |
|---|---|---|---|
| ~~MR 15 68~~ | | | |
| AP 2 68 | | | |
| | | | |
| RETURNED | | | |
| MR 13 70 | | | |
| RETURNED | | | |
| MAY 25 MAY 2 4 1993 | | | |
| NOV 1 4 | | | |
| NOV 7 1996 | | | |
| MAR 2 6 2002 | | | |
| | | | |
| APR 1 8 2002 | APR 1 8 2002 | | |
| MAY | | | |
| | | | |
| | | | |

WITHDRAWN FROM
OHIO NORTHERN
UNIVERSITY LIBRARY

GAYLORD | PRINTED IN U.S.A.

HETERICK MEMORIAL LIBRARY
621.312429 W72i
Williams, Keith R. / An introduction to fu     onuu

3 5111 00139 8951